P9-DVQ-682

EX
LIBRIS

Romance
Treasury

THE ROMANCE TREASURY
ASSOCIATION

NEW YORK · TORONTO · LONDON

These stories were originally published as follows:

RETURN TO TUCKARIMBA
Copyright © 1975 by Amanda Doyle
First published by Mills & Boon Limited in 1975

HOLD ME CAPTIVE
Copyright © 1976 by Margaret Pargeter
First published by Mills & Boon Limited in 1976

GREEK BRIDAL
Copyright © 1976 by Henrietta Reid
First published by Mills & Boon Limited in 1976

ROMANCE TREASURY is published by
The Romance Treasury Association, Stratford, Ontario, Canada.

Editorial Board: A. W. Boon, Judith Burgess, Ruth Palmour,
Alice E. Johnson and Ilene Burgess.

Dust Jacket Art by David Craig
Story Illustrations by David Craig
Book Design by Charles Kadin
Printed and bound by R. R. Donnelley & Sons Co.

ISBN 0-373-04073-3

Printed in U.S.A.

A073

CONTENTS

RETURN TO TUCKARIMBA

Return to Tuckarimba

Amanda Doyle

CRAIG

Tuckarimba was for sale! Nonie couldn't believe her luck! She would buy back her childhood home; she and her sister, Prue, would go back to the rural Australia Nonie had always loved.

It came as a crushing blow to finally arrive at Tuckarimba and discover that Jacey Lomax, the present owner, had changed his mind and withdrawn the homestead from the market.

So Nonie returned to her home as an employee instead – caring for Jacey's crippled brother, Raynor.

But could she stay? Nonie's life became an emotional agony when she fell desperately in love with Jacey Lomax. Could she bear to see him marry the beautiful Delphine?

CHAPTER ONE

WENONA ALLOWED HER EYES to travel once more curiously over the profile of the man standing just ahead of her in the line.

She had forgotten her own impatience and the unstamped letters in her hand, temporarily at least, because there was something about the simple elderly figure of that man that tugged at the strings of her memory, pulled at them irresistibly in fact. *Should* she know him? *Did* she know him?

It was one of those tantalizing and uncertain moments that we have all encountered at some time or another—a sense of familiarity with something that reason assures us must be totally unfamiliar, whether it be the curve of a mountain we recognize yet have never known; the path of a road, untrodden, yet whose hidden direction we can somehow predict; the planes and hollows of a stranger's face, the composition of features and form all unfamiliar yet welding themselves together into a fleeting vision of some past memory, as this man's features now were fusing themselves before Wenona's doubting eyes into an image that was at once foreign and yet distractingly nostalgic.

The line shuffled impatiently.

"Next, please."

It was almost her turn. Wenona received a small push from behind to tell her that she was dreaming.

"Sorry."

She stepped smartly forward to close the gap and the old man half turned. Again her memory was taunting her,

yet she knew she must be wrong. There was no hint of
recognition in the faded blue eyes that dwelled for just a
moment on her own pale oval face with an impartiality
that was convincingly total.

And then the counter clerk solved the whole problem
for her in one swift, concise query.

"Yes, Mr. Bunford?"

Ted Bunford! The mailman out at Tucka!

"Bundy," the children on that run had known him as.
Bundy, who had come each week in a rattling old lorry
with waterbags flapping from its rusting sides and two
spare wheels affixed primly to the top of its peeling cab.
They looked as gaudy and improbable as a cocktail hat on
the dyed curls of an aging harlot—an unlikely yet compelling combination. The lorry had been crammed with station stores, parcels, bags of sugar and flour, machinery
spares, canvas mailbags with stout leather collars and
padlocks, tins of groceries, packs of butter in a deep
wooden chest, swirling about like fat yellow barges on a
pond of melting ice. Bundy's pockets had held not only
tobacco wads and cigarettes and papers, but boiled sweets
in assorted colorful stripes and peppermints with holes in
the middle. Bundy had been the event of the week in that
lonely outback area.

The old man was getting coins from the counter, sliding
his gnarled brown hand under the grille between him and
the counter clerk and scooping the money into his cupped
palm and from there into his jacket pocket. The dollar
notes he counted systematically before folding them carefully and placing them in his wallet. His fingers were
shaky but somehow determined. It looked as though it
had been a long time since they dealt out tobacco wads
and striped bull's-eyes with the firmness Wenona remembered so well. As indeed it was. A long, long time. An
eternity in Wenona's mind as she groped to recall things
that were suddenly more important than plugs of tobacco

and sticky boiled sweets. Her brain, trembling on the brink of remembrance, somehow could not bridge the gap of time. Her failure to do so made her want to cry.

Now Bundy was turning away, walking slowly out of the building. Out of her groping recollections.

Wenona followed, her place in the line, her unposted letters, forgotten.

"Mr. Bunford? Mr. Bunford? Bundy?"

The old man stopped as she used the diminutive, his faded eyes sharpening.

"It *is* Mr. Bunford? From . . . from Tuckarimba?"

"Yeah, that's right, miss. An' *you* called me *Bundy*." He made it sound like a presumption.

Wenona flushed.

"Yes, I did. I . . . we used to call you that. I hope you didn't mind, but I had to stop you somehow." She took a breath. "I'm from Tuckarimba myself, or used to be. Wenona. Maybe you remember? Fat and short with fair plaits? I wore glasses then, too."

"Wenona? Yer don't mean *Nonie*?" He stared, incredulous now. "Well, skin the flamin' lizards if it isn't little Nonie Dermot!"

"Nonie Gotthart. My . . . my mother married again. I took my stepfather's name."

"Yeah? Well, I reckon yer mother did the right thing there, eh?" The old man grunted agreement with his own statement. He was still gazing at her in some amazement. "S'truth, yer growed some, didn't yer, Nonie? Who'd 'ave thought that that tubby little sheila 'ud turn into a bee-oot-iful long-legged young dame like you? Except, maybe, y're a bit *too* skinny now. I reckon. Yer've gone the other way now, see. Too thin." He continued his frank assessment.

They stood there together on the pavement, looking at each other with the rows of Norfolk Island pines behind them and the beach wall behind those, and then the sand

and the pounding white-frothed breakers. The wind
soughed gently through the needled foliage. It ruffled Mr.
Bunford's white locks and lifted Wenona's long blond
tresses, whipping them across her pale cheeks.

"Look, Bundy, could you spare time for a cup of
coffee . . . or even a beer, maybe?"

"I reckon I could. It ain't every day I meet someone
from the old life." He shuffled willingly along at her side,
and she matched her steps to his.

When they stopped it was to sit down at an outdoor café with small tables set back from the pavement.
Wenona chose coffee and bought Bundy the promised
schooner.

"Have you been back, Bundy? How long is it since you
left? How long have you been in Sydney, and whatever
are you doing *here*? You're the last person I'd ever have
expected to see here on the corso at Manly!"

The old man put down his beer and grinned.

"Well, you're a bit of a surprise yerself, come ter that,
Nonie." He wiped the froth off his tobacco-stained mustache with the back of his hand. "I've been here a good
long time now as it happens. Ten years about. And . . .
let's see. You were only eight when your dad . . . when
you, er, left. And I was there at Tucka a good five years
after that, so that makes you—"

"I'm twenty-three."

"Funny, that. An' I'm seventy-six." He sighed. "Little
Nonie Dermot, twenty-three."

"Gotthart."

"Eh?"

"Gotthart. Nonie *Gotthart*. My mother married again.
Remember I've already told you? And I took my stepfather's surname." She paused. "I've actually got a little sister, too, Bundy . . . a half-sister from my mother's second
marriage. Pru is eight herself now, just about the age I
was when I left Tuckarimba."

"That's nice. A young sister, eh? And is her . . . is yer stepfather a decent bloke then, Nonie?"

"He was a darling," Wenona told him warmly. "He's dead now, Bundy," she added without embarrassment, "but he was the very best stepfather a girl could have or wish for."

"Well, yer ma deserved that at the very least. She deserved a break. Where is she now, yer mother, Nonie?"

"She died, Bundy, when Pru was born. No, don't look like that, of course you had to ask. The doctor said she shouldn't have had such a late child after all she'd been through. It didn't work out for her, I'm afraid, that's all."

She swallowed, looked away so that he wouldn't see the quick tears that even after all this time could spring to her eyes so easily when she remembered her mother, so gentle and kind, patient and happy and yet always with a brooding sort of sadness tucked away behind the cheerfulness, a lurking wistfulness, almost as if she had known that she was never going to hold the child that she was carrying.

"I'm sorry, Nonie." The old chap's voice was gruff. "Like I said, she deserved better luck than that. It took it out of 'er, that whole business about yer dad. She kept 'er head up, too, right ter the day she left. Defended 'im right, left, 'n center, but I'll bet it took it out of 'er, more than she'd ever 'ave admitted. Reckon we all liked yer mother, Nonie. We admired 'er, see. That's why we all went along with 'er about yer father's accident. Well, it *could* 'ave been one, couldn't it? I mean, there was no *note* or anything like that."

A coldness feathered over Wenona's skin. Her eyes were beginning to widen.

"You mean . . . ?" She hesitated, schooled herself to calmness as the implication of what he had said was borne in upon her.

She made herself look at him with candor.

"I never knew that there was anything . . . I never knew exactly how my father died, except that he was drowned."

"Well, that's all that *anyone* knew, but there was plenty of speculation." Mr. Bunford scratched his ear uncomfortably. "I should know at my age when ter keep my big mouth shut, shouldn't I?"

"No, it doesn't matter. Truly, Bundy." Wenona shrugged a little ruefully. "The people most concerned are often the last to hear these things; I realize that quite well. I've learned to be realistic about things, Bundy . . . I've had to be, you see, with Pru to bring up on my own. I've had to look facts in the face, even unpalatable ones, and I think I've realized all along that my father couldn't have been a very strong or dependable character. But he was kind . . . good fun, *great* fun. He loved me."

" 'E was a . . . a *whimsical* sort of fellow yer dad. A bit of a dreamer, Nonie. Providence—the hard 'outback' sort of Providence, I mean—ain't all that kind ter dreamers, yer know. It's the hard-bitten sort that make a go of it out there. Floods an' bushfires an' droughts an' duststorms aren't fer dreamin' fellers like yer dad."

She smiled gently.

"I know. I think I realized that even then, young and all as I was. And yet all my memories . . . my *happiest* memories . . . are of Tuckarimba. My . . . I suppose one could say that my father was a failure, Bundy? And yet, at Tuckarimba even that didn't seem to matter, not to a child anyway. They were idyllic days, safe and secure, filled with sunshine and warmth and laughter, and the interest and variety of the changing country scene. I can think of no better background for a small child to grow up with."

"Huh. It ain't all beer and skittles like *you* make it seem." But even Bundy sounded unconvinced, nostalgic.

She sighed, half closed her eyes.

"I've often wondered what happened to it all after we left."

"D'yer really want ter know?" The old man hesitated. "Reckon I don't want ter shoot down any more of them ideas of yours."

"Do you know?"

"Reckon the bank had a bond on the place when yer dad died, Nonie."

"So that was why we never had any money! I was too young to understand, but looking back I'd have guessed anyway if I'd really thought about it. I realize now what a struggle it must have been for mum, from the time we left right up to when she married Stroud Gotthart. What *did* happen to it, then?"

"The Tintoola Pastoral Company took it off the bank and put in a manager. It's a good property, yer know, but the drought years hit 'em pretty hard right from the word go."

"Who are the Tin—whatever it was you said?"

The old mailman looked askance at what he obviously considered a display of abysmal ignorance.

"The Lomax outfit. Strings of stations farther north... west, too. In the end it got so bad that Jacey Lomax himself came down ter lick things inter shape."

"Jacey Lomax? He'd be the, er, the head?"

"Yeah, the boss uv the works. Young, tough, full uv drive like 'is dad was before 'im. I guess wherever Jacey goes 'e gets things done, and that's what 'e did at Tuckarimba too. In fact, 'e fell in love with the place an' stayed. Funny ter think of a *Lomax* fallin' fer a bit of real fancy country like Tucka. They're all north men, that lot— plains-'n-ranges, don't-fence-me-in sort of fellers—but no, Jacey fell smack in love with Tuckarimba I reckon. It's a small place by *their* standards, just thirty-odd thousand acres, but it got under 'is skin, see. Once 'e'd got it how 'e wanted it, 'e found 'e didn't want ter leave it."

"And he's there now?"

"Yep, 'e is. They say 'e's away a lot, of course. Flies

around visitin' the other stations, takin' a dekko at what's goin' on, but Tucka's 'is base."

Mr. Bunford alias Bundy drained the dregs from his schooner, took out a large gray handkerchief and passed it along his mustache from one side of his mouth to the other.

Wenona finished her own coffee in silence, trying idly to imagine what the place would be like now, now that this Jacey Lomax had "licked it into shape."

"Funny me runnin' inter you like this, Nonie," the ex-mailman mused pensively. "I 'aven't seen so much as a cat's whisker of the folk from Tucka fer years, and then in two days I do a double. 'Ad a letter from Mickey Doolan—'e used ter be at the store, but I doubt if you'd remember Mickey. Well, Mick's got a little show of 'is own now out at Innamincka, an' 'e went ter see 'is aunt at Tucka a couple days ago, an' 'e happened ter mention Tuckarimba. And then I run inter you. That's what I mean by funny."

"What did he say?" Wenona leaned forward eagerly.

"Said the old homestead's fer sale."

"Sale! You mean Tuckarimba? Our old house?"

That hurt, somehow. It didn't add up, either, with the fact that Jacey Lomax had fallen in love with the place. Nonie had found herself harboring quite a soft spot for the great Jacey Lomax for having the good sense to fall in love with a place like Tuckarimba in spite of the dimensions of all his other interests. It showed him to be a man of soul and sensitivity. But now, to want to *sell* it . . . .

"Are you sure?" she asked Bundy dubiously. "Sure you've got it right, I mean?"

"Most certainly I'm sure. Dinkum sure. It's only the house an' the orchard 'e's sellin', because it's right at the town end of the property as yer know, an' Jacey didn't like the site."

"Didn't like the *site*!" Her opinion of Jacey Lomax and

his soul and sensitivity were altering fast! "Why, it's a beautiful site. A . . . a *heavenly* site!"

"Well, Jacey don't hold your views on that, apparently. Too shut in down there on the creek flat. I *told* yer Jacey's lot are don't-fence-me-in fellers. 'E's built 'imself a ruddy great new homestead farther up the river where 'e can look right down the valley an' see what's goin' on, Mick says."

"The lord of all he surveys?" she broke in, and was amazed at her own waspishness.

"Yeah, that's Jacey," agreed the old man imperturbably, unaware of her sarcasm. "Fer a while there was an overseer in the old place, but now Jacey's wantin' ter get quit of it. Now 'e's livin' there 'e doesn't need a full-time overseer. He's the sort that likes ter keep the tabs on things 'imself if 'e can, see. Mickey says 'e shoved in ten acres of creek flat along with it, with the idea that someone might make a market garden out of it, being at the town end of the run, yer see."

Wenona found it all hard to believe. That anyone could *prefer* another site! That anyone could *want* to be quit of it!

It was difficult to visualize the old homestead, admittedly in an advanced state of antiquity, cut off from the rest of the place to which it had always belonged for so many years. Cut off. *Fenced* off, along with a mere ten puny acres. *Spurned.*

It was an insult! And they called him a don't-fence-me-in feller!

"Are you certain?" she persisted, but very feebly because she now knew exactly the sort of hands into which poor old Tuckarimba had fallen.

"Dead certain. Mickey said 'e took a run out, and there's even a great big For Sale notice stuck on a pole near the old wattle tree."

"The wattle tree! You used to stop the mail lorry right beside it, Bundy!"

"That's the one. A big white board with black letterin'," Mick said. Said 'e felt quite sad ter see it, but times change, I reckon." He stood up, and Wenona scraped her own chair back too. "Well, Nonie, it's been good ter meet yer like this, talkin' about old times an' all that."

"Yes, Bundy," she agreed. "You live here now in Manly?"

"With Florrie, me sister. She's me youngest sister, like. Never got 'erself hitched. There was a bloke once—a shearer—out on the Paroo...." he gestured vaguely.

"It's nice that you've got each other now though. Maybe I'll see you around, Bundy. We must keep in touch after this."

"Yeah, that's right, Nonie. We'll keep in touch. Thanks fer the beer, then." He clasped her hand for a brief moment. "S'long, Nonie."

"So long, Bundy. See you around," replied Wenona automatically, but already she had the strangest feeling that she wasn't going to *be* around—not here in Manly, anyway. Already she had a suspicion that she knew just what the inevitable outcome of this conversation was going to be!

And why not, she asked herself cautiously as she walked slowly back to the room that she and Pru shared together. They not only shared the room with each other, but the bathroom and kitchen facilities with the other residents in the same building. What sort of existence was *that* for Pru, compared with the freedom of a rambling corridor of rooms to themselves and the chance to shout and sing and jump and skip out there at Tuckarimba where there were no other people to keep on telling her to be quiet, keep down her voice, shut the door, stay on her own stair, pull down the blind, leave the flower beds alone.

Wenona let herself into the building, glanced at her watch. Soon Pru would be home from school.

She took off her jacket, went through to the shared kitchenette and began to clear the crumbs off the table. The bread knife looked as if someone had spread jam with it and then put it straight back on the board. It wasn't *her* bread knife. Not even *her* crumbs.

Strange that such a tiny, irritating detail as that could be responsible for a whole chain of decisions, a whole string of events, but it was!

Wenona ran the knife under the hot tap, her mind busy with the obstacles, tackling them in turn, eliminating them one by one. As her fingers went on cutting the bread for Pru's tea she was almost unaware of her own actions, so taken up was she with her thoughts.

What sort of a life was this for Pru, she asked herself again. Coming home each day to the same dingy place in the same dingy back street, the same dull routine, the same tedious restrictions? And what about Wenona herself? Wenona, the part-time . . . part-time *what*? How could she accurately describe herself or this mad life she led? Part-time sign writer because she had taken a course in it once; part-time picture framer because it was something she could do right here at one end of the bed-sitting room while she was looking after Pru, and a notice in the local newsagent's window occasionally put customers her way; part-time typer of envelopes because the money was good even if her typing wasn't; part-time cleaner because in return for doing out the landlady's own flat, which took up the whole of the top floor, she was "let off" four dollars a week in rent; part-time gardener because she got another two dollars off for keeping the path to the main front door free of weeds. Part-time jack-of-all-trades, and master of absolutely *none* of them, that's what she was, and she was thoroughly tired of the whole setup! Where was it getting either herself or Pru? Precisely nowhere!

She had three thousand dollars saved.

Well, nearly, if you included the bit Stroud had left that

wasn't actually in trust for Pru when she grew up. If you added that on to what she already had herself, it was nearly three thousand.

Surely that would be enough for a down payment, a loan or something to get that crumbling, *dear* old homestead that the Lomax man didn't want? The orchard could be productive almost straight away. She could maybe bottle fruit, too, and sell homemade jam, and that lovely alluvial soil down on the creek flats would grow fabulous vegetables. She might even try things like mushrooms and asparagus, which needed special beds and temperatures. She had no idea just *what* they needed, but she could soon read it up and apply the knowledge she had gleaned, like she had done with the picture framing. And all the time she was doing these things there'd be the sunshine, the open air, the scent of the wattle tree, the sound of bees in the gum blossoms, the peace and variety and freedom that were Tuckarimba's. They would be hers and Pru's to enjoy as freely as they pleased.

IT TOOK TWO DAYS to get away.

Wenona was quite surprised that it had taken even that, so determined was she upon her new course of action, but in the end there had been an alarming number of things to which to attend.

She had had to pay the landlady right up to the end of the month in lieu. That had been a bit of a setback but she supposed it was really fair enough. Tenants weren't supposed to go haring off into the blue at a moment's notice after all, but it would be worth it in the end, because if she didn't get out to Tuckarimba quickly someone else might see the For Sale notice and get there first, and that would be too unbearable even to contemplate now that her mind was made up.

Next she had had to transfer her account to the bank at Tucka. The manager of the local branch had looked dubi-

ous when she explained just why, but he had shaken her
hand in rather grave dismissal after agreeing to her request, and had even wished her well with a doubtful smile
on his lips. Wenona had been glad that she had got
around him so easily. It had been somewhat chastening to
have to stand there and listen to his paternal lecture on
the inadvisability of rash and impulsive decisions, but she
had done so knowing that she had no intention of being
talked out of anything.

Then there had been Pru's teacher to see and initial inquiries as to the relative merits of correspondence courses
and lessons at small country schools.

After all that, traveling arrangements and finally packing up. The packing didn't take long, because even
between them there was not much to pack. Wenona
wrapped her mother's old photographs and pictures and
other simple trinkets tenderly in tissue and then in more
brown paper before laying them carefully in the big trunk
that she would send by train to Tucka railway station. She
could collect the trunk at the other end, once she knew
what her movements would be and where they would be
staying.

They themselves were going by plane. Expensive, yes,
but again there was this urgent need for haste, and therefore Wenona felt such untoward extravagance was war-
ranted.

Strange to think that before very long these small, humble treasures of her mother's would be back on the
shelves they had known long ago. It all seemed oddly appropriate, that. It helped Wenona to believe in what she
was doing. It made her more certain that it was the
correct—the only—thing. Tuckarimba, fenced off together with its little river plot, spurned and unwanted by
the big Lomax overlord, would know itself to be loved
and needed and remembered. It would come alive again,
and with its revitalization would come the rediscovery of

some of that same happiness and sense of belonging that
Wenona had experienced there as a child. And this time
Pru, too, would have her share.

In the plane she was still preoccupied, exhausted now
too. She flopped back thinking. Beside her, Pru's thin
brown legs were swinging, her sandaled feet not reaching
the floor of the aircraft as the safety belt held her small
cotton-frocked body against the back of the seat. Her
mouse-brown hair stuck out in fine spikes, cropped short,
and she peeped excitedly out of the window with wide-set
eyes. They were peat brown in color, tilting at the outer
corners in a way that gave her animated face a slightly
startled pixie look. They were her mother's eyes, and unlike Wenona's own. Hers were her father's, she supposed,
Irish eyes, deep lake-blue with thick black fringes. Eyes
that could sulk and brood like descending mist on a lough,
eyes that could storm with all the dark threat of a Conne-
mara mountain raincloud, eyes that could sparkle and
dance as mischievously as the dappled waters of Killarney
itself. Dermot's eyes. Dermot, "the free one."

Dermot, the dreamer, more like, she corrected herself
practically. Poor Dermot. Poor Father.

No one there would know that she was his daughter,
and she didn't intend that they should...not until she had
"made good," as she meant to do. It wasn't that she
wanted to *deny* him; no one understood or forgave human
failings better than she did herself, but in the meantime,
for Pru's sake, things had better remain as they were. Pru
had never known about Dermot and her mother's "other
life." It had seemed terribly important at the time that
they should be a complete family. Wenona had been too
young to take part in the decision that changed her surname to that of her stepfather, but she had loved Stroud
Gotthart and she hadn't minded in the least. Later, after
her mother's tragic death, it was with his tacit agreement
that she had allowed Pru to grow up thinking from the

very start that she and Wenona were full sisters, and not merely half-ones. Wenona, after all, was the only female influence in little Pru's life now that her mother had gone. It seemed imperative that the relationship would appear total, and indeed Wenona could almost have believed that Stroud *was* her own father, because that was the way he had always acted, instinctively and irreproachably.

Pru didn't know about Tuckarimba either. She had never even heard of it until two days ago, when Wenona had mentioned it for the first time, taking her quite by surprise.

Pru was now wriggling with anticipation, her thin fingers laced through the harness of the seat belt as she edged nearer the glass to peer down over the silver wing-tip.

"What'll it be like, do you suppose, Nonie?"

"What, darling?"

"What'll it be like, Tucka?"

"You mean the town itself? Oh, just a tiny little place, a country township. It'll probably have a park where you can play among the trees when we go in to sell our vegetables and fruit. And a railway. And some shops and a sprinkling of houses. From up here I should think it will look like a tiny toy village, don't you? Everything looks so small from up here. Those trees down there are just like little dabs of plasticine, see, and that thin brown ribbon is really a big, wide river."

The plane droned on and Wenona let her head fall back against the seat again. How weary she was! And yet it was a merely physical weariness because of all the organizing she had had to do in order to get them both away. There was no Stroud now to do the things a man normally took care of, like tickets and travel and trunks. There hadn't been Stroud for years, really. Not for years and years. When Wenona thought seriously about the constancy of her struggle to support herself and Pru, to be father and

mother and breadwinner combined, she wasn't altogether
surprised at her physical state. Mentally she had coaxed
herself into a sort of wooden torpor, an if-I-can-get-
through-today-I-can-get-through-tomorrow sort of attitude that had not permitted her to think too broadly of
her situation, or too far ahead. That, she had told herself
now, was how she had managed to cope, how she had succeeded in being a stumbling and not very efficient jack-of-
all-trades who yet achieved the daily tasks successfully
enough to keep herself and Pru adequately clothed and
fed.

Now she was for once allowing her imagination the luxury of a free run. In her mind's eye she could visualize the
new Tuckarimba that she was going to make, could smell
the blossoms on the fruit trees, see the boughs sagging under their load of warm ripe fruit. Down nearer the creek
she would have rows of tomatoes neatly staked, trellises
of beans, melon vines on the rampage with their pretty
white and orange flowers, pumpkins and artichokes and
cool green cucumbers.

She would need to get a suitable vehicle, too, to transport her produce. One of those commercial vans probably, with double doors at the back that would open up so
that she could slide things in without squashing them.

She'd think about school for Pru once they had settled
in. Daily attendance along with children would probably
be preferable to correspondence lessons. It would provide
companionship, a little discipline, while allowing Pru the
freedom to run wild at Tuckarimba itself . . . something
the poor scrap had never been able to do in the whole of
her miserably confined eight years.

"That's it, Nonie! Look! And it's not a little toy town at
all. It's a *big* one!"

It was, too. Tucka township was much, much larger
than it had been in her day. It had arrived, no doubt
about it.

As the plane banked low she saw that it now sprawled extensively over the wedge of land between the two rivers that gave Tuckarimba Station its name, "the joining of the creeks." Wide streets were planted with oily-leafed kurrajongs that glistened in the sun. Clusters of cedar and willow and soaring heaven trees were where the tiny park had been. Now she could see an S-shaped swimming pool, spraying fountains, an orange-tiled pavilion and what was in all probability a golf course. The houses, the wide shaded streets, stretched endlessly, broken by green plots of lawn and bright splashes of color that were flower gardens and shrubberies. To the left, right out on the fringe, were the sale yards, silos, railhead, airstrip that characterized all country towns of this sort.

Tucka was almost a city. There would be plenty of demand for fresh garden produce if she worked things properly, got the right contacts. There was obviously a large, busy population, too, compared with the handful of people in her own childhood, and no one would ever connect a too thin, too pale, tall young blond woman called Wenona Gotthart with the pudgy, brown, bespectacled eight-year-old Nonie Dermot, if they remembered the latter at all. Besides, Nonie Dermot had been an only child, and here was the young Miss Gotthart with a sister as well . . . yes, my dear, they've just bought the market garden, the new people—and the old Tuckarimba homestead along with it—quite a pleasant young woman . . . city of course but still—and the sister's a dear little thing with spiky fine hair and a face like an elf.

Wenona's lips twitched. She unfastened Pru's seat belt and her own and gathered their bits and pieces together before following the other passengers from the plane.

On the way in from the airstrip Pru chattered incessantly.

"Oh, look, Nonie, there's the park. Swings and everything, see, and a slippery-slide, a roundabout, a hurdy-

gurdy thing—and look at that fountain—oh, isn't it
beautiful, water coming right out of the fish's mouth. Do
you think he's supposed to be a dolphin, Nonie? He *looks*
a bit like a dolphin, don't you think? He's smiling, and
they do smile, dolphins, don't they? I love Tucka, don't
you, Nonie? Don't you think it's just *beaut*? I think it's a
gorgeous place."

Wenona booked in at one of the better hotels, and
when they had washed and brushed up and had taken
some afternoon tea, she took Pru out and found a garage
that hired out self-drive cars. There should just be time to
reach Tuckarimba before darkness came. She wanted to
read that sign, see in whose hands the transfer of the
property had been placed. It was sure to be a local agent,
either a stock and station firm or a solicitor. Whoever it
was, she would see him first thing in the morning and start
proceedings to acquire the place. Wenona could hardly
wait.

She chose the bigger, better car. It was important to
keep up appearances, wasn't it? Just for the present they
must seem to have some "substance" behind them, some
financial substance, that is. Where business deals were
concerned, you had to think of all these things.

She put her foot down impatiently on the accelerator,
and they sped along, bouncing over the corrugated road,
leaving a flurrying dust trail behind them. Memories
nudged her at every turn. Yes, she remembered that
clump of wilgas and the signpost nailed to that old yellow
box tree. And here was the wooden bridge over the meet-
ingplace of the creeks—the Boogillgar to the right and
Whalebone Creek to the left.

She took the left fork, along the narrower track flanked
by silvery willows watched over by lofty paperbarks,
around the corner that was called Catfish Bend. Ahead
upstream were the serrated outlines of the rocks that gave
the creek its name. Limestone outcrops, smoothed by

wind and water, they spanned the creek from one bank to the other in an oblique arc like the vertebrae of a beached whale corpse. How many times hadn't she leaped glee-fully from stone to stone, from one bank to the other, throwing pebbles and sticks into the hurrying channels that rushed among the rocks and eventually merged with the slowly frothing pool below!

Another bend and they would see Tuckarimba.

She bit back the words that she had almost spoken aloud. Pru must not guess that she, too, was not a stranger to this track.

"Do you think we're nearly there, Nonie?" Pru sounded a little anxious. "It's beginning to get quite dark. The lady at the hotel said it gets dark awfully quickly out here in the country."

"Not to worry, poppet. It can't be far now. I've been measuring the miles on the speedo, you see. And I've got a torch. We won't stay long. Once we see who I have to contact tomorrow, we'll go back to town and have a proper meal. You'd like that, wouldn't you? We can come back in the daytime to see it all properly. Are you tired?"

"Mmm, I am. Aren't you? All that packing. I hate packing, don't you, Nonie? I hope we never have to move again, not ever, once we get our very own house like you said we will. I'm longing to get into it, and I won't have that narky old Mrs. Beeston telling me to 'keep my voice down' all the time and 'shut that door,' and 'just look at your sandals, they're *covered* in sand, you've brought in half the *beach*!' "

Wenona couldn't help smiling. Pru was a born mimic and could imitate the landlady's falsetto carpings to per-fection. It was naughty, though, and to be discouraged. Wenona would have checked her for it but she felt too keyed up right now to bother. It couldn't matter, anyway. Not *now*!

As the car rounded the bend and crested the brow of the hill, she braked and pulled in at the side of the road.

"Look, Pru, that's . . . that must be it down there. You can see the roof through the trees, and the creek looping around behind."

"That big place, Nonie? Right up the far end with the hills just behind it? I don't see any creek though. I mean, it's way *above* the creek. But isn't it huge? Quite fabulous!"

Wenona swallowed in dismay. She had only just spied the outline that Pru had been looking at away in the distance, the outline of a great long homestead poised in a magnificent position that commanded a view of the entire valley.

The new Tuckarimba, tucked into a fold in the hills, sheltered from the elements, remote from the public highway beneath, appeared as secluded and mysterious in this hushed bush twilight as a Tibetan monastery.

"I don't mean up there, I mean down here, right beneath us. See?"

"Oh, yes, I see. What a dear old house, Nonie! It's got fingers of roof going out in all directions, hasn't it? It looks all muddled and wobbly, as if it didn't know which way to grow next. Oh, Nonie, I love it already! Let's go down and see it closer."

"Yes, let's." Wenona's voice was suddenly husky. She started the engine again and took the car down to the creek flats slowly, savoring every moment of this homecoming of hers.

It was like a dream, and yet the poignant reality of it sent delicious tremors through her thin, weary frame. She was here! She had made it! Nonie had come home to Tuckarimba . . . and, this time, so had Pru!

And then, as the homestead came properly into view right on the level of the creek flat where the car was now cruising slowly along, Nonie saw that something wasn't quite as she had expected it to be. Lights were on in that squat, sprawling old house, and even as she slowed to a halt and stepped out, another light blinked on, winking out at her like a warning signal.

It wasn't empty! The house wasn't empty!

Unreasoning panic gripped her throat. Something of her urgency reached out to little Pru, skipping along at her side.

"What is it, Nonie? What's the matter?"

She put out her hand and Nonie grasped it, dragging her sister along in haste.

"I don't know. Perhaps it's just a caretaker, but perhaps it's . . . it's been . . . sold. Perhaps we're too late. Quickly, darling, hurry. Let's see if we can see the noticeboard. There's a big notice that says it's for sale."

But there wasn't. Not now. Playing her torch over the ground near the wattle tree, Nonie could see where the boarding had been. But now there was nothing. Nothing at all.

"It's not there!" Pru's voice was a thin wail.

"No, it's not."

When Pru began to whimper, Nonie turned and gave her a savage little shake.

"If . . . you . . . dare . . . to . . . cry, Pru," she said very slowly, emphatically, in a strangely strangled voice that held an unfamiliar note of desperation, "If you dare to cry *now*, Pru, I'll . . . I'll *whip* you, so help me, I will!"

"Oh, no, you won't!" A voice spoke from the shadows behind them. It came with a suddenness, a severity that sent the two of them into each other's arms, clinging together in fright.

"Oh, no, you won't. You'll do no such thing while *I'm* around to witness it, my impetuous young madam! And you don't know much about children, either, if you can't tell that that kid's almost out on her feet, plain tuckered out."

"Who are you?"

Wenona disengaged herself from Pru's skinny, clinging arms with as much dignity as she could muster and gazed at the tall emerging figure of the man who stepped out from the trees behind them. He was leading a horse by the reins. He loomed near her in the dusk, and the horse's hooves crackled on the dried, fallen leaves as it followed its master haltingly, stopping obediently when he did a few feet from Wenona herself. His broad-shouldered outline was near enough to seem menacing, towering over her in the gathering darkness.

Nonie took a grip on herself. She wasn't the nervous sort, she told herself firmly.

"Who are you?" she asked again, cursing her voice for its betraying tremor, because already she thought she knew!

CHAPTER TWO

"JASON LOMAX. What are you doing here?"

"Not . . . not *Jacey* Lomax?" Her confidence ebbed immediately as her worst fears were confirmed.

"Jason Lomax. My initials happen to be J.C., certainly. That's why my friends call me Jacey," he informed her in a forbidding tone that said *she* wasn't one of those friends, or likely to be! "You are trespassing," he added coldly.

"Inspecting a property that's up for sale can hardly be termed trespassing," she retorted, matching the man's chilly tones.

"You mean the house?" He jerked his head toward the shadowed bulk of the sprawling buildings.

He had taken off the wide-brimmed felt hat that he had been wearing, and now he was twirling it between his fingers, watching her in the dwindling light of dusk. The horse, whose reins were looped carelessly over his arm, nuzzled gently at his back with soft, snuffling noises.

"Yes, the house." She was more relaxed now. "I'd like to buy it."

"I'm sorry but that's not possible." He didn't sound very sorry, though, merely casual in a definite sort of way.

"It's not *sold*?" Her heart sank.

"No, but it's not for sale either. As far as you are concerned, there's relatively little difference."

"But it was. It *was* for sale?" Her voice rose in spite of all her efforts to appear calm. "There was a big sale notice, right there by the wattle tree. I saw where it was. The stand itself is there yet."

"The stand, but not the notice." He sounded maddeningly indifferent.

"But why?"

"I've changed my mind in the meantime," he informed her discouragingly in a voice that also told her clearly that he did not consider his reasons to be any business of hers.

"In the . . . meantime." Nonie brightened, hope reviving. "Does that mean that you *will* be selling it?"

"It means I may," he returned brusquely. "Sometime," he emphasized, as if aware of the need to quell her newly springing optimism.

"Then I'll stay around, Mr. Lomax. I've . . . I've come a long way to get this house."

"In that case, it would be unfair to mislead you, Miss . . . ?"

"Gotthart, Wenona Gotthart. This is my sister Pru."

"It's not worth waiting for, Miss Gotthart." He chucked Pru under the chin with long brown fingers. "It could be a fair time."

"It's worth it to me." There were tears in her voice; in her eyes too, just a little. "It's worth it to *me*. We've come a . . . a very long way, but I can wait. If you'll just give me the first chance of it, when you sell?"

"It could be years."

"Years?" She was startled at the way he'd said the word. He had made it sound like forever, an infinity, eternity.

"Well, a couple, anyway. On the other hand, I might put it on the market again fairly soon. It depends very much on several contingencies of a personal nature."

"Oh, I see." He obviously was not going to elaborate upon what the contingencies were. "Well—" she squared her shoulders, reached for Pru's hand "—I can wait, Mr. Lomax. I'll stick around."

The man was peering at her intently. His face above hers was darkly tanned, merging into the night itself. It was a long face, square jawed, heavy browed, that was all that she could tell. She couldn't see his expression at all.

In a way that was a comfort, because it meant that he couldn't see hers either!

"I don't think I would stick around, if I were you," he advised her more gently. "I think the wisest course where you are concerned would be to go home."

Home? Home is where the heart is, Mr. Lomax, or didn't you know?

"We don't, er, have a home, exactly, just at the moment." Her voice faltered a little, uncertainly, as she debated with herself as to how much she should tell him. "But I'll stay in town, and you can contact me when it becomes available. Who is your man of business?"

"The Tintoola estate office is in the main street. You can hardly miss it." His tone was dry.

"Oh, I see. Well, when I—when we find somewhere permanent to stay, I'll let them know so that they can contact me."

"Don't bank on it."

"I've learned never to bank on anything, Mr. Lomax," she retorted, stiltedly, because that was just what she *had* done, wasn't it! "Come, Pru."

She turned away stumblingly toward the car, and the man put his hat on his head once again and began to lead the horse back in among the trees. She could hear them crashing through the scrub together.

Nonie put Pru into the car and got in herself. When she had closed her door, she put her hands on the steering wheel without attempting to start the engine. Then she put her head forward and rested her forehead against her hands. Sitting there, slumped against the wheel, she tried to get a grip of herself. She must get herself in hand, overwhelming though the disappointment was. Maybe things would work out in the end. Maybe he'd put the house up again quite soon. She'd need to find a job and lodgings. They couldn't stay in that expensive hotel—

"Move over."

"What?"

She looked up, dazed. Her mind was almost too weary to alter course and take in the fact that the man was back.

He had her door open and was leaning into the car.

"Move over. Hop into the back, young 'un, and give your big sister some room."

"What are you doing?" Nonie gazed at him blankly.

"Driving you back to town, what else?" He sounded abrupt, impatient.

"You're doing no such thing."

"Like to bet?" Already his bulk was forcing her to shift grudgingly from her position at the wheel.

"I'm perfectly capable of driving myself, thanks."

"That's debatable. I don't think you are."

"I am!"

His eyes narrowed, glinted dangerously.

"You're damn near snapping point, if you ask me. The signs are all there, and I've no intention of having a hysterical female on either my property or my conscience. Besides, your kid sister wants to get home to bed, and I'll get her there quicker than you will."

There was no point in arguing. Nonie could see that he was not in the mood to have his decisions disputed. Probably no one *ever* disputed decisions that were made by Jacey Lomax. They wouldn't dare. He was the kind who'd always have an improbable ace tucked up his sleeve, and if he didn't he'd invent one!

He was also the kind who could drive a car, even an unfamiliar rented model, with quiet competence and impressive speed. His hands went unerringly to all the right switches. The dashboard light lighted the panel and also lit up a hawk-nosed, craggy profile. The engine whirred to life and headlights swept the road ahead as he turned the car expertly and took them back toward the town.

Nonie lay back against the lumpy upholstery, seething. A hysterical female, he'd called her!

Finally she broke the silence resentfully.

"I hope you don't think I *meant* it when I said I'd whip Pru. I've never so much as laid a finger on her, quite honestly. It was just a—a—an empty threat."

"Was it?" Skeptically.

"Well, of course it was!" she replied indignantly. "You don't really think—"

The wide shoulders shrugged, maddeningly.

"Leave it, little one. What does it matter what I think?"

He had a point there certainly. Nonie, rebuffed yet still strangely dissatisfied, relapsed into a huffy silence.

She could not keep it up for long.

"What have you done with your horse?" she asked now, unable to contain her curiosity.

"I've bushed him."

"Bushed him?"

"Turned him loose."

"Won't he wander away?"

"He won't go far. He's lame . . . cast a shoe. That's why I was leading him in the first place."

"Oh, I see." A pause. "Had you led him far?"

His lips twitched.

"Far enough, Miss Gotthart, but I'm hardly decrepit yet, fortunately. If I hadn't been taking a shortcut home on foot, I wouldn't have seen you standing there in the dark like a lost Sioux princess."

"A—*what?*"

"Winona, the Indian firstborn daughter." He was laughing at her. "Didn't you know that's what it means?"

"It's spelled with an *e.*"

"Same thing, *i* or *e.* It's not a usual name."

"My friends call me Nonie." She couldn't resist that one, spoken with precisely the same inflection on the word "friends" as he had given it himself.

He ignored the thrust, except perhaps for the faintest tightening of the level mouth.

"That fairness isn't Sioux. It's almost Teutonic . . . Gotthart. Are you German?"

"Our father was."

Our father. Our father, which art in Heaven. No, that was Father, capital *F*. *Our* father was German, small *f*. And *my* father was Irish. And *my* father's in Heaven, too. Poor Dermot. Poor dreamer.

And poor firstborn daughter. No, not firstborn but *only* born. Only daughter, because poor Dermot hadn't waited in this world long enough to have another child. Poor Dermot had . . . had . . . .

No, maybe he hadn't after all. It *could* have been an accident, even Bundy had admitted that much. It *could* have been.

Oh, Lord, what a mess life could be! Such a muddle—

"Please! Could you stop the car?" she managed to gasp.

"What?" The man glanced her way swiftly.

"I'm going to be sick," Nonie said urgently.

"Nonie always gets sick if she's a passenger," explained Pru helpfully from the back seat "Nonie gets sick even in the front. Nonie always says it's different if she's dr—"

But the man didn't wait to hear. He had already brought the car to a skidding halt, leaned across and flung open Nonie's door, and Nonie staggered quietly out into the night and away among the trees. There she knelt at the bole of a mottled eucalyptus, leaned dizzily against its sustaining trunk. She leaned there until someone pulled her away firmly and held her head quite expertly.

She felt the man's hand clamped calmly across her brow, and when the spasm had passed he pressed a handkerchief into her palm. She accepted it wordlessly, allowed herself to be drawn back against his chest, helpless, humiliated beyond belief.

"I'm terribly sorry."

"No, stay there a minute yet. You'll be better soon."

His hand was still there, keeping her head against his shirt. Presently he turned her around to face him and wiped the dew from her forehead, watching her speculatively.

"Better now?"

She nodded. "I'm terribly sorry," she muttered again. Her voice trembled with the sheer shame of it.

"No, it's I who am sorry." He helped her to her feet with grave, unembarrassed courtesy. It seemed that Jacey Lomax could be quite kind when he chose. Kind, provided that *you* were weaker than *he* was, she decided shrewdly . . . and she undoubtedly was, right now! She was oddly reluctant to abandon the support of his arm around her. Nonie almost groaned aloud. The indignity of it—that she couldn't stand properly without his help, that he had been there to see her like this!

"All right?" His eyes were crinkling in the moonlight almost as if he had guessed her thoughts.

"Yes, thank you." She would have pulled away but he kept an iron hold on her arm right back to the car.

There he paused, asked solemnly, "Would you prefer to drive?"

"No, I'll be all right. I think I'm too tired to drive. You were right, I'd have made a hash of it."

A grin hovered. "Is that an olive branch by any chance? A pipe of peace from the Sioux maiden?" She could see his teeth gleaming in the swarthy tan of his face as the grin spread and his lips parted. "I think I prefer the Teutonic tigress to the submissive Sioux after all," Jacey Lomax taunted lazily as he saw her seated once more.

"So you *did* think it funny," she flashed, anger bringing an immediate stain to her pale cheeks. "I knew you did! I just knew you were laughing all the time!"

"Let's just say that I didn't expect to see you on your knees quite so soon after that bristling display of independence back there," he admitted satirically.

"I think you're hateful!" Her words were muffled, choked with rage.

"Yes, I know. You thought it from the word go."

How that soothing tone could irritate! He probably knew that, too.

"I hope I never set eyes on you again, *ever!*" she stormed furiously, her blue gaze flashing darkly. And then she remembered to whom it was that she was speaking, after all. To none other than Jacey Lomax. The owner of the house that she wanted so very, very badly. "I mean...what I mean—"

"You're thinking of the house," he supplied uncannily. "Well, don't worry, Miss Gotthart. If it becomes available, you may deal directly with my estate office. I know how you feel. You're sore as hell at being sick in front of a man, but believe me you needn't be. I've a pack of nephews and nieces, and it's not the first time I've helped out. You must have seen for yourself I'm a dab hand at it."

Monstrous creature, she thought wearily, leaning back and shutting her eyes. First he'd called her a hysterical female and now he was as good as telling her that she was just another child.

When they reached the hotel, it was to discover that Pru was sound asleep. In her skimpy cotton print frock, she was lying full length along the back seat, one hand on her cheek, the other dangling over the edge of the bench.

"I'll take her. Where's your room?"

Already Jacey Lomax had stooped and gathered the child carefully into his arms. Without speaking further he followed Nonie up the stairs and into the bedroom, where he laid Pru gently on the bed without waking her up. He'd probably done that hundreds of times too, with those nephews and nieces of whom he spoke.

At the door he turned. "Good night, Miss Gotthart," he said levelly.

"What about the car? How will you get back to Tuckarimba?"

"I'll take it back now. One of my men can bring it back in the morning. I'll square the garage."

"Thank you all the same but *I* shall pay the garage," she corrected him crisply. "I hired the car after all. Besides, I prefer not to feel in your debt in even the smallest way."

"Not even the smallest?" There was a glint in his eye that told her he was recalling, as she was, the indisputable comfort of his hold in her recent distress, the steadying contact of that rough masculine palm against her perspiring brow. The right touch at the right time!

"You've done quite enough," she told him stiltedly, unable to subdue a rosy blush. "Goodbye."

The man inclined his head, twirled the wide-brimmed hat in his brown fingers. "Good night." And he was gone.

"Mr. Lomax?" Nonie opened the door and dashed after the long, retreating figure.

"Well?"

"Mr. Lomax, what was your asking price for the old homestead . . . *if* you sell, I mean?"

A pause.

"Twelve thousand dollars."

"Twelve *thousand?*" Her breath caught on the words.

The Lomax man was watching her. In the light of the hall his eyes were a clear, hard gray, cool as a mountain waterfall. They flickered, narrowed.

"Does that seem a lot to you?" he asked. The question came with a sort of quiet, deliberate care.

"No. No, of course not." She looked away. "It's worth all of that, I'm sure."

"It's a gift at the price. There are the orchards and river land included. That puts a mere token value on the house and outbuildings. I'm not out to make a profit on it. Rather, let's say that when and if the time comes I prefer to dispose of it to the right person, who will of necessity be my close neighbor."

"Yes, I see your point," she conceded awkwardly. "Well, thank you for telling me anyway."

She didn't look back, but Nonie had a feeling that he was still standing at the end of the hall when she reached her room again and shut the door behind her.

Next morning over breakfast, she pondered her problems. Twelve thousand dollars was an awful lot of money. She had barely a quarter of that amount. It was enough to raise a loan maybe, but with interest to pay too, it was imperative that she keep what capital she had intact. Not only intact, she'd need to try to *add* to it somehow. That meant a job and moving out of here to cheaper lodgings immediately.

Nonie sighed. She had a feeling that she had been through all this before. It was tough on Pru, too, that her promised freedom would have to be postponed. She told the child as gently as she could.

"But at least we'll be in this pretty town, Pru, and we can get to know the people while we're waiting. You'll be able to start school on Monday. It's right next to the park. I'll take you down and show you, and then you can play on the swings and roundabout for a while, and I'll make fresh arrangements for us."

"Okay, Nonie."

Oh, to be eight years old and have the decisions and responsibilities taken out of one's hands. Pru had taken the news with philosophical cheerfulness, knowing that Nonie would soon come up with some other alternative. She always did!

"Can I go swimming?"

"Better not, just for this morning. I may be quite a while. Stick to the swings and things just for today, poppet."

"Okay, Nonie."

Afterward, Nonie consulted the proprietor of the hotel. He was middle-aged, quite understanding, even helpful in an avuncular sort of way. He eyed her doubtfully.

"A job? The only easy job to come by is domestic work; nobody wants that these days. The little girl could be a problem there, unless it was in a hotel or something. No, we've nothing at all here in the way of vacancies, miss, as you can see. Your best bet would be the Pink Pelican. They're always short-staffed because nobody ever stays for long," he informed her depressingly.

"Would they take Pru as well?"

"They'd take Pru and your granny too, if you were willing to sign on. You'd better go down and ask. The big ugly pink place at the far end of the street going out of town. You'd have passed it coming from the strip. You can't miss it."

Well, he was right about that, thought Nonie soberly, as she walked across the concrete courtyard to the door of the Pink Pelican. It wasn't the sort of place one could overlook. In fact, it was almost incredible in its ugliness and dinginess. The walls were of that nasty, unsubtle, candy-pink shade often referred to as "lolly," and the window frames were brown, peeling in places to show that before that they had been cream and by the look of the odd deeper chip even green at one time. The pelican that dangled from his rusty hinges over the portico wasn't pink at all and probably never had been. He was a dirty gray color with an orange beak with a broken tip, and one of his legs was missing. Or maybe he had only ever had one leg, standing on it in contemplation in the way a heron does.

Inside the Pink Pelican, Nonie's request to join the staff was met with even more enthusiasm than predictions had led her to expect. They were very shorthanded, they explained, and, no, they didn't mind the youngster as long as she kept out of the public premises and away from the front of the building. There was a place at the back where she could play while Nonie herself was occupied, and if Nonie didn't mind long hours she could earn some overtime pay as well. The money was good if people were willing to work for it.

Nonie trudged back to the park to report to Pru on her success. Then they went back to have lunch, and in the afternoon they moved their things down to the Pink Pelican. On the way Nonie called at the car-hire garage, and paid her account. The car had been returned that morning by one of Mr. Lomax's station hands, just as he had promised.

The room that Nonie was to share with Pru was in an annex at the back of the place. The annex was hardly more than a long weatherboard hut whose single width was taken up by one identical room after another, with access from a corridor running down the side. This long shed had obviously been added on as staff quarters, but at the moment all of the rooms were empty except for their own and one other, occupied by a plump, henna-haired woman in her forties who told Nonie that she was the "stillroom maid." Nonie was to discover, in the weeks that followed, that the "stillroom maid" had a roving commission, rushing from place to place wherever she might be most urgently wanted, just as Nonie herself had to do because of the inadequacy of the help on hand.

That first night she spent altering the hems of the black uniforms with which they had provided her and running in the sides of the garments to give them a better fit. She turned the procedure into a fun thing for Pru's benefit, folding and tilting the white caps at the different angles, and there was much giggling between them as they pirouetted in front of the mirror, posturing and making faces at each other. But inside herself, Nonie could not quell her doubts and misgivings. She knew this was not the sort of place she would have chosen to take Pru, yet it seemed the best that offered at the moment. Her misgivings extended further, to her own abilities, her lack of experience. What if she proved to be inefficient and they dismissed her?

She need not, as it turned out, have worried on that score. Far from dismissing her, they worked her to the bone, but as they had promised they paid her well for doing so. She was kept at it till late at night, and therefore she hardly saw Pru after school but was able to arrange her hours so that they could at least breakfast together before she saw the little girl off in the morning.

In the first few weeks, the early rising and late nights, the heavy physical activity, took their toll of Nonie. Her muscles ached, her limbs felt leaden and her hands became red and raw although she creamed them diligently each evening before she flopped thankfully into bed. If she had been thin before, she was almost ethereal now.

And then, after a month or so she seemed to get her second wind. Not only was she more accustomed to the constancy of her varied chores, but there was also the satisfaction of finding that Pru, too, had reached the same stage with her schooling. She seemed to be enjoying her lessons by all accounts and made proper friends with whom she stayed playing in the park until teatime. Once Nonie had assured herself that there were responsible attendants at the baths, she gave her consent to swimming sessions as well. Pru would come in from these with a ravenous appetite, and the plain, reasonably wholesome food at evening tea would disappear in a flash. All the time, the pay mounted regularly, and anytime Nonie was particularly weary or inclined to be a little depressed, she would buck herself up by remembering her goal, the dear old homestead at Tuckarimba, with its little orchard and the extra acres for the market garden that she hoped some day to make hers.

This evening she had had an especially trying day and was now in the room behind the bar, sluicing glasses and slinging them back through the hatch to the counter. It was a Friday night, and the "stillroom maid" had chosen to take her halfday rather than count it as extra hours, which was what she had always done before. Nonie had been sent to fill in for her, and so far things hadn't gone too badly.

The noise was deafening. It came in great gusts of sound every time the stillroom door swung back on its hinges. The place was packed. Every time Nonie went through to scoop up an armful of used glasses, she marveled at the thickness of the atmosphere, the wafting clouds of smoke, the sticky smell of heavy beer.

And they called this fun!

She had just returned a tray of clean glasses through the hatch and was in the act of gathering up some more empty ones at the end of the counter when the scuffling broke out in the corner where she was. Scuffling, at *first*. But with the most alarming rapidity it developed into what could only be described as a good-going fight.

Nonie cowered against the wall. Nobody seemed to be taking any notice of her at all, which was of some comfort, as she was effectively hedged in all of a sudden. The men about her were by now too busy hurling lewd epithets at each other and battering each other with clenched fists that seemed to her widening eyes as big as outsized hams. She had never seen anything like it in her life! She could only stand there, ducking instinctively as she saw the blows landing, gasping with horror as blood began to spurt and bruised eyes to close.

"Stop! *Stop* it, I say!"

But of course they ignored her pleas. To be truthful, Nonie doubted if they even heard them.

Her horror increased. She had to get out of here. She *must* get out! Somehow she stiffened her faltering limbs and sidled along the wall toward the door.

"Not going, gorgeous?"

He was young, quite good-looking in a way with his white shirt and tie, his best town garb. He was also very drunk. He pulled himself away from the table where one of his adversaries had just flung him, leering amiably around as if enjoying the melee. As Nonie dashed past he made a grab at her.

"Hey there, c'mon! The party's only starting!"

She snatched herself away, felt the bib of her neat white apron torn from its pin. As the young man's fingers caught her cap, that too, came off and fell to the floor, somewhere in among the pounding feet.

"Let me *go!*"

She groped among the flailing legs, retrieved the crumpled remains of her frilly white headgear and at last managed to escape into the air outside.

Nonie had never been so relieved in all her life. For a moment she simply leaned against the wall, panting to recover her breath. Then she held her cap between her teeth as she attempted to pin up her tumbling, fair mane into the neat coil upon which the little white bonnet had been perched. Her fingers were trembling to such an extent that the task was well-nigh impossible.

"Drat it!" she muttered in frustration, then her hands paused in their task as a man came with long strides over the concrete toward the entrance near where she stood. A tall man, he was. A man in pale, neatly creased drill trousers and polished boots and a crisp white shirt with a cravat knotted casually at the throat. A man with thick black hair and scowling brows, and eyes that were a piercing gray in the mellow light from the doorway.

"Good grief! *You!*" The eyes had fastened themselves on her huddled form in the semidarkness a little way along the wall.

"What are *you* doing here?" Jacey Lomax sounded surprised and somehow angry.

"Oh, Mr. Lomax, *please*—" she pushed herself away from the wall, relief washing over her at the sight of someone she knew; someone *responsible* "—please, Mr. Lomax, go in and stop them," she gasped. "They'll listen to you! They . . . they're killing each other in there. Do hurry! They'll *listen* to you, you see." Her eyes were wild, her voice taut, high with strain.

Nonie's fingers returned distractedly to her hair. Oh, this wretched hair! It had tumbled down all over again, spilling over her shoulders almost to her waist. The comb that had secured it fell too. She stooped to retrieve it, then followed the direction of the man's gaze. Ineffectually she tried to cover the rent in the front of her dress where the pin had caught and torn it.

"Here, let me." Jacey Lomax took the pin from her fumbling fingers and turned her toward the light. His face was completely without expression as he brought the pieces of black material together, covered them with the flap of frilled white cotton that was her apron bib and slid the pin through, fastening it deftly. He took not the slightest notice of the thuds, curses, bumps and shouting that still emanated from the room beyond them.

"Why are you here?" he said again. "Miss Gotthart, will you leave that blasted thing for the moment and *answer* me?" he barked suddenly, taking the squashed cap from her and ramming it into his pocket.

"I work here. But what about you?"

"I've come for my men. They're in there." A careless jerk of the dark head toward the door.

In there? His men? And he sounded as though he couldn't care less!

"They're not men, they're monsters. Jungle beasts, or worse. If they're yours, I advise you to get them out as speedily as possible," she urged him coldly, "before they succeed in bashing each other to a pulp."

He shrugged. "It wouldn't be the first time."

"*And* they're wrecking the place . . . the furniture . . . some of the tables are matchwood already and . . . and chairs . . . glasses. . . . " Nonie gestured impressively, yet he remained unimpressed.

"Not the first time either." The man seemed to find her remarks amusing. "The usual procedure," he went on to inform her, "after *this* sort of spree is, I pay the pub and the men pay me. In other words, they don't mind paying for their fun."

"Fun! You call that fun?"

"*I* don't, but *they* do." A smile lurked somewhere in the depths of the level gray eyes that were still looking down at her. "Haven't you heard how the song goes?

> When we go to spree in town
> We live like pigs in clover?"

"No, I haven't—" her voice was tart "—but the words are apt, that much strikes me quite forcibly!" She shuddered in spite of herself and then found to her dismay that somehow she couldn't stop. Even her teeth were chattering, although it was a warm night.

"Did they hurt you?" he asked instantly, and Nonie guessed by the swift concern in his voice that she must look as white and witless as she felt.

"No, not me, but each other." Her voice trembled. "They'll murder each other, I tell you."

"The hell they will. They never quite manage to go as far as that, although I reckon there'll be a few jokers in there feeling pretty sorry for themselves in the morning. You should know better than to intervene."

"I... wasn't... intervening." She pushed her hair back indignantly, looked up at him with candid, hollow eyes that still felt glazed with fright. "I was trying to get away, and I nearly did, I was ... qu-quite n-near the d-door when one of them grabbed me. I don't think he even knew wh-what he was d-doing—"

"Possibly not." He pressed his lips together. "Come with me."

Jacey Lomax took her arm and led her around the side

of the building toward the portico where the dirty gray pelican danced sadly on his one leg from the iron hinges. She had no option but to go where he was taking her, because his grasp was firm and curiously unrelenting.

When they reached the porch, she resisted.

"I'm not supposed to go in the front. I don't think you understand."

"At the moment you are my guest," he told her crushingly.

Inside, he pushed her down into a chair in the lounge and jabbed at the bell on the wall.

"Yes, Mr. Lomax?" The proprietor's eyes widened as they took in the identity of Mr. Lomax's companion.

"Bring me a beer, please, will you, and a brandy for the lady. And a pot of tea for two." Jacey Lomax's snapping eyes were forbidding questions.

"Yes, Mr. Lomax."

"I reckon things are getting a bit wild through there at the back. You'd better send Fred and Stanley to cool them down. I'll settle with you later, as usual."

"Most certainly, Mr. Lomax."

"Are all those men yours?" asked Nonie weakly when the proprietor had gone away.

"Only four. The others are from surrounding stations, and some from the town itself. Thanks, Barney. Just put them there."

Jacey Lomax waited while the other man placed the drinks and tea on the table between them, and when he had gone away again passed her a small glass with the brandy in it.

"Skoal!" He held up his own tall tankard of frothing beer.

"Er, skoal," she replied gallantly, matching his gesture with hers. She loathed spirits, but tonight she had a feeling that she needed this!

Nonie sipped in silence and then, because the taste was

so repellent, took the last part of her drink at a gulp and lay back, closing her eyes as the fiery stuff coursed through her bracingly. She heard the chink of crockery as he poured the tea, and then a subdued rustling brought her eyes open again.

Jacey Lomax was rolling himself a cigarette, tilting the rubbed tobacco carefully from his brown palm onto a wafer of paper.

"You don't object?"

She shook her head. "Please do."

"Take your tea now." His lighter flared and he leaned back drawing deeply on the neat cylinder he had just fashioned. When he had made sure it was alight satisfactorily he looked up. "Feeling steadier?"

"Yes, thank you."

"Then maybe you'd care to answer that question I asked you several times out there, and which you thought you'd successfully dispatched."

"I don't understand."

"I think you do. Why *here?*" He leaned forward, his eyes hard.

"Why what here?"

"Why work here?" He was being heavily patient, his voice level.

Nonie put down her cup and shrugged, a little flippantly.

"Why not? Some people have to work for a living, Mr. Lomax."

"Granted." He watched her through a curl of smoke. "Now try again."

She licked her lips. The man's composure was extraordinarily unnerving.

"The . . . the pay's good," she said defensively. "And they don't mind having Pru along with me. Her board and lodging are thrown in. That's quite a big consideration."

Jacey Lomax smoked in silence for a while. It seemed to be a very thoughtful silence indeed.

"Haven't you and the kid really got a home to go to?"

"We're waiting to get into it," she told him pointedly, and she was rewarded to see a tinge of color darkening his tan. There was something about this domineering creature that made her itch to needle him, and Nonie was inordinately pleased with herself at having succeeded.

"Haven't you a home to go *back* to? You know perfectly well what I mean! Where did you come from? Sydney? They told me you got off the Sydney plane."

So he'd been making inquiries, had he? Well, in a way that was natural, to want to know where a potential buyer for your house had come from, especially when the old and new homesteads happened to be so close to one another. She had better be reasonable over this, although she felt resentful of his interference, tempted to tell him to mind his own business.

"Yes, Sydney."

"Well, then?"

"We only had rooms there, the same as we have here. There was no point in returning. In any case, traveling can be expensive, and I want to be easily accessible to your, er, estate office."

"What sort of work did you do in Sydney? Not this?"

"Not exactly this."

"What?"

"Oh, this and that." She shrugged a little helplessly. "It's difficult to explain. I'd done a course in design and sign writing, but the commercial prospects are overrated. I mean, once you've got a sign you don't think about changing it for years. Somehow everyone seemed to have signs after a while."

"What else?"

"Oh, all sorts of things. Picture framing. There was an art gallery that used to put stuff my way. But I don't see an art gallery in Tucka and everyone has signs already, haven't they?"

"Your parents?"

"They're dead." Her tone didn't invite sympathy. She got up, smoothed her apron down over the drab black crepe of her dress. "Thanks for the tea and the drink, Mr. Lomax. You probably saved my life, and certainly my honor!" She laughed a little huskily, turned toward the hall and remarked brightly, "Well, I'd better return to the nether region or I might be feeling as sorry for myself in the morning as those men of yours, if for different reasons! Chambermaids aren't encouraged to loll around in the front lounge drinking brandy with the patrons!"

She hadn't gone two steps when he caught up to her. It had taken only one of his long strides to do it. Another brought him in front of her, right in her path. Now she felt both her wrists grasped firmly, halting her in her tracks.

"You stubborn little fool!" Jacey Lomax's voice had gone deep and rough. His eyes held the gray steeliness of controlled anger. "You can't go on with this business, and you know it. Hell, you'll fade away, crack up. You're white as paper, thin as a wraith and your nerves are jangling like fire buckets underneath all that calm. In fact, you're as taut as a fiddle string and you look like nothing on earth, if you want the truth."

"Well, *thanks*," she drawled sarcastically, and there was a flash of pure rebellion in her own eyes as she tried to draw away.

His mouth leveled. A muscle flicked at the side of his cheek.

"You know well enough what I'm trying to tell you. You must see what you're doing to yourself? Why, if I hadn't seen that pale hair dangling around your face out there in the half-light, I mightn't have recognized you at all."

"Then perhaps it's a pity you did," she retorted coldly, and that made him release her wrists instantly.

"If that's how you feel about it, then I, too, regret it."

The man's eyes were as cool as his tone. "I'll say good night, Miss Gotthart."

There was just the hint of a formal bow, and then he went back to the table, stubbed his cigarette butt into the cheap tin ashtray with the beer advertisement running around the sides.

"Mr. Lomax?" Nonie had remembered something. "Could I have my cap, please?"

He took it from his pocket without a word.

"Thanks." To her dismay, Nonie's voice was wobbling and tears had unaccountably filled her eyes. She hated making enemies and it seemed that tonight she certainly had. "I'm sorry if I seem ungrateful," she told him in a tight voice. "I know you meant it kindly."

He was searching her face. His own features were set in granite lines. The sheer inscrutability of the man made Nonie dither.

"I—I don't expect you to understand," she said a little desperately, looking away, "but I simply can't afford for people to be *kind*. It's a quality just as easily withdrawn as it is bestowed, and if it's *there* one is tempted to lean on it. It's a risk I just can't take. Please say you understand? Just a little bit?"

Her eyes came up to his, misty with pleading. His were unreadable. Unmoved.

"I'm not as slow as you appear to think," said Jacey Lomax slowly. "I had got the message already."

There was a quiet irony in his voice that told Nonie he hadn't really got it at all. Her explanation had been completely misunderstood.

The knowledge of it filled her with an unfamiliar fatalistic despair as she walked away to resume her duties. She had emerged from this encounter strangely bruised, and there was a curious little pain that lingered yet, somewhere inside her chest.

CHAPTER THREE

"SEEMS LIKE you ain't ter relieve me in drinking hours ever again, after last night's escapade," said Doris of the henna hair next morning. "So that's the last of me Friday nights out till they can get someone else ter do it instead."

"Who said so?" Nonie was indignant. "It wasn't *my* fault they all started fighting like a bunch of grizzlies, was it?"

"Jacey Lomax said so. Gave it ter Barney straight."

"And what business is it of his, may I ask?" Nonie found that she was really nettled. The Lomax man still seemed to have that particular effect upon her, and a few additional ones as well that were far harder to define!

"I reckon Jacey don't like his men lookin' like a case of squashed plums when 'e's wantin' them ter do a muster for 'im next mornin'," explained Doris nasally. "You gotter be *firm* with 'em, ducks, these blokes. You gotter be *tough*, see. It's the only language that lot recognizes." She sighed. "Maybe it takes an older woman ter keep 'em in order, more experienced than what you are."

"It's not *my* place to discipline Jacey Lomax's men, or any other," Nonie returned tartly.

"Funny, that's just exactly what Jacey was sayin' ter Barney when I come in last night, them words exactly. Yer didn't get together on it by any chance, did yer?" Doris's tone was dry.

"You know I didn't, Dorrie. I—I can't stand the man. He's nothing but an interfering autocrat."

"Big words, fer a big fella." Doris giggled. "You better not let the rest of the town hear you talkin' about Jacey

like that. He's the kingpin around 'ere, yer know, and 'e's
real popular too. Does a lot of decent things fer people on
the qt, does Jacey. And yer gotter admit 'e looks ... well,
wow! ... real class." She shrugged her plump shoulders
comically. "I wish 'e'd take *me* ter the front lounge fer a
bit of a booze-up now and then. I could really go fer them
big, lazy gray eyes 'n lovely white teeth, and if 'e put 'is
arm around *me* and led *me* to a chair like Barney said 'e
did with you, cripes, I'd pass out on the blinkin' spot."

"And where would that get you?" asked Nonie practically.

"Well, I don't *know* about *where*...." Doris's voice
trailed away dreamily. Her pouchy eyes were narrowed in
what was obviously some sort of pleasant speculation.

"Oh, come on, Dorrie. I've got work to do, even if you
haven't."

Nonie flounced away impatiently. She had heard and
seen enough of Jacey Lomax to last her a lifetime, and
she did wish that everyone around here would let the subject drop.

After that, she was not asked to perform that particular
duty again, which meant that Barney must be in as much
awe of the Lomax man as the rest of the population. The
days wore on and the incident receded in Nonie's own
mind and apparently in everyone else's too, since it was
not referred to again. As it turned out, she was given
other things to think about anyway, surprising things.
Worrying things.

She gazed at the headmaster in horror.

"You mean Pru hasn't been going to school each day,
as I thought? All this time when I've been congratulating
myself upon how well she has settled down, she has in fact
been playing hooky?"

"So Miss Wilson in Primary Two tells me."

"For ... for how long? I mean, how many times has she
done it?" asked Nonie faintly, trying to grasp the import
of the information she had just received.

"Too often," responded the headmaster grimly. "We don't know the specific number of instances because at first the teacher thought she'd been unwell. Then, when she demanded a note from you, as her guardian, none was forthcoming. I admit that she's not alone in the crime, but you understand that we have to nip it in the bud, otherwise the idea of skipping lessons will soon spread. We had no choice but to inform you, Miss Gotthart, and seek your cooperation in the matter."

"Yes, of course, I understand that." Nonie sat down weakly. "I can't think . . . I mean, why should she begin to do a thing like that? She never has before."

"Possibly it's as Mr. Lomax says . . . a lack of stability in her background."

"Her background?"

"Her home life. In fact, in a nutshell, a *lack* of home life."

"Mr. Lomax! How does he come into it?" Nonie's eyes were resentful. She could feel them growing round, incredulous, as spots of uncomfortable color stained her cheeks at the mere mention of that man's name.

"He's the convener of the education committee. It came up at the monthly meeting."

"Why wasn't I told before it reached that stage? Surely, if it's been going on for a while, I should have been the first to know?"

To think that Jacey Lomax knew things about her little sister that she didn't even know herself! It was an impossible situation!

"Each case is treated individually. In this particular instance, it was regarded as preferable to allow the child's teacher to try to deal with the matter first. Had she been successful, you would not have been worried with it at all."

"And she hasn't been successful? I see." Nonie swallowed miserably. "Well, I shall speak to Pru in no uncer-

tain terms, you may be sure. It does seem as if now is the
time to play the heavy parent."

She attempted a smile but somehow it didn't quite
come off. Pru playing truant! It had never happened before and she hadn't the foggiest idea as to how she was going to tackle it.

"That's just it, Miss Gotthart." The schoolmaster
looked grave. He wasn't even trying to answer her tentative smile. "As Mr. Lomax said, you *aren't* a parent.
Therein probably lies the root of the problem."

"It will be no problem," Nonie asserted, suddenly cool
and formal and very firm indeed. "You may safely leave it
to me. I've managed perfectly well as a substitute parent
up to this moment, and Mr. Lomax oversteps himself in
presuming to comment on that angle. He knows extraordinarily little about our case, so little that I regard it as
presumption on his part to even pass an opinion!"

The other shrugged, unwilling to commit himself.
"You'll see about it, then?" The headmaster raised his
hat and Nonie, still seething, managed to see him politely
to the door.

To her dismay, Pru's own reactions confirmed all too
clearly that there was some foundation at least in Jacey
Lomax's analysis of the situation. Nonie felt first surprise,
then dismay and finally a sort of winded helplessness.

"But, Pru, why? Why?"

"I didn't think you'd mind, Nonie."

"Not mind? Darling, of course I mind. I mind very
much indeed. Whatever could have given you such an
idea?"

The little girl shuffled her feet uncomfortably.

"Well, I mean, you're never around, Nonie You're
never *there* anymore, are you? You don't worry about
what I'm doing when I muck around by myself at the back
of this stinky old building, so I didn't think you'd care
about the daytime either."

"Well, I *do* care! And in *school hours*. Oh, Pru, how could you be so deceitful? And here was I, thinking how well you were getting on with your lessons."

"I wasn't, though," mumbled Pru unhappily. "It's all different, what we have out here. I couldn't get my arithmetic to add up and I'd never done geography; I can't begin to understand it. I wanted to ask you sometimes but you weren't around. You always seemed to be so busy doing something else. And I meant to tell you too, the first time we played up and didn't go to school but you were so busy then too, and I . . . well, I just didn't, that's all. I'd have probably said it to you, like I used to when you were doing the picture frames in the corner or something, or when you were typing I could have, or weeding the path. We used to tell each other everything, didn't we, only here there isn't much of a chance. . . . Not that I don't like it *much* better here," she hastened to add, her eyes fastened in some anxiety on her sister's anguished face.

"No, Pru, I . . . I can see how it happened. It was as much my fault as yours, darling. But that doesn't mean it can happen again. It mustn't, *ever*, do you understand? Promise me on your honor, Pru."

"Cross my heart and spit my death."

"And—" Nonie hesitated "—this won't be for much longer, Pru, living this way. It's just . . . a very temporary arrangement. I know it's not very satisfactory for either of us, but it was the best I could do at the time. I'll try for something different, better, but I don't suppose I'll have much luck." She stifled a sigh. "Schooling is important though, and from now on I'm going to make myself available for a while each afternoon when you come back, and we'll go over everything you did that day in lessons. That way I'll know whether you really *have* been to school or not."

She made herself sound severe, but inside she could only feel a mute self-reproach.

The unhappy, trapped feeling persisted. Even though she kept her word and met Pru each afternoon for as long as she could possibly spare and made up the time she had taken with extra work after the child was in bed, Nonie found that she was still worrying, sleeping badly.

When Jacey Lomax appeared out of nowhere a couple of weeks later, he, too, seemed as aware as she was herself of the way in which her skin was drawn so tightly over her high cheekbones and of the new hollows that made smudgy shadows beneath her dark-lashed blue eyes.

"Are you well?"

Jacey asked the question abruptly, spinning his broad-brimmed hat onto the small round tea table in the lounge to which he had summoned her, and turning to where she waited politely in the doorway.

"Perfectly, thanks."

"Hmm." He gave her an assessing look but made no further comment as he saw her seated, then hitched the legs of his khaki moleskin trousers and took a chair himself, stretching out his long limbs in their polished elastic-sided boots.

He came straight to the point.

"I've come to offer you a job."

"But I already have one." She looked at him in some surprise.

He made a dismissive gesture. "What I have in mind could be more suitable." His mouth leveled as he observed her expression. "It's not working for *me*," he emphasized bitingly, "so keep an open mind for a few minutes if you *possibly* can, will you, Miss Gotthart?"

"Who is it for, then?" she asked cautiously.

"For my brother, actually." A pause. "Out at Tuckarimba."

"Tuckarimba?"

"At the old place."

"You mean at the old homestead?" Her eyes widened as he nodded half impatiently.

"Raynor is there now recovering, we hope, from a polo accident. Unfortunately there's a doubt as to how complete that recovery will ever become, which is why I postponed the disposal of the house in the meantime. He's accustomed to country life and was fretting badly in the hospital, so it seemed a good idea to get him up here, near enough to me to keep an eye on his progress but where he could at the same time be reasonably independent."

And how independent could you be, Nonie was asking herself somewhat acidly, if Jacey Lomax himself had decided to keep an eye on you? Poor brother!

Aloud she asked, "What is the matter with your brother exactly, Mr. Lomax? I'm afraid I have no nursing qualifications whatsoever."

She watched him searching his pockets, slapping them one after the other in his hunt for his tobacco and papers. When he found where they were he took them out and began to roll himself a cigarette with slow preoccupation.

"Ray's past that stage now, more or less," he told her, rubbing the tobacco between his palms half absently. "What he's needing now is a different approach altogether." He gave her a direct look. "You see, Miss Gotthart, Raynor can't walk. He's in a wheelchair, and that's where he'll very likely remain for the rest of his days unless he can in some way be persuaded out of it." He sounded grim.

"I see."

"No, you don't, and neither do the rest of us. The doctors confirm that there's now no apparent medical reason why he shouldn't be able to walk again, but the fact is that he can't and won't even attempt it. There was a certain amount of spinal damage at the time of his fall, but not so serious that it should have resulted in permanent disability. They're convinced that Ray could walk if he'd only try it, but for some reason he won't even put himself to the test."

Nonie wasn't looking at Jacey Lomax now, because she didn't want him to be aware of the compassion she was feeling for the young man whose life had been so cruelly altered by what must have been a terrible misfortune. Compassion was a weakness, and Nonie knew that if Jacey Lomax spotted it, he'd ferret it out and play on it because that was probably what it suited him to do. She also knew that she wasn't up to this kind of thing at all, which was why she looked not at him but at his polished boots. Those elastic-sided boots that all the stockmen out here seemed to wear, with a defined heel and a welted sole and a little tab at the back to pull them on and off.

"I couldn't do it, Mr. Lomax. I couldn't do anything for you brother. I can hardly do anything for myself and Pru, let alone anyone else." She could not hide her bitterness. "I'd be quite inadequate."

"You foolish child!" Nonie's gaze shot upward at the strange harshness of his tone. "Do you think I'd saddle *you* with *that* sort of responsibility, when—" He broke off, ran a brown hand through his hair in a way that was somehow quite uncharacteristic of Jacey Lomax's usual calm. "Just credit me with a little sense and judgment, and trust me, will you?" he said indistinctly. "You haven't heard me out yet."

"I'm sorry," she apologized meekly.

"Your role is only a background one, quite simply."

The way he said it was reassuring enough to make her pay attention once again. Even while she was registering with vague resentment the fact that he had said "is" and not "would be," she was also thinking how nice Jacey Lomax's eyes were when they softened like that. They had become kind and comforting, and their color was a deep, almost caressing gray that held none of the waterfall coldness.

"I don't intend to put more responsibility your way, but rather less," he was now continuing matter-of-factly, like a general giving a briefing to a particularly dim underling. "When Raynor had this accident he broke off his engagement... I'd better put you in the picture about that properly. Ilse was very upset about it indeed, but he insisted on releasing her ... did the noble thing, in his own eyes if no one else's. Look, isn't there somewhere else where we can talk? You're obviously on edge in here. Why?"

She shrugged apologetically, lifted her white apron and let it drop again rather helplessly.

"I didn't mean to make it obvious. But you're right, of course. I'm not supposed to be here, chatting to ... to the, er, clientele. It makes things a bit awkward with Doris and the rest.

He stood up.

"When are you free?" he asked abruptly. "I'll come back."

Nonie hesitated.

"I have an hour and a half each afternoon now, when Pru comes back from school, so that I can be with her to, er, to hear how she got on and things," she added lamely.

"Have you always done that?"

"It's a new arrangement," she confessed awkwardly, blushing furiously and hoping he'd leave it. "I make it up later—the time, I mean."

He did leave it, thank heaven. She couldn't have borne a lecture from a member of the education committee at this point, when she was doing everything she possibly could to get Pru on the right lines again!

"We'll discuss it over a walk," said Jacey Lomax unexpectedly. "Pru can come with us and play in the park while we discuss it. I'll be back at—" he glanced at the wristwatch strapped to one hairy brown wrist "—say, four o'clock."

"Very well."

"Be ready."

He was gone.

Now why did he have to spoil it all by adding that brief command at the end? It snapped Nonie out of the pleasant state into which she had been gradually sliding, an almost companionable state! Nonie found that she was in two minds about her walk with Jacey Lomax. One half of her was back to hating the man for his bossy attitude to all and sundry, the other was contemplating the outing with a faintly tingling anticipation that was at once unfamiliar and disturbing.

She put on her navy linen shirtwaist, and brushed out her long fair hair carefully, but something perverse inside her decided against further preparation or the use of makeup. Her pallor was regrettable, certainly compared with most of the lovely golden-skinned girls she had seen in the streets of this country town. And she could no doubt have improved her reflection with the application of some additional color. As she gazed in the mirror, she noted with dissatisfaction that the only vestige of color in her whole face was the natural pinkness of her lips and the dark glow of her eyes, which had gone the same deep navy as the dress itself.

Yes, she could improve things, but for *that* man, never!

Be ready, he had said, and she was.

Nonie had trouble in keeping up with his long strides as they made their way toward the park. To outpace him she'd have had to run as Pru was already running, a little ahead of them, and that would have been even more undignified than panting along beside him like this, giving only the odd half-skip to keep herself level. If she had envisaged a companionable stroll, then already she was doomed to disappointment!

In the park itself, Jacey Lomax looked a little uncomfortable, slightly out of place, as if he seldom if ever went there. Other people must have thought the same thing, because one or two looked openly surprised as they recognized him and said a mumbled " 'Day, Jacey" in passing.

"We'll sit here and Pru can go to the swings." He indicated a wooden seat with a slatted back and iron legs. "Have you given some thought to what I was saying earlier?"

Trust Jacey Lomax! Always the disconcertingly direct approach!

"I've been busy," Nonie hedged.

"Hmm. I can't blame you for not wanting to commit yourself until you've heard the whole setup." He sighed. "The present position is a type of mental and emotional deadlock as far as my brother is concerned. It will impede his hopes of recovery unless some sort of change takes place. Ilse is herself a physiotherapist. She wants me to dispense with the nurse since Ray can virtually look after himself now anyway, and Ilse proposes to come up and stay, providing I can find some sort of chaperon-cum-housekeeper." At the look on Nonie's face his lip curled sardonically. "Not a chaperon in the accepted sense of the term, Miss Gotthart. These two are mature people, and Ray is still dead set against taking up where he left off with Ilse . . . through what I consider to be a misguided highmindedness."

"Perhaps your brother doesn't see it that way."

"No matter what way he sees it, Ilse's feelings are involved too. She wants this chance, and I'm determined that she shall have it. You will merely be another presence, to defuse the atmosphere and give the setup as much normality as possible. She thinks it's better to come primarily in the role of masseuse and professional therapist and play down the ex-fiancée bit. It was Ray, after all, who insisted on calling the whole thing off. Ilse still hopes he'll come to his senses about their plans for the future. She thinks that, with returning health, propinquity and so on, this can be achieved. Do you follow me?"

"I think so. It sounds worth a try. But—" hesitating "—I still don't honestly see where I come in."

"As I said, your role is a background one. Can you cook?"

"I'm not much good, Mr. Lomax. As I once told you, I'm a jack-of-all-trades, but cooking has never featured either prominently or successfully."

"As long as you don't actually poison them, you'll do." His lips twitched.

"I don't think you understand," she responded worriedly. "The only cooking I know is what I've taught myself. I can knock up simple dishes but I can't pretend to be competent."

"You'll manage all that's required of you," he told her with certainty. "It's only a question of filling in on Hattie's weekends off. She's been there cooking for the nurse, and she'll carry on for as long as I ask her to. You will be primarily a companion for Ilse."

Nonie turned to him on the bench, doubt clouding the soft darkness of her glance.

"You don't need me there, Mr. Lomax, do you, if we're to be honest? What's the use of pretending? I . . . I have the feeling that you . . . that you're *creating* a place for me in your brother's household where there isn't really a place at all."

"Rubbish!" Jacey Lomax sounded impatient. He looked at her oddly. "Why would I do a thing like that?"

"Pity? Charity? Disapproval of my present employment?" She shrugged. "I don't like people feeling sorry for me. I thought I'd made that clear."

His lips tightened in a forbidding manner. So did the muscles in his jaw. In fact his features congealed into an awesome severity that made Nonie wonder if she should have been quite so outspoken.

"Listen to me, Miss Gotthart. When I am *sorry* for people, they're not left in any two minds about it, I can assure you." The words were strangely clipped. "My pity I reserve for Raynor and Ilse, bogged down in this emotional mess they're in. My charity I keep for those who deserve it, which I can't say I reckon you *do*. As for my feelings about your present work, you know darned well what they are, and I haven't attempted to hide them, have I?"

"No, you haven't, and that's why I find myself wondering now... I mean..." Nonie floundered dubiously.

"What does it take to convince you, Miss Gotthart? If you stop thinking about yourself for a second or two and turn that introspective little mind of yours outward for just a moment, perhaps you'll acknowledge that your presence and the child's at Old Tuckarimba could serve a genuinely useful purpose. You'll be expected to do your share in the house, I warn you, and for what you do you will be rewarded commensurately, with board and lodging properly deducted. Does that sound like charity? Like pity? I don't think so! You strike me as having a certain amount of common sense and perception, so you'll appreciate that cheerful feminine company for Ilse and a child's amusing chatter could be the right background touches for both of them just now. Besides—" he narrowed his eyes in the direction of Pru's bright, cotton-clad form, pirouetting over the grass "—there's something very relaxing about a child playing around the place, don't you agree? And Ray has always had a sneaking fondness for kids. That about sums it up, Miss Gotthart. Take it or leave it."

His brusqueness had a strangely astringent impact upon Nonie. Her mind had been racing, her thoughts tumbling over themselves one after the other. Now the process had steadied itself into an analysis of a quite objective sort.

How could she refuse this chance? It could be painful finding herself back in her old home in these particular circumstances, but it would be better than the present setup—anything would be! And for Pru it would mean a

more family-style life than her impersonal existence here
at the Pink Pelican. Tuckarimba was a true home, a place
where she would have the freedom to run about where
she pleased instead of being confined to the dingy back
premises of this public house except for daily rambles in
the park. She and Nonie could be with each other a lot of
the time out there. That was what Pru had been missing,
her sister's influence. That was why she had been so
naughty, playing truant from school. Indeed, Nonie was
finding it increasingly difficult to get through to Pru these
days. There was a lack of communication that was beginning to cause her constant and gnawing worry.

"I'll take it, thanks," she heard herself say, with every
bit as much brusqueness as his.

"That's settled, then." Jacey Lomax stood up, swung
around as a musical feminine voice called from the path
behind him.

"Jay . . . cey! Jacey, it *is* you! What a peculiar place to
find you in, darling!"

The woman's tone was underlined with a quite satirical
amusement that brought a grin to Jacey Lomax's swarthy
features.

"You, too, Delphine. One could hardly describe the
public park as your, er, natural habitat."

"I'm taking a short cut to the golf club, actually." The
young woman's pretty face held a definite question. What
are *you* doing, Jacey, she was asking, just as eloquently as
though she had spoken the words aloud.

She was a very attractive person indeed, of medium
height with a slender figure and the shapeliest legs that
Nonie had ever seen. Perhaps the most striking thing
about her apart from those legs was that beautiful auburn
hair that waved away from her high forehead in burnished
glory. Instead of the pale cream complexion that so often
goes with rich auburn coloring, this girl's skin was a surprise. She was deeply tanned, the dusting of freckles was

curiously fetching, and her long green eyes had the composed glitter of a jungle cat's, the same bold challenge too.

It seemed that Jacey Lomax intended to ignore the unspoken question.

"Miss Gotthart, Miss Simpson." He introduced the two women, continuing easily, "I'll walk a bit of the way with you, Delphine. Excuse me just a moment, I'll be right back."

He had settled the broad-brimmed hat back on his head. Now he tipped it in a polite gesture to Nonie and strode off over the grass to join the girl who waited there, a small, satisfied smile lurking round the corner of her gay red mouth.

Just like a kitten that's got first to the bowl of cream, thought Nonie in some amusement, watching the tall broad figure and the dainty feminine one as they walked past the fountain in the direction of the building over there among the trees, presumably the clubhouse.

The two were deep in conversation. Nonie wondered idly if they were speaking about her. She supposed that Jacey Lomax would find it necessary to explain his unexpected presence there on a bench in the public park.

When he came back, he gave no indication whatever of the possible nature of his conversation with his woman friend. He was jingling the loose change in his trouser pocket in a rather absentminded manner, as if perhaps his thoughts were still with his recent companion.

He brought his mind back to Nonie with a slight frown.

"Yes. Well, let's see. Where were we?" The beetling brows scowled a little. "You have agreed to take the position?"

"Yes."

"Splendid. Then I'll speak to your present employer and fix things up. No need for you to be personally involved. I'll handle it for you. I daresay Barney won't be too surprised. He'll manage to get someone else to come for a while. Nobody stays there for long . . . in fact, I must say you've stuck it out longer than the rest." He looked at her shrewdly. "Something's worrying you. Was it that or something else?"

"It's about Pru . . . her schooling. I'm concerned about her. She's only just settled down here, and now she'll have to change again. It's bad for her."

"Not nearly as bad as living in the confined circumstances in which she finds herself just now, in some dump where she hardly sees the only relative she has," he pointed out tersely, adding in clipped tones, "And has she settled down as successfully as you would have me believe? It struck me and my committee that the number of days young Pru attended class and the number of days she didn't were running pretty well neck and neck."

Nonie's color rose at that.

"I'm doing my best for her, aren't I?" she said defensively, angry at his implication of neglect.

"No one is disputing that, little one." There was, surprisingly, no censure in the level gray eyes. Even the man's voice was noncommittal. "There are times, however, when even one's best isn't good enough. In your case just let's say it can be improved upon if you lower that prickly barrier a little and face the thing squarely. Independence—especially the feminine variety—can be quite a tedious commodity if it's overdone."

"Look, Mr. Lomax—" she flushed angrily "—is it a job you're offering me or a lecture? The fact that I've just accepted the one doesn't automatically give you the right to proceed with the other. If you want to know, I find your whole attitude insufferably superior and dictatorial!"

"And I find yours stubborn, headstrong and not a little immature." He grinned maddeningly. "It must be a part of that excessive independence of which I spoke."

"The *feminine* variety." She mimicked his own phrase a

little acidly. "What have you against females, Mr. Lomax?"

The grin broadened and Nonie seethed. The dancing lights in the depths of his wide-spaced eyes under the beetling brows told her that he was enjoying himself.

"Nothing against them at all, collectively," he replied suavely. "Indeed they're an admirable invention. Even individually they have their points. You can hardly have failed to notice that I have just given myself the pleasure of conducting one particularly charming and decorative member of the sex as far as the golf club, with positively no show of reluctance whatever. I can assure you that had I disapproved I shouldn't have bothered."

Nonie stood up. "Come on, Pru!" she called. "We'll have to get back now, darling." She turned. "When do you wish me to go to your brother?" she asked in a tight, formal voice.

"We'll give Barney a week to find someone. I'll speak to him when I take you back just now, and come for you on Sunday. Right?"

"You don't need to take us back. We can walk there ourselves," she pointed out a little ungraciously.

"But it's my pleasure, Miss Gotthart," he emphasized, teeth glinting in a smile so smooth and silky and sarcastic that Nonie felt she could have screamed.

"I suspect you doubt my sincerity," he added, amusement crinkling the lazy gray eyes.

She pressed her lips together and set off, scarcely waiting to make sure that her little sister was following. How this man could pique and annoy her! Nonie could only hope that once she had settled down at the old homestead with his brother and the ex-fiancée she would see little, or preferably nothing, of Jacey Lomax himself.

Once more she found herself packing up, but this time there was not much work involved. The unattractive black uniforms she had been wearing went back into the

staff pool, and her other personal effects were few. A
good thing that she had not even opened the stout tin
trunk that contained her mother's things. The ornaments
and pictures were still wrapped in tissue exactly as she had
placed them before leaving Sydney. They would have to
remain there for some time yet, she acknowledged, re-
placing the lid with a sigh and snapping the brass catches
shut once more. Although the trunk would accompany
them out to Tuckarimba, the time had not yet arrived to
unpack it. That time would not arrive until the old home
got back into Nonie's own hands, and since Jacey Lomax
had made it clear the he would not consider selling until
his brother was well again, it was as much in Nonie's interests as his that Raynor Lomax should make a quick
recovery and that a reconciliation should take place
between him and Ilse.

Nonie's lips quirked ironically. Strange to find herself
in complete accord with Jacey Lomax over something, if
for differing motives. Yes, he could certainly count on
Nonie to do all she could to help Raynor on to his feet
once more, although he need not be made too much
aware of the underlying reason for her cooperation. Perverse man that he was, it would be just like him to decide
not to sell at all if he guessed how much she really wanted
that old place!

On the following Friday Nonie went along to the school
and waited outside for the children to come out. She had
promised Pru that she would be there on the final day to
help the child to carry the extra books and other odd-
ments that she had accumulated in her desk during her
months in town.

It was a bright, still day, almost stiflingly still. The sky
held the harsh glare of pale heat that Nonie could remember well from her childhood sojourn in this inland climate. It was a dry heat without the humidity of the coast
that she always found so sticky and trying. Nonie ac-

tually enjoyed this beating, dry heat that set the landscape shimmering under a hard blue sky. She sat on the wall outside the school, bare legs dangling, tapping her heels gently against the bricks in time to the tune she was humming as she waited.

And then she ceased her humming as a long gray car came up the street in her direction. Even at this distance Nonie could recognize the fiery glory of that auburn head in the passenger seat. The driver's identity remained a mystery right to the moment when the shiny vehicle swished past.

Nonie gazed after it, sighed. She might have known it would be Jacey Lomax at the wheel with the delectable Delphine at his side. The kitten smile had been playing around her red lips as she glanced through the window as they passed, but Nonie doubted if she herself had been recognized by either of them—certainly not by Jacey anyway. His face had been half hidden beneath the wide slouch hat, and at the speed he was traveling his eyes had doubtless been fastened upon the road.

Just as well he hadn't seen the girlish figure balanced on the wall in the sunshine or he might have stopped and Nonie was bound to admit she'd have felt at a distinct disadvantage, barelegged and untidy as she was, beside the beautifully groomed presence of that Delphine woman.

IT WAS THE SAME GRAY CAR that called for them on Sunday. It slid into the front yard quietly, so quietly that if Nonie had not been watching from the window she might not even have known it had arrived. She found that her whole body had been stiff and tense, waiting here for this moment.

Somehow she forced herself to relax, gathered up the smaller articles about her and called to Pru.

"Are you ready?" Jacey Lomax stood in the doorway. If he noticed the whiteness about her mouth, the uncertainty in her strained blue eyes, he didn't comment. "Where are your cases?"

"There are just the two. And a trunk in the porch."

Nonie and Pru followed him out into the yard in silence. He stowed the luggage swiftly, heaving the trunk into place with an ease that secretly amazed Nonie. She climbed obediently into the front seat and Pru scrambled willingly into the back one. Then Jacey Lomax closed the door and took his own place at the wheel

As they swept around in a circle past the entrance to the dingy building, the pelican danced a final, sad farewell on his creaking hinge. Nonie couldn't stop looking at him, so desolate and despondent did he seem, hopping on his one webbed foot.

"Sorry to be leaving?" Jacey had seen her backward, lingering gaze.

"No, not at all." She shrugged. "I was just saying goodbye to the bird. He looks so lonely, somehow. It's an awful place to have to be for the whole of one's life. For him, there's no escape."

"But for you, yes. I'm glad you see it in a sensible light and have agreed to come." He shot her a swift, appraising look, took in the sudden wetness of her thick dark lashes.

"I didn't know pelicans *were* pink," Nonie heard herself say stupidly, hurriedly, in a husky indistinct voice.

"They're not as a rule, except for the beak. I doubt if that one was ever pink either, although it's hard to tell underneath all that dust." A pause. "In ancient times the pelican was reputed to wound itself with its own beak in order to feed its young with its blood."

"How . . . horrible!"

"Not entirely." His tone was dry. "In those days it was considered a symbol of selflessness and piety. That pelican dangling over the door back there is just about as much out of his element in that place as you were yourself. Be thankful that he's only a tin one. Do you want to drive?"

"What, this?" Nonie looked askance at the mere suggestion. The gleaming dashboard held almost as many buttons, switches and dials as a full-sized airplane.

"You won't, er, feel sick?" There was the suspicion of a humorous gleam in his eye.

"Thank you, no. I took a tablet," she replied stiffly. Then, as she saw the gleam deepening. "I've no intention of finding myself in that undignified position again, I can assure you."

"Or of being beholden for my timely assistance either? I get the message. However, far from *you* being beholden to *me*, you're actually doing me a favor by agreeing to come out to Tuckarimba. Just remember that, will you, any time you get to wondering about it."

Nonie glanced at him curiously. Could he possibly *believe* in what he was saying?

It seemed that he did. There was no teasing glint in the level gray eyes that met hers for an instant, no satirical lift to the corner of his mouth either. Jacey Lomax appeared quite solemnly convincing—and as inscrutable as the Sphinx.

"Does your brother know we're coming?" she asked, feeling suddenly more apprehensive about the whole thing, suddenly aware, too, of the actual physical nearness of this big, broad man in the car beside her.

For some unaccountable reason, the impact of his nearness was affecting her in a most unpredictable manner. Nonie felt her breath break short, and a tiny shiver ran right through her.

"We're nearly there," Jacey Lomax told her, evidently—and fortunately—misinterpreting the shiver, which hadn't escaped his eagle gaze. "You needn't be worried. Ray and Ilse are looking forward to having you, and Pru's presence will buck them both up, I'm sure. The nurse left a couple of days ago, and Ilse flew up to take over the running of the place as soon as she had gone. She asked Hattie to prepare your room. It used to be two rooms at one time, I believe. It's a big one that you can both share."

"Looking out to the tankstand?"

"You know it?" Jacey Lomax seemed startled.

"No, n-not really." Color rushed to her face. How idiotically careless of her to make such an unthinking remark! "I . . . we walked around the outside a bit that night," she lied confusedly. "There seemed to be what was probably a bedroom facing on to the side veranda."

"The side *away* from the wattle tree where I ran into you. Yes, there is."

She licked dry lips.

"It . . . it's very kind of Ilse . . . to have given us a nice big room to ourselves, I mean."

"There are plenty of rooms in the house, and she's expecting something in return, of course—your support, companionship, understanding, patience. Raynor's not an easy man at times in his present restricted state and he was against Ilse's coming up from the outset. I'm sure you'll manage, though, so don't look so haunted."

But "haunted" was what she was feeling at this precise moment, could he but have guessed. Haunted by remembrance, as the big gray car crested the ridge and swept down toward the creek flat. Haunted by nudging memories that jostled for pride of place in her racing mind. Her mother, in a striped apron and canvas shoes, feeding chickens near the water trough. Her father, Dermot, riding in through the clump of timber with a screwed-up, faded blue gaze that saw beyond the plains and the valley and dreamed of success that somehow never came.

She swallowed.

"Welcome to Tuckarimba," said Jacey Lomax gently,

taking her arm and drawing her out of the car, completely unaware of the irony of his remark.

Welcome *home*, Nonie corrected him under her breath, as in a daze she began to walk slowly over the grass toward the house.

CHAPTER FOUR

ILSE BJORNIG WAS OLDER than Nonie had expected. There was a completely mature beauty in her serene face that was both striking and somehow sad, at one and the same time. The radiant smile of welcome with which she received Jacey Lomax couldn't quite disguise the lines of strain about her controlled mouth once the smile had disappeared again, and Nonie couldn't help noticing the momentary anguish in her pale blue eyes as she glanced swiftly behind her, just once and only fleetingly, at the man whom she had left in his wheelchair on the veranda before coming down the shallow steps to meet them.

Jacey Lomax raised his broad-brimmed hat, and somewhat to Nonie's astonishment kissed this quietly beautiful woman upon her smooth, tanned cheek. Nonie would not have imagined him to be the sort to bestow that particular kind of kiss at all! One didn't associate tall, tanned, forceful "don't-fence-me-in" fellers with the nonchalant air of polished gallantry displayed by Jacey Lomax just now in greeting the woman who might one day become his sister-in-law.

"How is he, Ilse?"

"A little depressed. I think your new arrivals are going to do him the world of good, though."

"I hope so." Jacey still held his wide felt hat in his hand. "This is Miss Wenona Gotthart, Ilse . . . Nonie to her friends—" the gray eyes glinted "—and here—" with his free hand reaching out and grasping the mercurial Pru "—is her little sister."

Ilse smiled gently down at Pru, held out a hand to Nonie.

"Pru, Nonie . . . I am so glad you've come. We must get your things inside, and then we can set about getting to know each other. But first you must come and meet Ray, since he can't come down here to you."

Another of those swift, anxious glances in the direction of the veranda.

"You take them up then, Ilse. I'll get the gear."

Nonie followed the other two up the steps and through the gauze door at the top. There was a dreamlike unreality about this homecoming of hers that left her too bewildered to do more than obey Jacey Lomax's suggestion mechanically. It was all so very different from the way she had imagined her return to Tuckarimba might be. Instead of the quiet thrill of rediscovery alone with little Pru, she found herself being ushered into her own house—the very place in which she had been born—with the formality of a guest and a stranger. Now she had to hide the conflicting emotions of the moment and walk up to greet the gaunt, pallid invalid who was wheeling himself impatiently toward her, as if this particular civility was the only thing in her mind at this minute.

"How do you do."

Raynor Lomax was quite unlike his brother—fairer hair, a nose that was wider, less hawklike, and a noticeably milder manner. It was difficult to compare his stature, because of the wheelchair, but by the look of those long, helpless legs it was a fair guess that he would have had much the same impressive physique had he been able to stand upright.

Instead of standing, though, he could only lean forward to spike Pru's hair into further disarray, treating her at the same time to a grin that was sudden and surprisingly amiable.

"Hello, scrap. Excuse me for not getting up to meet you."

"Hullo."

"Come here and let's have a look at you, since we're going to be playmates."

Pru stepped nearer and put one finger on the arm of the chair.

"You can't play with me in that," she told him uncompromisingly, running her gimlet eyes disparagingly over his cumbersome prison.

"Pru!"

Nonie was agonized, her cheeks hot with embarrassment at her young sister's lack of tact. It wasn't as though she hadn't been well warned, either!

"It's all right," Raynor Lomax's amused voice pronounced. "I understand kids, and they understand me. Besides—" here a meaning look that was obviously directed toward Ilse "—I prefer directness. The honest approach is most refreshing, and somewhat unfamiliar these days."

Pru, bless her, seemed to be the only one among them who remained unaware of the general tension this remark had created.

"What's that thing for?" she asked.

"That's the brake."

"And that?"

"That goes back and fore to turn the wheels. See?"

"Can I do it, d'you think?"

"Have a go if you like. Or, better still, you can push me from behind if I release the brake first. Now."

"Like that?"

"That's it. You can give me a ride right down the veranda and back if you want to."

"I'll just go and see about our things, if you'll excuse me," murmured Nonie, secretly marveling at the suddenness of the rapport that had sprung up between her unpredictable little sister and the invalid brother whom Jacey had described as "often difficult."

Ilse, too, seemed happy to leave the situation as it was.

"And if you'll excuse me for a moment too, I'd better see what Hattie is doing about the evening meal."

Still dazed, Nonie stepped into the hall. It took a few moments for her eyes to become accustomed to the dim interior after the harsh glare of light on the veranda. When she could see properly, the milestones of memory emerged one after another from the shadows. Here was the same oak bench along one wall, with a wobbly lid that lifted off to reveal a zinc-lined interior. Beside it was a stand full of polo clubs that must be Raynor's, but the long mirror on the opposite side was where it had always been, too. So was the tall-backed rush chair in the corner. Nonie remembered asking her mother why they weren't taking it with them, for it had long been a family favorite, and her mother had brushed the question aside, taking trouble instead to lift the mirror off its hook and show Nonie the faded patch on the wall behind it.

"We must leave *some* things for the people who come after us, Nonie," she had temporized, and in the end there had just been the trunk full of small, more personal items, plus their few suitcases of clothing.

She ran her fingers along the oak seat, sat down on it, mindlessly. After a while she stood up again, walked over to the mirror, moistened her lips and inspected her reflection.

Strange to be looking at the wide-eyed, pale reflection of a young woman's face, when what you actually felt you should be seeing was the plump, jolly, round-cheeked image of a pigtailed eight-year-old. That was what she had always seen in that particular mirror before.

Nonie pushed her blond hair back behind her ears and gazed at herself critically. She wasn't a person at all right now, she decided objectively, just a bundle of piquant memories that jostled each other for position in a nostalgia that was half pleasant, half painful.

Well, wasn't it what she should have expected, this feeling of dual personality that had taken possession of her? Wasn't it what she had prepared herself to face, half anticipating, half dreading? One couldn't step back into the past without being very much aware of the experience, especially after all these years spent in yearning to recapture it.

Nonie walked away from the mirror, through the other door, turned left and into the bedroom. Their cases had already been deposited on the floor near one window, and Pru's coat and school beret lay on one of the beds.

She put her handbag on the dressing table and looked around her. The proportions of the room were unfamiliar, yet vaguely reminiscent of the place as she had known it. A ridge of plaster above her head soon told her why. This must be where the partition had been. As Jacey Lomax had already told her, two rooms had been knocked into one to make a pleasantly large and spacious bedsitting apartment that stretched the entire width of the west wing of the house. Yes, now she had it! That was where one door had been, and the door to the other room had opened from the veranda. In actual fact, she was now standing at the window of what had once been her very own, smaller bedroom.

Nonie wandered to the other window, the one away from the tankstand.

From here you could see right down over the creek flats to the river itself. There was the engine shed behind the oleanders, and a little beyond that the windmill. Between the two wound the path up which they had carried the shrouded form of her father on that fateful day. Nonie hadn't realized at the time just what it was that they were doing, but she had known from the conversations going on about her and her mother's ill-concealed consternation that something dramatic and irrevocable had happened and it was from this very window that she had watched the mysterious procession approach. She had never seen her father again, and it wasn't very long after that that her mother had broken the news to her that they would have to leave Tuckarimba for good.

Nonie remembered that bleak moment very well indeed.

Thinking about it now—but with the implications of old Bundy's revelations ringing in her head—she felt weakness assailing her limbs. A dew was breaking over her forehead and there was a sudden, painful swelling in her throat. Had Dermot really felt so hopeless about the future that he had simply chosen not to have a future at all? Had he cared about them, her mother and herself? *Really* cared, that is? Had he loved them, even if he couldn't find it in him to love this place?

Nonie clenched her hands together. She would never know the answer, and maybe it was better that she shouldn't. Yet it was with complete, despairing honesty that she admitted that the answer suddenly mattered in a way that she could not have been expected to anticipate. It mattered because she was *here*. With absolute clarity she knew now that she should not have come back. Not ever.

It would have been better for everyone if she had never happened to run into the old mailman at all. Then the pungent, bittersweet memories would not be haunting her, crushing her, now . . . because she wouldn't have got the idea of coming back at all, would she? It was typical of her, this, wasn't it? She had always been inclined to be too impetuous, headstrong. This time it hadn't paid off, that impulsiveness of hers.

She had fooled herself, telling herself that it was the answer for her and Pru, the solution to everything. It hadn't been so far and it wouldn't be now. It hadn't been the right thing to do. What had it brought them but tension and strain and enforced breaks in Pru's schooling, and even more uncertainty about their future than they had had back there in the city?

She had done the *wrong thing*, and in this moment of acknowledging it, Nonie felt more wretched, more alone, than she had ever done in her entire life.

"What is it?"

Jacey Lomax's voice came from the doorway, and she turned instantly to see him standing just inside the room with the tin trunk tilted upon one broad shoulder.

"What's up?" he asked again, putting down the trunk with little effort and crossing the room to where she was standing.

"I'm tired, that's all." Nonie pulled a wry face, moved back from the window.

"No, it's more than that." His presence checked her. "Look at me," he commanded. Already his fingers were tipping her chin. "It's more than that," Jacey Lomax stated again quite positively. "You look . . . tortured over something. What's the matter?"

"Nothing that time and a good night's sleep won't cure," she returned briskly. "Thanks for bringing in the trunk."

For a moment she wondered if he was going to argue the point, but instead he merely shrugged. Then he went over to the window, leaned with both hands upon the sill and stared out at the very same view at which she herself had just been looking. He appeared not to see the view, though. Not consciously, anyway. He seemed almost absentminded, screwing up his eyes into slits in the brownness of his face as he studied the sun-drenched distances abstractedly, almost as if he wasn't seeing them at all.

Nonie saw the muscles in his tanned forearms rippling as he flexed his fingers against the ledge. Then he stretched to his full height once more. The wide shoulders squared themselves and he turned around and fastened her with a curiously impersonal look.

"You've probably realized that the house is in a much, much worse condition than you'd have been led to believe on your brief inspection of the outside that evening in the dark," he said levelly. "A good deal of money would need to be spent to get the old place into reasonable order if one were intending to reside here permanently. Is that what's worrying you?"

She shook her head a little stupidly, trying to take in what he was saying.

"I only stayed here for a short time," he continued, "while my own place was being got ready. But it was long enough to be aware of the shortcomings. I put a lot of the old junk out in the room behind the kitchen quarters, and that did something to improve the look of general dereliction. Without all those bits and pieces lying around it does look a little bit better, and we can go through them and burn them before a new owner takes over, but I realize that there's still a basic problem, a structural one of some magnitude."

"It's not that at all, Mr. Lomax."

"Because if it is—" he paused, inspected the toe of his elastic-sided stockman's boot as if it held some momentary but absorbing interest for him "—if it *is*, then I'm sure that something can be arranged, when and if the time comes, some adjustment...."

Nonie shook her head again.

"It's nothing like that," she muttered huskily, cursing the treacherous tremor in her voice. What a fool he would think her if she confessed now that she wasn't interested in buying the house after all! What an abject, stupid, shilly-shallying little fool!

"The price I quoted to you was merely a guide, you know. I hadn't really made up my mind. You mustn't let it bother you too much for the present. Don't meet troubles halfway."

Halfway!

Halfway, the man said! Little did he realize that she wasn't a mere halfway to trouble but—thanks entirely to her own rash actions—up to her very neck in the stuff.

"It is not *anything* like that," she stressed again with rather desperate firmness.

"What, then?"

He asked it in a way that *invited* an answer. He was standing very near now, and his voice had deepened in a way that was gentle yet compelling, and in his gray eyes was an expression that undoubtedly communicated sympathy, that tempted the telling of one's confidences.

There was also a certain rocklike quality in the man's stance, a steadfastness in the unflickering grayness of his faintly speculative gaze, that threatened Nonie's resolution altogether just then. She had a sudden quite shocking urge to fling herself against the broad khaki chest that blocked her escape, confess the predicament into which she had got herself and Pru and beg for a little sensible, objective, *male* advice. Those sinewy arms could be quite comforting in moments of distress; she had found that much out from previous experience.

Horrified at the trend of her own thoughts, Nonie drew back hastily, concealing her inward dismay.

"Mr. Lomax, the fact that you are now my employer hardly gives you the right to probe so persistently into my personal affairs, I think."

How cold and discouraging that sounded! Even more cold and discouraging than she had intended it to be, but she was still in a state of dire alarm at the turmoil of her own thoughts and emotions, not to mention the direction that they had just taken!

"Forgive me if I've spoken rather bluntly," she added less certainly.

"But wasn't that just what you *meant* to be, Miss Gotthart—blunt?" His own voice was chillier than she could have imagined possible, and the warmth had drained from his eyes, leaving them flinty as a saber's steel and as coldly penetrating. "Why apologize when you meant exactly what you said? Honesty is always more preferable than either hypocrisy or false remorse after all." A pause "I take it—or may I—that you have no intention of going back on your word about coming here, about staying here with Ilse and Raynor at least for a while, even though the prospect appears to have rather *thrown* you in some strange way."

Nonie's chin went up. "It hasn't thrown me at all," she assured him tartly, stung by his tone. "I have every intention of keeping to the arrangement we agreed, for however long you feel I may be needed here."

"And...?"

"And what?"

"After that?"

She looked up, startled, recovered swiftly.

"After that," she stated calmly, "I shall see. Haven't you just been telling me yourself, it's a mistake to meet trouble halfway?"

"Touché." There was the faintest lift to the corner of the leveled mouth. "In that case there's little more to be said at the moment, is there? If you'll excuse me, I'll leave you to get on with your unpacking."

She didn't turn, even when she heard the crisp staccato sound of his boots crossing the pinewood floor to the door. She just went on standing there, numb and wooden.

In the hall came Ilse's voice.

"You'll stay and eat with us, Jacey."

"No, Ilse, thanks. Not tonight."

"But I thought—"

"Something's cropped up.... I'm sorry, my dear. Give Hattie my apologies if I've disappointed her."

"When will we see you, then?"

"I'll look by tomorrow if I can."

Nonie took Pru's beret and coat off the bed, hung up the coat on the hook behind the door and threw the beret in the top shelf of the wardrobe. She eyed the tin trunk with misgiving and decided not to unpack it at all. Not just yet anyway. Maybe this confusing welter of emotions might sort themselves out if she gave herself time, and then she would know more clearly what to do. At present she'd better leave things as they were. The contents of that particular case had been there long enough already, so it wasn't going to make much difference to their condition whether they remained a few weeks, or even months, longer anyway.

Nonie found the key in her handbag, unlocked the padlock that held the metal clasp in place and lifted out the few bits of clothing that she had placed on the top for want of room anywhere else. A couple of light jerseys, too warm for just now, but they would need a press to steam the creases out. Two shirts that Pru would need for school and a pair of sandshoes that she had pushed down the side.

Back at the window again, she could see that the light was fading. Night gave little warning of its approach. It just dropped a soft gray blanket over the hills, swamped the last faint rose flush from the western sky, and then the stars sprang out, one after another. The Evening Star. Hesperus, big and bright and single, over there above the pump shed. Glowing and blinking in solitary splendor. Then, as the color ebbed from the sky altogether, there was suddenly myriad sprinklings and scatterings of stars all over the heavens. Constellations of them—the Giant Saucepan, the Southern Cross—all shimmering and winking over the still nighttime hush of the Australian bush.

Nonie sighed. If only she could find the same peace within herself as that great, still tranquillity outside, everything could have been just perfect. But it wasn't perfect at all, was it? Far from it. It had been a mistake to think that she could ignore the bad bits and recapture only the happy moments in coming back here. With a new and adult understanding she was aware that her memories had been a child's memories, whereas now she was a woman, with enough experience of the rawness of life to know that things were never as utopian as a child's-eye view would have them. Children were apt to oversimplify. Life was full of ups and downs, and just as she herself had always done her best to cushion Pru against the "downs," her parents had probably done exactly the same with her. Children had a right to be happy, didn't they, because as they got older, complications were bound to set in— things like lack of money and finding congenial work and getting on with people for whom they seemed to have a built-in antipathy. Like Jason Lomax, for instance. She just couldn't seem to be with him for two minutes on end before they were striking sparks off each other. Each time they met she was determined to remain civil, to hide the irritation that his authoritarian manner aroused in her, and each time she was unsuccessful. It always seemed to finish in the same way, with her having to reassert her independence, maintain her rights as an individual.

Nonie found him a disturbing person altogether, for even while she recognized him as autocratic and over-bearing, she had to admit that there was a sort of magnetism about the man that was hard to resist. Yet resist she must and would! With *that* sort of man you had to, didn't you, or before you knew where you were he'd be ruling your life, jerking the strings to make you dance, like he did with all of those human puppets of his. Nonie had the idea that Ilse and Ray were two of the puppets, perhaps unwilling ones, and Pru would do almost anything for Jacey Lomax. She, Nonie, wasn't going to be a puppet too, and the sooner he accepted that fact, the better.

She wasn't at all sure—and it would be all to the good if she were proved right in this—that Raynor was going to be as difficult to handle as his brother had said, in spite of Jacey's warning on that score.

When she went back to the veranda he was playing checkers with Pru, and the two of them were laughing softly over a move that he had apparently missed.

"I'm out of practice." Raynor Lomax snapped his fingers, chuckling. "What a fool, not to see that you'd get that second one."

"Do sit down, Wenona." Ilse put down the piece of tapestry she had been doing and indicated one of the cane chairs that were strewn haphazardly about the veranda. "Mind that loose board, do. I really must get one of the men to fix it for me."

"You see, I am completely useless and therefore can't," Raynor Lomax stated with what seemed unnecessary venom.

Ilse flushed. "I didn't mean that, Ray, and you know it," she said quietly. "I didn't even mean for Jacey to do it. One of the station hands could easily put a new piece of wood in for me, or even the blacksmith if I asked him, I'm sure."

"Would you like a drink, Nonie? You don't mind us calling you that? It's going to be hard not to, since Pru does it all the time."

"But of course. I hope you will."

Raynor had wheeled himself over to a cabinet upon which stood an array of bottles, an ice bucket and a jug of orange juice.

"Just orange, please, then. Is it fresh? How lovely!"

"We've been hearing all about you from Pru." He passed her a glass. "It came as a bit of a surprise to hear that you'd been actually thinking of buying this place. Jacey had omitted to mention it for some strange reason."

Nonie bit her lip, vexed that Pru had unwittingly said something already that she'd hoped she wouldn't.

"We did look at it," she admitted as calmly as she could, "but that's as far as things had got. In any case, it's not for sale at present anyway, is it, so I'd sort of shelved the matter in my own mind for just now."

"Hmm. Well, I hope for my sake as well as yours it's not going to have to be shelved for too long. Not that it wasn't decent of Jacey to make it available. I was going slowly out of my mind down there in the city—doctors and nurses pushing and pummeling at one from morning till night. Visiting hours under restriction, meal hours, bells going all the time—no peace, no privacy. I can tell you it was a relief to get away, and it was a red-letter day when Jacey sent that meddlesome nurse away from here, too, even if it does mean putting up with these tiresome sessions of Ilse's instead."

"It's only twice a day, darling, and it's always progress when the physiotherapist ousts the nurse, remember," Ilse reproved him lightly. "Whatever makes you want to come to a place like this, though, Nonie? You're young and gay; you should be down there in the bright lights, in the center of things, instead of tucked away out here in the country, shouldn't you?"

"Me an' Nonie *love* the country," chimed in Pru reproachfully. "We've been in the city and it wasn't all that much fun. Bossy old landladies and everyone telling you where to go and where not to go all the time, and nowhere to play and not much to do. We're going to *love* it here. I do already, don't you, Nonie?" Her thin face was glowing with enthusiasm. "I've been doing lots of exploring already, and it's just like you said it'd be, Nonie. Just."

"Well, at least you'll have had a chance to live in the place, and if Jacey does ever decide to put it on the market again, you'll know all the shortcomings. Not many would-be purchasers have the chance of a trial run first. You'll be able to recite all the drawbacks and beat him down," Raynor pointed out somewhat flippantly.

"Ray! What a thing to say."

"Well, so she will. You know as well as I do, Ilse, that the place is practically falling apart. Anyway, it'd do Jacey the world of good to be beaten down by someone, to meet his match just for once."

Nonie couldn't resist exchanging smiles with him. She was beginning to warm to Raynor Lomax. They appeared to agree basically over at least one essential point, and that was brother Jacey's almost unbearable domination. On the other hand, she had already developed a sneaking sympathy for Ilse. Gentle Ilse. Those barbed remarks and pointed gibes of Raynor's were undoubtedly intended for her, and they mostly reached their target too. They must have been particularly hurtful, and yet Ilse accepted them with calm and dignity, successfully concealing her true feelings. In fact, had not Jacey already put Nonie in the picture she would have found it hard to believe that these two had actually been engaged to be married at the time of Raynor's accident. One didn't intentionally set out to hurt the very person whom one loved, surely . . . and yet Raynor's remarks were cruelly calculated to do just that to Ilse. Just as if he were punishing her for something.

Poor Ilse.

And poor Raynor too. There was a trapped, restless look about him as he sat there in his wheelchair. For such an intelligent and previously athletic man it must be a prison indeed! Perhaps sheer frustration drove him to wound Ilse in this way.

When Hattie called from the end of the veranda they all went in for tea. Or dinner, as it turned out to be.

Nonie, hungry by now, found herself more than ready for the delicious roast of mutton that was set in front of Raynor, with vegetable dishes in accompaniment, holding peas and cauliflower, and a sauceboat of rich gravy. The apricot pie that followed was nothing short of a culinary work of art. Eyeing its flaky, shiny top decorated with small pastry leaves and a twining border, Nonie was already having secret misgivings as to how she was going to take Hattie's place in the kitchen when that lady was having one of her weekends off. She hadn't tried to conceal her lack of experience from Jacey Lomax but he had paid scarcely any attention to her protestations all the same. Now she was quite sure that she would make a fool of herself when the time came, and she didn't exactly relish the prospect. Nonie inspected the pie with even greater attention, wondering dubiously if she could ever produce one something like it. A good thing if she could, since it was obviously popular with this particular household, and after second helpings all around there was only one wedge left—for Hattie herself.

Later Nonie excused herself and Pru.

"Yes, you'll want to unpack properly. I'm sure, and have a proper night's rest." Ilse was immediately understanding. "Jacey said you certainly weren't getting much peace in that place you were in in town . . . I forget what he called it. By the way if you want a bath the chip-heater is lit. It's a bit archaic but it does get results. I'm sure you'll manage."

"We'll manage all right, thank you, Ilse. Good night. Good night, er, Raynor."

She followed her sister in the direction of the hall, then across it to their room.

Archaic it might be, but Nonie found the bathroom—it was a washhouse, really, with a cement floor and laundry tubs at one end of it—a comfortingly familiar place. It didn't have the acutely painful associations of the view from their enlarged bedroom window anyway, and that was a comfort. She must not get back to thinking about *that*, however, or let the present uncertainties and doubts make her more tired and depressed than she already was. Enough to acknowledge that she had been wrong to come, and leave it at that.

The trouble as far as that particular line of thought was concerned was that it, too, led to an unsatisfactory conclusion. Pru herself was the conclusion! It did look as though Pru, in her childish and innocent excitement, was already regarding Tuckarimba as her future home. Al-

ready it obviously held for her the same uncomplicated
delights and charms that it had once upon a time held for
Nonie. At eight, you didn't see the drawbacks. You
weren't aware of the undercurrents, and you *certainly*
didn't appreciate the difficulties inherent in living so near
a man like Jacey Lomax! Right under his eagle, and interfering, eye!

From the darkness of the veranda once she had tucked
Pru in and heard her prayers, Nonie could see the oblong
row of lights that must be the windows of the new Tuckarimba homestead. They lay well above the level of her
own eyes, halfway up the hillside where the house
crouched in its sentinel position at the head of the valley.
Nonie could just distinguish dark figures moving about
against the light. Soon after that another light blinked on
a little way from the main building, and after that came
the noise of a car's engine revving up. The sound seemed
to slice through the night, reverberating around the valley
before finding itself hemmed in by the hills and thrown
back upon itself from their rugged barriers.

Presently the twin shafts of headlamps' beams swept
the road and Nonie backed almost instinctively, cursing
herself for a fool as her heart's beat increased its rate.
Why be frightened, when he couldn't possibly see her or
know that she was here, a slender pajama-clad figure in
the darkness behind the gauze?

He wasn't coming in, in any case, because the sleek car
now raced on down the track beyond the sprawl of the
original homestead in the direction of Whalebone Crossing and the town. Jacey Lomax obviously had other fish to
fry tonight. Nonie had a feeling, though, that whatever it
was that had "cropped up" had been of his own on-the-
spot invention, which he was now converting into fact.

For a long while after that Nonie lay in the darkness,
unable to get to sleep. Finally she got up again, pulled on
her seersucker wrap without even bothering to tie it in
place and trod silently back to the veranda.

If only she could sort herself out! For the present, of course, she had to remain where she was because an undertaking was an undertaking. It was *afterward* that worried her now. Should she carry on with what she could at last see had been an extraordinarily ill-conceived idea or abandon the entire notion and go back to Sydney?

The place here was certainly in shocking repair. After a down payment on it there would be obvious repairs required that couldn't possibly wait very much longer. Jacey Lomax had no intention, naturally enough, of throwing good money after bad on this crumbling edifice. He was a businessman not a sentimentalist. *Certainly* not a sentimentalist! The repairs would be up to Nonie, and she couldn't see herself left with nearly enough capital to get her market garden going, let alone buy her little van. Without transport, the thing wouldn't be viable at all, so even supposing that she could overcome the disappointment of her personal reaction to these reawakened and painful memories, it was extremely doubtful if she could ever get the venture off the ground.

Unless, perhaps, Jacey were to make some "adjustment."

Out of the question. Nonie couldn't bear to be beholden to a man like that, not even for a *small* adjustment, and it looked as though she'd need a very large one indeed if she were to carry out her former plans.

Easy enough, the decision, if it were only for herself. But the awful thing was that Pru liked it here. *Loved* it here. She wanted to stay. Indeed, as far as Pru was concerned they had arrived at the end of the road, they had reached their Shangri-la. To turn back now? How could she possibly justify such a contradictory action to her little sister? She'd think her quite, quite crazy. She'd think she'd taken leave of her senses, and in fact Nonie was beginning to wonder if perhaps she hadn't done just that!

"Couldn't you sleep either?" Raynor's voice came from the other end of the veranda.

Nonie, glancing along that way startled, saw that he, too, was in his pajamas, having just wheeled himself around the corner. He was sitting in his chair smoking a cigarette.

"It's because you're in strange surroundings," he added with unconscious irony as she approached rather timidly. "It often works that way."

"Yes, you're probably right. What about you, though, Mr.—"

"Raynor. Why hesitate? Your little sister says it already."

"Are . . . are you in pain?" she suggested a little uncertainly.

His crisp directness of speech had reminded her a little bit of his brother just now, and it had the effect of disconcerting her.

Raynor Lomax grimaced.

"A little. Ilse tells me it's a healthy sign. For too long I didn't feel anything, so maybe there's something in what she says."

"I'm sure there must be. I think Ilse is a—a sweet person."

"Do you now?" He studied her with interest. "That's a snap judgment, surely. Or has Jacey been extolling her virtues in advance by any chance?"

"What an odd thing to say." She seated herself in one of the substantial cane chairs, drawing her wrap about her and wondering at the sudden bitterness in his tone. "I'm a good judge of character on my own account," she added firmly.

"Hmm." Raynor shifted his position. "What would you say about *me*, then? Let's hear the worst."

"You? Why, I hardly know you!"

"You know me as well as you know Ilse," he pointed out logically. "Come on, Miss Good-Judge-of-Character. You must have formed some opinion, so let's have it."

Nonie was tongue-tied. She was wishing now that she had never got herself involved in this strange nocturnal conversation with the enigmatic Raynor Lomax.

"Would you say I'm, for instance, a *reasonable* man?" he insisted, and she could see his mouth twisting in amusement at his own question.

"Except when you're busy enjoying yourself by baiting people who you know are already at a disadvantage and can't answer back."

"Meaning you?"

"Meaning me. You know perfectly well that I am in your brother's employment, and I've no intention of involving myself in an analysis of the family's personalities on my very first evening here."

"You mean you need more time?"

"I mean not now, not ever," she replied crisply. "It . . . it wouldn't be proper."

"What you're trying to say is, Jacey wouldn't like it," he elaborated for her slyly. "That's Jacey, spoiling things as usual."

"Is that fair, Raynor? I should think you should be grateful to Mr. Lomax."

"Grateful!"

"Well . . . I mean—" she floundered helplessly "—I suppose he took a lot of trouble arranging for you and Ilse to come back here. And he meant it for the best, getting *us* here too."

"I suppose he did," agreed Raynor surprisingly gently. "I'm not getting at *you*, child, or your kid sister, either. I was very genuinely glad when he said you were coming. I've already told you that, and it's the truth. Ilse and I were getting on each other's nerves, and you'll be company and a welcome distraction. That's what you're being right this minute, Nonie. But don't talk to me about gratitude in connection with anything Jacey does, Nonie, or you'll be making a very big initial mistake. That brother

of mine never makes any decision without a reason . . .
And that reason is never one that doesn't suit his own
particular book, you can take it from me."

Nonie wiggled her bare toes and watched them expres
sionlessly. She had no intention of being drawn into any
form of comment where Jacey Lomax was concerned
even though, silently, she half agreed.

"Careful little creature, aren't you?" Raynor's teeth
glinted in the dim veranda light. He changed tack.
"That's an enchanting young sister you've got, and no
mistake. We're going to be friends, she and I, I can tell."

"I hope you will be. Pru loves it here already."

"She lacks your cautious approach."

"I'm not always cautious," Nonie replied candidly,
adding a little bitterly, "Sometimes I'm far too impetuou
for our own good, hers and mine, I'm afraid."

"Like landing yourself in that Pink Pelican place in
town? Jacey told us about that. He reckoned you'd be
better out of it, I gather."

Nonie licked her lips. "Is . . . was that partly why he go
us here?"

Raynor shrugged carelessly. "Who knows why Jacey
does things? Even if you asked him he wouldn't tell you.
Jacey never does. Jacey never explains his actions to any
one; it's almost a principle with him."

"Maybe that's the sort of principle that can rebound on
one," Nonie said wisely. "Maybe one's actions can be
misinterpreted sometimes if one just doesn't bother to ex
plain them, wouldn't you think?"

"Hmm." A pause. "Perhaps you think I'm tough on
him with what I've just been saying."

"You sounded as if you meant it."

"You consider me bitter, don't you? Bitter and a little
unfair?"

"I'm thinking this is the strangest conversation to be
having in the middle of the night with someone I scarcely

know," she told him evasively. "And I can't see where it's getting either of us. What I think doesn't matter in the slightest. If you're being unfair to anyone, you'll know it yourself, won't you? As for being bitter, I can understand that you must feel terribly resentful and frustrated not being able to get about in the way that you used to."

"Can you? Can you really understand that?" Raynor studied her earnest face thoughtfully. "Yes, I believe you really can, my dear. You have a sensitive, imaginative little face and a capacity for feeling and caring about other people." He reached out a hand, touched the side of her cheek gently. "I think you're going to be good for us all, do you know that, Nonie?"

The satire had died from his face, the smoothly ironic tone from his voice. Raynor had spoken with a sort of quiet wonder that touched Nonie to the very core. It was the first time in their brief acquaintance that she knew him to be completely sincere in what he was saying, and his sincerity had been about *her*.

Pity stirred in her. Pity for this big, restless, bitter man confined so despairingly to his wheelchair. Pity for the gentle Ilse, whom he seemed bent upon wounding with his barbed repartee and who obviously loved him enough to suffer his churlish treatment with what amounted to almost saintly patience.

She longed, then, to help them all in whatever way she could, although she couldn't see how her own presence could make much difference. Maybe Pru's would though. Because Jacey Lomax had told her that his brother loved children, and this at least was true.

"I hope so, Raynor. I hope we'll be good for everyone," she said a little huskily. She stood up abruptly. "If you'll excuse me now, I think I'll go to bed after all."

"Sleep well, Nonie. And I think I shall, too . . . better than I'd been going to anyway. Good night."

"Good night."

CHAPTER FIVE

It was a long time before Nonie fell asleep that night, and when she woke up she found that the sun was well up in the sky. Glancing at the clock, she was horrified to find that it was almost eleven o'clock. Eleven! And no one had been to waken her or even to see where she was and why she had not yet appeared.

She had a quick shower in the yellowish water that was pumped up to the homestead from the creek—cold water today, since the heater had not been lit. Indeed, the ashes could be seen lying in a depressing little heap at the base of the cylinder.

Nonie dressed hastily, then cleaned out the fireplace and went kitchenward to seek out some paper and kindling to reset it. There she made the acquaintance of Hattie, a thin sparrow of a creature with critical black eyes beneath a frizzy mop of wiry graying curls. Hattie appeared quick and active and extremely efficient. She showed Nonie where the kindling was stacked, then went out the back door with a basket full of dish towels and drying cloths that she had been boiling in a pan on top of the big black cooking range.

No one else seemed to be around this morning. It was only when she stepped out through the hall to the front of the house that Nonie found out why. On the veranda there appeared to be a morning tea party in full progress. Ilse was presiding over a trolley upon which lay an assortment of cheeses and biscuits, plain white cups and saucers and a large brown enamel teapot. Raynor's chair was strategically placed near a small wicker table, and in a canvas deck lounger beside him sprawled the long-legged figure of Jacey Lomax. On the other lounger, twin to Jacey's, reclined the decorative Delphine Simpson. The fiery splendor of her rich auburn hair was complemented perfectly by the unrelieved white of the simple tennis dress she was wearing. Her shapely legs in their short white ankle socks and canvas shoes were crossed in a way that accentuated the rounded curves of her body. From one hand she was dangling a pair of extravagantly framed sunglasses, while the other reached idly for a biscuit from the plate on Ilse's trolley. She was just about to bite into the dry cracker with her neat white even teeth when those long lynx-green eyes caught sight of Nonie, poised uncertainly in the hall doorway.

"Why, Jacey darling, look who's here. Your little protegée in the flesh." The tones were husky, slowly amused.

Everyone in the gathering turned then to look at the object of Delphine's remark.

"Ah, Nonie, do come and join us in a cup of tea." That was Ilse's voice, tranquil and kind.

"Miss Gotthart." Jacey's own deep murmur of acknowledgment just reached her as he drew up his long legs and scrambled lazily to his feet.

"Oh, please . . . don't anybody get up—" but her embarrassed protest came too late, of course, for Jacey Lomax was already hooking his elastic-sided boot beneath another chair, drawing it nearer and indicating that she should sit in it.

"I'm afraid I'm disturbing everyone," she muttered apologetically.

"Not me, you'll have noticed, and I don't intend that you should. I'm conserving all my energies for tennis later." Delphine popped the last piece of biscuit into her mouth and passed Ilse her cup. "Some more if it's there, please, Ilse. I've such a dry throat this morning. It must have been that smoky atmosphere in the club last night."

"Why go there, then?" Raynor spoke for the first time, sliding one of his blatantly cynical looks at Delphine's pouting mouth.

"Because, darling, I was asked to go there. Asked in a way that made it quite difficult to refuse, and by a man who, in spite of his indisputable charm in many directions, doesn't like to take no for an answer."

"Jacey, I suppose." Raynor's scowling gaze swelled disapprovingly upon his teacup.

"Who else?" agreed Delphine sweetly. "Although it's perhaps hardly flattering to him that you recognized my definition of your dictatorial brother quite so promptly. Why shouldn't I whisk him away sometimes? You don't have any objections, do you Raynor? I should think you'd have been quite pleased, actually."

"And what do you mean by that?"

"Well—" slim shoulders shrugged a little deprecatingly "—I just thought you *should* be, that's all. If his attention's on me, then it can't be anywhere else, can it? I thought you'd welcome a little, um, timely diversion for Jacey's attentions just now, if you follow me."

"Stop it, Delphine." Jacey spoke with lazy authority. "Just because I've agreed to drive you over to this crazy tennis party of yours it doesn't give you the right to start talking in riddles and innuendos, especially at this hour of the day. Drink up your tea and we'll get going."

"It's not a riddle to Raynor, though. *He* understands me, don't you, Ray?" She slid him an oblique look from beneath her long lashes, then pouted back at his brother. "Anyway, I can't think why you won't stay and play tennis yourself, Jacey. You were invited too, you know. It's not very fair just taking me over and dumping me like a piece of unwanted baggage." Her tone dropped to a wheedling softness, to which Jacey Lomax seemed completely impervious. Or was he? Just for a moment Nonie could have sworn that his firm lips were threatening to curve uncontrollably. Instead they pronounced with inscrutable solemnity:

"A piece of baggage, certainly. The 'unwanted' bit is obviously thrown in as a challenge, but I refuse to be goaded, Delphine." He got to his feet, scooped his broadbrimmed hat off the table. "Come on, then, we'll go."

"Why *won't* you stay the whole day, Jacey?" she persisted, getting up and putting her cup back on the tray near Ilse. "It would do you good to relax for a while. You can be much too serious at times, my pet. I suppose you're going off instead on some of that horrid business of yours, as usual."

This time his lips did twitch.

"That's perfectly correct. And I reckon it'll be time better spent than hitting lollipops over the net to you girls."

"Dear Jacey! Now you're being humble, which is *quite* out of character, since we all know you can produce the most devastating drives when you like." Delphine replaced her sunglasses on her pretty freckled nose and followed him toward the gauze door that led to the front steps. "You will come back for me, though?"

"Haven't I said so?" Jacey Lomax paused with his hand on the door, and Nonie was quite taken by surprise when she found that she herself was now the object of his momentary attention. "You slept well, Miss Gotthart?" The gray eyes raked her. "You still look a little peaky to me."

Raynor swung his chair around deftly.

"*Did* you sleep well, Nonie . . . after our little midnight chat?"

Color rushed to Nonie's cheeks. She was well aware that Jacey Lomax's gray gaze had sharpened perceptibly, and she could have cursed Raynor for that unnecessary revelation.

"Quite well, thanks," she mumbled confusedly, finding that her voice had gone thick with embarrassment, for again every eye seemed to be fastened upon her as though the quality of her slumber had suddenly become a point of quite universal interest.

"A midnight chat?"

Jacey's controlled voice demanded an explanation, just as she had guessed it would. Raynor must have guessed as much too. Was he doing this deliberately? He certainly seemed to be enjoying the situation, at any rate.

"That's right. Or after midnight, actually, to be precise. What time would you say our tête-à-tête took place, Nonie? One o'clock? No, later, I believe. I distinctly recall the hall clock striking two, don't you?" He chuckled as he studied his brother's changing expression. "Now, don't come over the heavy brother, Jacey, for God's sake. It was all quite proper, I can assure you. We were simply getting to know each other a little better, that's all, and it was as delightful a process as was possible in my present condition, so you can stop scowling in that arrogant manner. You know damn fine I'm quite incapable of getting up to any mischief at the moment, even if I wanted to. In any case—" he grinned that sudden, devil-may-care grin that could so quickly transform his pain-lined features to a roguish boyishness "—she looked about ten years old standing there on the veranda in those stripy pajamas and little bare toes. One can't go around seducing ten-year-olds, can one?"

"What a cozy picture you paint though, Ray!" Delphine put in creamily. "And how quickly your little innocent seems to have made herself at home, Jacey, don't you think?"

"It would certainly appear so." For all his deep tones were so clipped, Jacey Lomax's tanned face was still unreadable as he nodded to the company at large, held open the gauze door for his companion to pass through and followed her down the steps without a backward glance.

A few seconds later the engine of his car whirred to life, and it slid away smoothly toward the main road leaving a trail of dust in its wake.

"That was unkind of you, Raynor." Ilse's voice was quietly reproving as she began to gather up the cups. "Not very nice of Delphine, either."

"I hope you don't think . . . they . . . you don't think—"

"I don't think anything, Nonie." Ilse's eyes were sympathetic as they dwelt on the other's distressed face. "And you mustn't let yourself become upset by Raynor's childish behavior. He's got a chip on his shoulder as big as that cedar tree out there. It amuses him sometimes to be cruel, that's all, and I must say Delphine eggs him on. You'll soon get used to it, like the rest of us have had to."

"No one's asking you to put up with me, Ilse, if that's what you're getting at," said Raynor hardily. "Why don't you just go? Go away and leave me if I'm as difficult as all that. It might be better if you did at that, for all the progress I'm making," he tacked on with gloomy cynicism.

"Now, darling, you mustn't say that." Ilse spoke soothingly, immediately contrite. "Of course you're making progress. I'm aware of a difference, an improvement, after each session . . . and I'm speaking now from a purely professional angle. It's there, Ray darling, truly it is. All you've got to do is to believe in it for it to happen, and it will." She put her hands on his shoulders and leaned forward and placed the gentlest of kisses on Raynor Lomax's scowling forehead.

"It's not as simple as that, and you know it," grumbled Raynor, still frowning, though obviously somewhat mollified. "You don't just get a thing in life because you *believe* in it. You, of all people, ought to know that by now, Ilse. Sometimes these naive philosophies of yours simply leave me breathless."

"One has to believe," she maintained firmly. "And it's almost a medical fact of life, Ray, where recovery's concerned. The will has to be there."

"And you don't think it is, with me?" His tone was bitter. "Hell, what do you know about it, anyway? Do you honestly think I *like* being here, half man, half wheel-chair, dependent upon you, on Jacey, watching you all doing the things I can't do—riding, driving cars, playing tennis, even simple walking? Just walking. The simplest of the lot and I can't even do that."

"But you will, Raynor, truly you will. In fact—" she shot a quick look at the neat black watch strapped to her wrist, made an apologetic face "—I'm sorry, but it's time for another session right now. Goodness knows where the morning has gone to!"

"Let me take these things out and deal with them," begged Nonie swiftly. "I know where my own morning has gone, alas . . . most of it simply in sleeping, so I might as well be useful for what's left of it, don't you think?"

"Bless you then, if you will. And thanks. After that you might like to look for Pru. She went exploring down through the old orchard, I think."

"There must be other things I can do first. I didn't come here for a holiday, Ilse, although Mr. Lomax might be forgiven for thinking so when I put in such a late appearance. It was just . . . well, I felt really terribly tired last night. Tired and sort of confused and apprehensive."

"You don't need to explain. Of course you'd feel strange on your very first night, but you'll soon get used to us all and learn to find your way around. The orchard is out that way." Ilse nodded in its general direction. "Go left outside the kitchen and you can't miss it. Okay?"

"Okay. And thank you, Ilse."

"Don't thank me. It was Jacey who arranged it after all, but I'm going to love having you here. We all are. Little Pru and Raynor are buddies already, and she's loving being here too. She was so excited about everything this morning, and so interested. She's the adaptable sort, it seems, but then children generally are," pronounced Ilse tolerantly as she followed Raynor's wheelchair inside, leaving Nonie to her self-appointed task of clearing away the tea things.

In the kitchen Hattie had returned from the clothesline and was busy scoring cucumber with a fork. Nonie washed and dried the few cups and saucers and then offered her assistance in other directions.

"Chop those chives then, if you like." Hattie's nimble fingers were arranging her cucumber slices around the edge of a large oval platter filled with salad. "I'll sprinkle it over the lot when you've done it. The board is just behind you . . . that wooden one there, and here's a good sharp knife."

"Have you been here long, Hattie? At Tuckarimba? I suppose you have."

"Not always, if that's what you mean by 'long.' I came down here when Jacey asked me to. I lived on one of the company's cattle stations when I was up north. My father used to be an overseer with old Mr. Lomax."

"With the father? And you came down after Mr., er, Raynor's accident?"

"Heavens, no, long before that. I was here with Jacey when he came here first. I came down to look after him. It's difficult to refuse Jacey a favor when he asks for one." A pause. "I must say it's funny hearing you calling him Mr. Lomax. Absolutely *everyone* calls him Jacey."

"We're not on Christian-name terms, exactly." Nonie swallowed a little uncomfortably. "Do you mean here in this house, Hattie? Did Jacey Lomax actually live here, then?"

Hattie scooped up a palmful of chives and sprinkled them deftly over her salad arrangement, stepped back to survey the finished dish.

"That'll do, thank you, Nonie. There's nothing nicer than fresh, crisp salads in this wilting heat, don't you think, and that loam in the garden grows the loveliest lettuces. Lovely everything, come to that. Everything we use here is homegrown," she added proudly, lifting the platter over to the fridge and placing it on one of the wire racks inside. "That's more than we could claim up in the top end. We couldn't even have a house cow up there. Tinned milk, it was, and tinned everything else almost, except for the sides of salt beef."

"Did he live here long?"

"Who?" asked Hattie vaguely, her mind already busy with other matters.

"Mr. Lomax...Jacey. You said he lived in this house."

"For a while, he did, yes."

"Didn't he like it here? I suppose he couldn't have or he wouldn't have wanted to sell it."

"Hmm. I've a feeling the move wasn't Jacey's idea alone. Delphine Simpson took a great interest in the plans for his big new house up there on the hillside, you know, so maybe it was as much her idea as his to part with this one. Who knows? Certainly she never liked it." Hattie sniffed. "Not nearly grand enough for the likes of her, I suspect."

"Nor for him either, I shouldn't think," murmured Nonie, remembering Jacey Lomax's disparaging, unsentimental look at the decaying boards and peeling paint before he had taken his leave of her yesterday. It hurt, somehow, that rejection of the old house by them all. It was like a—a personal rebuff, although it was silly to think of it that way when they couldn't even know that she had ever been remotely connected with it, and especially as she herself now realized what a mistake it had been to come back like this. If Bundy hadn't told her the things that had been surmising about her father's death she might have felt differently, but now that she had had that inkling of how things really were, the pain and uncertainty of it all were just another small and agonizing burden, along with the unsatisfactory way Pru had been behaving lately. And her own consequent lack of confidence in herself and her own decisions made everything that much harder to bear, particularly as there was no one in whom she could confide. She was stuck with her own rash decision now whether she liked it or not.

"Are they engaged, or something?" Nonie dragged her mind back to present realities. "When she takes such an interest, I mean."

Hattie snorted.

" 'Or something' might be near the mark. There's nothing official; that's what I'm saying by that. Not that Miss Delphine Simpson wouldn't *like* there to be, mind you. She works hard enough at it, heaven knows."

"You don't like her?" Nonie studied the housekeeper's indignant face curiously because she realized with some surprise that there had been a certain genuine vehemence about the way in which the older woman had just spoken.

Hattie drew herself up to her full, not very impressive, height and said, "It's not my place to like or dislike friends of Jacey's, is it? All the same, I can say I'm surprised at someone like him, someone who's known more women in his day than I'd care to count, falling for that barley-sugar line of hers. That's if he *does* fall for it. Like I've always said, you never really know with Jacey. You never really know what he's thinking and what he's not. He always liked to keep people guessing, ever since I've known him. He's a deep one, Jacey. He's never been the transparent sort, not like *her*. It's not hard to guess what *she*'s after. You'd probably spotted it yourself already."

"She's . . . well, very attractive," Nonie pointed out, albeit with reluctance because she hadn't been able to like Delphine's manner out there on the veranda just now. She hadn't liked that silky sarcasm in her voice or the meaning way her eyes had slid from Jacey to Raynor and back to Jacey. And she hadn't much cared for the proprietorial way in which Delphine had rested her manicured hand in the crook of Jacey Lomax's brown forearm as they'd walked down the path to the car.

"Huh, you wouldn't say she was so attractive if you'd

heard her sending your little sister about her business the moment she arrived."

"*Did* she? Did she really do that? I hope Pru wasn't being a nuisance?" Nonie looked suddenly anxious. "She can be, you know. Where is she now, I wonder?"

"Jacey took her up to show her the kittens under the woolshed. She was quite happy to stay there playing with them. And if I know children the way I think I do, that's what she'll still be doing."

Nonie found herself unaccountably touched by that gesture of Jacey's. It had been kind of him to intervene like that to rescue Pru from Delphine Simpson's scathing tongue. But then he always seemed to be rescuing someone from something, didn't he? He enjoyed having lame ducks around just so he could rescue them, it seemed. It was the *way* he rescued you that Nonie didn't like. That high-handed manner and the way he just *took charge*. When Jacey Lomax took charge, no one else stood much of a chance of doing things in any way but his way, that's what really annoyed her most of all about the man. She'd been doing things her way for years—hadn't had much option, really, since there'd been nobody else to ask in any case—and she meant to go right on doing them her way. Independence was a precious thing, even if you did sometimes make decisions that were stupid and ill-conceived, like the one she had made to come here. Nonie meant to keep her independence no matter how the Lomax man reacted.

Still, it might have been easier to resist his interference if he wasn't quite so—well—*nice* about it. It might have been easier if he hadn't been so kind all along to Pru, either. And it would certainly be easier for Nonie to decide what she should do about the situation she'd got herself into if only little Pru hadn't been going about looking *quite* so happy, *quite* so childishly enthusiastic over positively everything at Tuckarimba.

Why, even the look on her face this very minute as she peered out from the semidark of the sloping space between the woolshed's slatted floors and the ground where she squatted to where Nonie herself knelt cautiously beside clumps of docks and nettles calling to her softly—even *that* look told Nonie that Pru was happier than she had ever been in the whole of her not-very-long life.

"Oh, Nonie! Look at them, Nonie, aren't they the sweetest things you ever saw? Come here, sweetness. You darling, come on then. Look, Nonie, this one's settled on my lap. I think it must like me."

"The feeling appears to be mutual. You can't go on calling it '*it*' though, Pru. You'll have to think up a name."

"Yes, that's what Jacey said, and I've named them all already; it's just that I forgot to say them." Pru grappled with the wriggling bodies, held them up in turn to introduce them. "I've called the mother Marmalade, like that ginger pussy we had once in Manly. And this is Manda and this is Reen. Manda*rine*, see. Marmalade, manda*rine*. See?"

"I see," nodded Nonie a little faintly, overcome by this stroke of original inspiration, as Pru obviously regarded it. "Did you tell Jacey what they're to be called?"

"Not yet. He left me while I was still thinking about it. He had to get back to Delphine, I s'pose." A pause. "I hate that woman, Nonie."

"Hate's a strong word, pet." Nonie did her best to infuse a measure of rebuke into that, but even to her own ears it sounded a bit lukewarm.

"Well, I *do*. She's always so . . . so smug, so . . . uppity. First she asked me what I was doing there and why wasn't I at school, and when I said I wasn't starting till Monday and Jacey was going to teach me to ride a pony so I can go on that, she said didn't I think I'd missed enough schooling without hanging about with the grown-ups all the time as well. And then she said, Run *on*, child—quite narky sort of. So I did . . . run on, I mean. Only I didn't really know where to run on *to*, and I was standing at the top of the orchard where I've got that hopscotch place drawn out, and that's when Jacey came out and told me he had something to show me. Wasn't that nice of him, Nonie? I like Jacey, don't you? I love *him*, and I hate *her*," Pru added darkly.

Nonie swallowed, amazed at the clarity with which Pru had defined her feelings on the subject. It wasn't going to help things if besides falling for Tuckarimba her small sister were to fall for Jacey Lomax as well!

"Don't get too dirty, will you? It doesn't smell all that nice under there, if you don't mind me saying so. You'll need a really good bath when you come back to the house."

"I know. Jacey said I'll have to, so I s'pose I will," agreed Pru with some resignation. "He said it was a condition, or I think that was the word, something like that anyway. He said they're only here while they're little, though, for protection, see. When they're a bit bigger, they'll come down around the homestead, and Hattie and me'll probably give them scraps."

"Hattie and I," corrected Nonie automatically.

"No, Hattie and *me*, because *I'm* in charge of them."

"Have it your way, poppet." Nonie grinned at her sister's indignant retort. "Only I'm talking about grammar and you're talking about who'll feed the kittens, and we seem to have got our wires crossed somewhere along the way. I daresay it'll take the schoolteacher to sort that one out."

"Mrs. Mooney, her name is. Jacey said she's really nice and she's got kids of her own, too, and they're in the class along with the rest of us. It must be awfully funny having your mother as your schoolteacher as well, mustn't it?

But like I was saying to Jacey, I can't imagine what it'd be
like having a mother at *all*, even if she was just an ordinary one and not a schoolteacher.'

Here was dangerous ground indeed.

"What else were you and Jacey saying?" Nonie heard
herself asking carefully, wondering if perhaps she herself
hadn't come into their discussions at some stage around
this point. Surely, though, he wouldn't criticize Nonie and
her failings as a guardian to Pru, no matter how incompe-
tent he thought she was? Not to her very own sister?

She was obviously not to be enlightened. All Pru would
say—offhandedly and with her voice muffled because she
had buried her face into one of the kittens' furry
bodies—was, "Oh, this and that, Nonie. I can't remember it all, because me and Jacey talk about heaps of
things. We tell each other *lots* of things, I mean, don't
we?"

"Do you, darling?" replied Nonie with some misgiving,
wondering why she should feel so troubled and uncomfortable over the fact that Pru should share so many confidences with Jacey Lomax in this way. They'd only be
childish observations and innocent secrets anyway, probably, such as the names for the kittens and things. Harmless chatter, nothing more.

No, she was sure it was nothing more, for in the weeks
that followed she took the trouble to observe them together in order to satisfy herself upon this point. Watching them together as Jacey gave the child her riding
lessons, listening to his patient instructions, his quiet teasing when he was with the little girl and the way in which
he listened so attentively to all she had to tell him, Nonie
was bound to admit that over this, at least, she might have
misjudged Jacey Lomax. He would never use the child to
further his own ends or to seek out information, and Pru's
chatter itself was harmless enough.

Actually, one couldn't help seeing that Jacey appeared

to genuinely enjoy Pru's company, and his censure he reserved for her elder sister. As always, he was—by his own stern code at least—completely just. The younger sister had not yet attained the age of responsibility. The elder one had and must therefore carry the burden for the joint conduct of their lives, and up to this point it seemed he hadn't much approved of the way Nonie had done things. Not that he wasn't always gravely polite and consistently courteous. He was, but in the most distant fashion. For Pru he had that sudden smile that could break up his rather hawklike features in an instant into scores of little lines that crinkled a fanning pattern at the sides of his dancing gray eyes and grooved a deep path in his weather-beaten cheeks. For Nonie those very same gray eyes held nothing more than an unwavering and inquiring steadiness, with perhaps at times a hint of quiet speculation that made her heart thump somewhat uncomfortably whenever she discerned it.

For the first two weeks Jacey rode with Pru to the school, a couple of miles farther along the creek beyond his own homestead. Each morning for the first week, he came down to the old place on the big bay horse, the same one he'd been leading through the timber that first time they'd seen him. There he would supervise the catching and saddling of Pru's small chestnut pony, and then they would ride off together on the bridle track along the creek.

At the start of the second week, he insisted that Pru herself must catch her pony and saddle up, and he would join her at a point below his house. By the third week she was deemed fit to do the whole thing for herself and make the journey alone.

"There's very little risk," he took the trouble to assure a concerned Nonie. "I wouldn't have let her do it if I'd thought there was, but out here in the bush children have to learn to stand on their own feet."

"And not just children either," chimed in Delphine sweetly from the doorway. "I've brought Ilse some more of that tapestry wool she was wanting, since she didn't think she'd have enough to finish the background."

"She's in the kitchen with Hattie, I think."

"Is she? I'm in no hurry anyway." And to prove her point Delphine took an apple from the bowl on the table and sank down gracefully on one of the cane loungers. "What are we talking about anyway, Jacey? Is someone not standing on her own little feet like she should be doing?" She shot a sidelong glance at Nonie.

Jacey's broad shoulders shrugged idly.

"No, Delphine, everyone's doing fine as it happens. But this is the first day Pru's tackled the ride to school entirely alone, and I'm just reassuring her big sister that she'll be okay. I've actually arranged with her teacher that if she isn't there by nine o'clock any day she must phone us, and we in turn will ring her if for any reason Pru isn't coming."

"Well, that sounds a watertight-enough arrangement, and you've devoted quite enough of your precious time to that child in the last few weeks anyway, if you ask me, Jacey."

"*Did* I ask you, Delphine?" he murmured mildly, raising a bushy brow in mock surprise and giving a tantalizing grin that took away any suggestion of a sting from his query.

He was rewarded by one of Delphine's most charming and conciliatory smiles.

"No, you didn't darling, and I've no intention of interfering. What could possibly happen to the child, anyway, just between here and there?"

Nonie intervened, still hesitant about the whole thing.

"I just thought, if the pony stumbled and threw her off . . . *you* know—" she gestured a little vaguely "—and then there's the river."

"The river?" Delphine's lips curled scornfully. "For heaven's sake, it's hardly more than a creek even at its widest, you silly thing. And she can swim, can't she? Even if she couldn't, you could hardly drown a cat in it, it's so shallow. The only person I've ever heard of coming to grief in it was that stupid fellow, the one who was here before your Tintoola lot, Jacey. What was his name, something-or-other Dermot? Only his wasn't an accident. He *meant* to do it, because he was a bit of a flop or something, so everyone said. Lord, you'd *need* to mean to do it to get drowned in that pathetic little bit of water." Delphine bit into her apple. "I daresay even *he* had trouble in actually managing it," she mumbled less distinctly, adding as she caught the almost inaudible hiss of Nonie's indrawn breath, "My dear girl, what on earth are you looking at me like *that* for?"

Nonie found that her hands were clenched against the edge of the table, the knuckles so white that already her fingers felt numb. A dew had broken out on her forehead and she was wondering a little crazily if, when she unbuckled her fingers from the edge of that table, she might not fall over altogether. She'd have to try it, though. She'd have to get out of here. Outside. Into the air.

Carefully she forced her hands to open.

"It's all right, Delphine." Could that breathless, far-away gasp really be her own voice? "I know you ... meant to be ... kind ... reassuring—" somehow her wooden limbs moved mechanically toward the door "—excuse me ... just for a moment—"

Nonie never remembered afterward how she actually got down to the creek or why indeed she went that way at all. She could only recollect that each dragging step was an incredible effort, as if each foot carried a leaden weight, and that she had to force her limbs into some sort of determined movement. Their direction, their destination were immaterial.

The trees blocked out the sunshine, the branches mingling, forming dizzy patterns about and above her. Finally she could go no farther and sank down in the grass at the edge of an arc of shingle lapped by peaceful shallows. There were water lillies in the pool beyond, their cups closed secretly in the dappled shade that dimpled the broad flat leaves lying so delicately upon the surface of the water. They were serenely lovely, tranquil, calming, of palest cream color flushed with a mere tinge of pink at the center.

A sound above her made her raise her eyes. Jacey Lomax stood at the top of the bank. He was hatless, which meant that he had left the house in something of a hurry. Jacey Lomax was *never* separated from that disreputable wide-brimmed felt hat of his. It was as much a part of him as the springing dark hair, the craggy sunbleached brows, the cool gray eyes, the firm mouth that just now was pulled into a thin, level line as he picked his way down the bank to where she sat.

Jacey hitched his moleskins and sat down beside her, and Nonie, numb and still as any statue, made a valiant effort to drag her mind out of its trancelike state. She'd need all her wits to cope with Jason Lomax right now, wouldn't she? God, what had she done, fleeing from the room like that?

Nonie drew up her knees and clasped her hands tightly about them, bracing herself to hide the trembling that still possessed her.

For a time Jacey said nothing, just kept picking up pebbles from the shingle and flicking them into the water with savage little flicks. He selected each pebble carefully, as if it really mattered.

"You seemed upset, Nonie," he observed at length, still not looking her way, and her heart gave an odd little leap of sheer surprise not only at his noncommittal tone but because that was the first time he had ever called her by her first name.

She swallowed. Out of sheer nervousness her own fumbling fingers found a pebble and she too threw it toward the pool. Nonie's pebble didn't reach the water. It landed with a tiny staccato click on the shingle at the edge of the creek.

"I'm sorry," she said tonelessly. "I'm quite all right now. It was just a...a...temporary thing."

"Temporary? Huh!" Jacey gave a snort of disbelief. "How long have you carried this thing with you without telling anyone?"

"What thing?" Her nerves tautened immediately.

Jacey threw away his last pebble without even bothering to see where it went, in a gesture of pure impatience. She knew that he was looking at her now, studying her profile with analytical keenness. Doubtless she was a sight to behold, she realized wryly. She could feel the perspiration setting coldly on her forehead, and her hair clung in pale, sticky tendrils to her temples and nape. A good thing she hadn't actually fainted back there or she'd be even paler than she probably was.

Jacey continued to study her thoughtfully. He seemed to be waiting. Waiting for *something*, only Nonie didn't know what the something might be. He seemed to be expectant, yet she had no idea what could possibly be expected of her in such a situation as this. It was uncomfortable, sitting there on the bank beside the quiet, expectant, *waiting* figure of Jacey Lomax.

Her nerves began to tingle. Nonie felt her spirit surging back, roused by the man's candid scrutiny. Maybe she could bluff the thing out, if she were clever enough, even though she wasn't feeling particularly clever just now.

"*What* thing?" she repeated, much more firmly.

Jacey's gesture was a peculiarly stern, telling sort of one. And the thing it told her was that her bluff wasn't going to receive the consideration she had hoped it might merit.

"You're Dermot's daughter, aren't you."

It was a statement, not a question at all. And Jacey Lomax had stated it with such certainty that it was obviously useless to deny it. Too late to bluff, Nonie. Much too late.

The fact that he knew her identity was like a physical blow. She could feel the thud of it as it struck at the pit of her stomach.

"Don't play with me, please, Nonie. I'm hardly in a mood for games." Jacey's hands bit into her shoulders, turning her toward him. "Look at me," he commanded, and when Nonie looked she saw that indeed he was not in a mood for games.

She swallowed again and this time she actually heard the difficult sound of it in her throat.

"Yes, I'm Dermot's daughter." She threw back her head, made herself meet his gaze unflinchingly. There was a defiant note in her voice as she gathered the shreds of her courage about her and added, "What if I am?"

Jacey's eyes were unreadable, holding hers. She couldn't look into them for long, especially as he didn't seem to be going to reply.

"H-how long have you . . . . known?" she asked bleakly, glancing away and pushing her hair back nervously. The numbness was draining out of her now and the old misery was flooding back to take its place again.

"Since the first day you came here to be with Raynor and Ilse," he told her levelly. "You never got farther than the wattle tree that evening you came out with Pru to see if the place was for sale. I'd been watching you from the edge of the timber when you were looking for that signboard, and you didn't go *around* the house that time; you were only at the side where the wattle is. When I brought you here myself you knew your way around too well not to have been here before. The bedroom by the tankstand, you said. Yet you couldn't have seen a tankstand that night. Even had it been light enough, it's on the opposite side of the house." His fingers had tightened, bruising the soft flesh beneath her shirt. "And then there was your re-action inside that day. Something shook you up pretty thoroughly, even though you tried to hide it, and I asked myself what." Jacey released her, shrugged. "It didn't take much to come up with some answers, and when I checked them out the whole thing dropped into place. Why did you lie to me, Nonie?"

It was her turn to shrug.

"Would you have asked me to come here with Pru if you had known who I was?"

"No, probably not. That's hardly relevant at the moment though, is it? You lied to me. You deceived me. Why?"

Jacey's face was set, and although his tone was con-trolled it was full of censure. So full of censure, in fact, that something inside Nonie seemed to snap. This was the old Jacey back—Jacey the god, Jacey the judge, Jacey the arrogant.

"Lie? Deceive?" She scrambled to her feet as she jerked out the words, and he in one swift movement fol-lowed suit. "Who are you to talk of lies, of deceit?" she asked on a rapidly rising note. "I deceived, yes, because I wanted to redeem my father's name. I wanted to make good, show that I could stick it out, prove I had the guts that you all seem to think Dermot lacked. I was going to paint up the house and start a market garden, and when I'd got it going, *then* I'd have told everyone, *then* I'd have said, 'Look, I'm Dermot's daughter, and it wasn't like you all think, because none of you knew him, not like he really was. He was a wonderful father and I'm proud of him, do you hear, *proud*, not because of what he did but because he tried. He was weak but he *tried*. He was hu-man but he *tried*.' We can't all be strong like the great Ja-cey Lomax, can we? But I'm . . . I was . . . going to t-try to be what my father couldn't be, and *then* I'd have told." The words were pouring out and Nonie couldn't stop

them. Not even when Jacey got her by the shoulders again
and shook her could she stop. "My deceit was justifi-
able," she told him shrilly, "but yours? Ugh! How low,
how deceitful haven't you been to me, knowing all the
time and stringing me along—"

"Stop it, Nonie!"

"I won't stop it, I won't! You *have* been stringing me
along. Did it give you satisfaction, Jacey? Did you have
fun? Knowing all the time, watching me playing out my
pathetic little pantomime for your edification and entertainment, enjoying it all from the sidelines while I carried
on with my poor little charade like the ignorant clown that
I was?" Her voice broke.

"Stop it, Nonie. I'm warning you . . . stop it!" His tone
was low, incredibly deep.

Nonie rallied, unaware of the dangers in that lowness
and depth of Jacey's voice.

"I won't, and you can't make me. I don't have to dance
to your tune like all the others do. I may be Dermot's
daughter but I'm free to say what I want and I'm saying it
now. You've had your fun, laughing at me behind my
back. Well, it's my turn now to say what I think. I hate
you, Jacey Lomax, do you hear? I hate you! I—"

Nonie's tirade was halted by Jacey's lips.

They came down upon hers with a savagery of which
she hadn't dreamed him capable. At the same time, she
was caught against him in such an abrupt and viselike grip
that she was unable to move, let alone struggle. Her head
was being forced back, and back, and back. She wondered dazedly that her spine hadn't already snapped in
two. And still that brutal pressure of Jacey's mouth went
on and on, seeking out the rebellion in her, draining the
hot protests that rose to her lips with his own lips so that
she couldn't speak, could hardly even breathe.

There was no tenderness there. It wasn't a tender kiss,
the way Nonie had always imagined that kisses between a

man and a woman must be tender. *Should* be tender. Not tender. Just cruel and punishing and . . . endless.

When he finally released her, Nonie found that she was actually clinging to Jacey's shirt for support. It was a khaki shirt, one of his everyday bushmen's ones, with shoulder tabs and buttoned flaps on its breast pockets. Nonie had quite a fistful of the khaki cloth clenched in each of her hands, and she had to make sure that she could stand there unaided before she could let go of the shirt at all.

She drew away cautiously, half stupid with shock and fright, aware that she was shaking in every limb. When she put the back of her hand up to her bruised mouth and looked up finally at Jacey, he was still looking down at her. It seemed to Nonie that he looked from a great height. His eyes were dark, unfathomable, certainly not repentant.

"Why did you do that?" she asked, cursing her husky, quivering voice.

"Why do you think?" His own tone was uncompromising.

"To p-punish me, I suppose. For the th-things I said?"

Jacey Lomax passed a lean brown hand over his face in a gesture that was curiously weary. Defeated, almost.

"Leave it, Nonie," he said gruffly. "You're just a child."

"No, not that. Anything but that. I haven't been a child for a long, long time. Not since the day my mother died just after Pru was born."

There was silence between them for a time. Then: "Where did Gotthart come in? Was he really Pru's father or did you adopt the name?"

"No, my mother married him after we left here . . . down in Sydney. Pru was his baby."

"I see. That's why there's no mention of him in the local registrar's records. And he actually adopted you legally?"

"Yes. I took his name. Pru doesn't know that I ever had another name or a different father. When my mother died, Stroud insisted upon it because he said it would bind us all close together. He died quite suddenly not long after that. I often wondered as the years went by, whether I should tell Pru or not. I didn't know what to do for the best, and there wasn't anyone I could ask, so I . . . I . . . well, I just sort of let things go on as they were. Maybe it was cowardly, but I didn't know what would be best."

A muscle flickered in Jacey's swarthy cheek. His expression was unreadable but the bite seemed to have gone out of his voice.

Nonie laughed. It was a nervous, embarrassed little sound.

"Well, Jacey, what do we do now? I mean, where do we go from here?" She gestured uncertainly.

"It's up to you, Nonie. Does it make so much difference to things, the fact that I know, have known for some time about you? I think not. I hope you'll stay as you promised, to help Ray and Ilse? Pru's happy here too," he reminded her levelly.

"Yes, and *that*'s going to make it harder when we go. Oh, Jacey, I seem to have made such a mess of things, such a miserable mess, and I didn't mean to. Of course I'll stay for as long as I can be of help to Ilse and Raynor though," she assured him hastily, stepping back nervously as he moved toward her, "a . . . a promise is a promise."

"That's right, Nonie." Jacey had come right up to her, but this time all he did, to her intense relief, was take one of her hands in both of his. He held it there for a moment, captured in a gentle prison of warmth and reassurance that calmed the rapid flutterings of her renewed alarm. He turned her palm over, studied it carefully. He seemed to be searching for the right words for what he wanted to say. "You mustn't worry, Nonie. I only want you to make me another promise though. It's nothing to do with the other one."

"What is it? I mightn't be able to."

"Give it a fair go here and put the past behind you. In time the pain will go and you'll feel differently about things. They'll sort themselves out; they always do. None of us has the right to judge another person, only ourselves, so don't let the past get in the way of the present. Pru doesn't know, and you were right not to tell her, *quite* right. No one knows but you and I."

"Not even Delphine?"

"Certainly not Delphine. Just you and I," he emphasized calmly. "It's up to you whether you ever want to tell anyone or not. I won't."

"Thank you, Jacey."

"And if I can help—"

"No, thanks, you can't," she was quick to assure him. "As you said, I'll get over it in time. I don't need anyone's help to do that. It's up to me, isn't it, and I'm sure it'll work out as you say. I'm sorry I was so silly this morning, rushing out of the room like that. It's just that it was so . . . so unexpected . . . Delphine's remark I mean, and I wasn't ready, I suppose. I wasn't running away, you know."

The weariness she was feeling couldn't help sounding in her manner somehow, although she did her best not to let it show. How tired she felt! How dreadfully tired! She wished that she felt stronger to face the thing squarely. Strong, as Jacey Lomax was. Instead she felt beaten, like someone with a gigantic hangover, except that you could sleep that off and her problems couldn't be so easily disposed of as that.

"I know you weren't running away," he replied quietly. "I don't believe that Dermot's daughter *would* run away, Nonie."

And looking into his eyes and seeing that he really meant what he was saying, Nonie found that she couldn't even answer. Swiftly she turned away and hurried back toward the house, leaving Jacey alone at the edge of the creek.

CHAPTER SIX

"CAN YOU GIVE THEM some milk and the bacon and toast scraps from breakfast for me, Nonie? Not till about midday, though."

That was Pru, her satchel on her back and her lunch already in her saddlebag, squatting down to say a last farewell to the kittens before setting off for school. They were down at the homestead now, as Jacey had predicted, and appeared to have made their home under the tankstand. Only food would lure them out. Although Marmalade, the mother cat, often lay on the concrete outside sunning herself or washing herself or simply walking up and down purring noisily, all that could be seen of her offspring were two sets of luminous eyes in the darkness beneath the stand.

It was maddening to Pru, who was too big to crawl underneath to play with them.

"One step at a time, kiddo," Jacey had told her, laughing at her impatience. "Give them a week or two to get used to the place and then they'll venture out. Remember everything down here is strange to them after the woolshed. Different sounds, different smells, and human activities thrown in. Wouldn't you be a bit alarmed by all that if you were a kitten?"

"I suppose so. Like me and Nonie when we went to the Pink Pelican. We thought we'd never get used to it, only she said we'd just have to, even if it was a pretty strange sort of dump. I expect that's what Marmalade is telling *them* too, don't you?"

"I reckon that could be so." Nonie could just catch Jacey's slow, amused drawl through the gauze of the kitchen window. "Put down some milk each day, Pru, and any little thing you think they'd like that Hattie can spare, and soon they'll come venturing out for it as they begin to trust you."

And that was what Pru had been doing, every day since then. At first Marmalade came out alone and carried selected morsels back to her babies, but after a couple of weeks they were edging out cautiously themselves, scuttling back to shelter only if they heard anyone approaching.

"Marmalade won't like the bacon but Manda and Reen will." Pru was giving some final words of advice as she unhooked Acorn's reins from the fence post nearby and climbed nimbly into the saddle.

"Why don't you come riding sometimes too, Nonie, with Jacey and me?"

"No one's ever asked me to, and I don't suppose there's a spare horse."

" 'Course there are. There are lots of them; they're taken into the yards every morning. They're all much bigger than Acorn though, so I don't suppose you'd get on very well anyway."

"I don't know much about it so I don't suppose I would," agreed Nonie humbly. But she was remembering all the same those far-off days when she herself had been about Pru's age and had had a fat pony of her own.

"I could get Jacey to teach you, if you like."

"Oh, no, you mustn't do that." Lord what would the child think of next!

"He would if I asked him."

"No, I'd rather not, truly. Pru, I wish you'd leave me out of things when Jacey's around, really I do."

"Why, Nonie? Don't you like him? I don't think you can much and he doesn't think so either."

"What rubbish you talk!" replied Nonie sharply. "It's

not a question of likes or dislikes. I think I'm completely impartial with absolutely everyone in this household if it comes to that. Certainly I try to be."

"What's impartial?"

"Well, it means I like them all the same and treat them all the same. I don't feel anything more for Jacey than for the others... or any less, either, come to that."

"Jacey says people who've got very hurt about something sometimes forget *how* to feel. I s'pose that's what im—impartial means."

"Not exactly that." Nonie felt her color rising. "I hope you and Jacey haven't been discussing me, Pru. I've asked you not to, lots of times."

Pru looked injured.

"There you go again, Nonie. You *don't* like him, do you? He was only being *nice* anyway, so there. And it was really me we were talking about mostly. You only came into it 'cos he said you'd be hurt if I played hooky from school again. He said that working so hard at the Pink Pelican and even *being* in a place like that must've hurt, and that me not going to school might make the hurt worse, that's what he was saying. It was *me* we were talking about, and Jacey's made me promise I won't do it again, and I *have* promised, and I won't."

"I'm sorry, darling." Nonie reached up contritely and patted Pru's bare brown knee. "I don't know what's got into me lately to sound so cross and unreasonable about everything. I truly am sorry if I sounded narky and I'm very glad you've promised Jacey that. It's kind of him to think about us the way he does. Now off you go, Pru, or you'll be late, pet. I'll see to the kittens for you." She waved from the top of the veranda step. "Bye for now, and take care, darling."

"So long," returned Pru in a fair imitation of Jacey's drawl, although the pitch was a good octave higher.

Nonie sighed as she went indoors. How the child wor-

shiped that man, she pondered to herself as she carrie
out the milk and scraps to the backyard before lunch a
she had promised. Every day, every week that passed
their relationship seemed to become more matey . . .
unlike Nonie's own.

She could only feel embarrassment in Jacey's presenc
these days. Remembering the scalding things she had sai
that time brought swift, uncomfortable color to he
cheeks whenever she thought of it, even when she wa
alone and there was no one there to see. Jacey had neve
referred to the incident again, almost as if he divined he
unease. She'd have like to apologize but couldn't thin
how. And then, as she remembered that brutal, remorse
less kiss, resentment would begin to smart within he
afresh.

Drat the man, why should she even think of saying tha
she was sorry after *that?*

"Hallo there. How's the kitten girl today?" Raynor'
chair came into view from around the corner.

Nonie smiled from her seat on the step. "Hello. Tha
sun's beginning to be almost too hot, isn't it? And if b
'kitten girl' you mean Pru, she's at school, as is usual a
this time of the day."

Raynor stopped his chair at her side.

"I didn't mean Pru. I meant you."

She pulled a face. "I'm hardly a kitten girl, Raynor. I'n
a . . . a *woman*."

Raynor's cynical mouth quirked a little as if the quain
dignity of that statement somehow amused him.

"To me you're a child."

"Why does everyone have to say that?" she asked
piqued. "That's just what Jacey called me too." Sh
flushed then, remembering.

"He would," agreed Raynor equably. "He likes hi
women mature, or hadn't you noticed?" A pause. "Lik
Ilse," he added slyly, and Nonie looked at him sharply

aware of the sudden barb in his voice. There he went again with his cutting remarks that were so calculatingly cruel and unfair! Nonie had no intention of letting him off with it this time. She felt she knew him well enough now to protest that it was quite unjust to connect Jacey's name with Ilse's like that.

"You know she's got eyes for no one but you, Raynor. Anyone can see that, and if you can't you're more of a fool than I think you are. Besides, it's Jacey and Delphine, isn't it? You're a fool if you can't see *that* when it's right under your nose too."

Raynor grinned, unoffended and unrepentant.

"So the little kitten girl's got claws. You're barking up the wrong tree, though, my dear, if you'll forgive a slight mixture of metaphors. What you really mean to say is, Delphine would *like* it to be Jacey and Delphine. She's aware that I'm aware how hard she's working on it too. But no—" he grimaced, moved irritably in his chair "—I'm not a fool, my pet, far from it. I know what I'm talking about. I'm older than you, remember. I know more about these things."

"*How* do you know?" she challenged him.

"I have the evidence of my own eyes, that's how."

"What evidence? I've never seen any."

"Because you haven't been in the right place at the right time, that's why."

Raynor sighed. It was a jaded sound, and when he looked up Nonie could see that he was deadly serious. In fact, the naked misery in Raynor Lomax's candid blue eyes could not be missed, and certainly not by someone as sensitive as Nonie. He really *meant* what he said.

Somewhere, sometime something had given him this sense of gnawing doubt and unhappiness that had nothing to do with his illness. He was nursing it and fostering it and torturing himself with it quite needlessly, Nonie was sure. Pity for him swamped her.

"Ray, I don't believe it," she told him gently. "Whatever makes you say such things?"

"Because I know them to be true." He couldn't keep the bitterness out of his voice. "You must have seen the way he kissed Ilse even that day you arrived. Or don't you remember?"

"I remember very well," replied Nonie with conviction. "It was a very nice kiss, I thought. A . . . a sort of gallant, *considerate* kiss."

Much more gallant and considerate than the one he'd given *her*, anyway, she thought fleetingly, and felt that wretched hot color flow into her cheeks anew.

"Pshaw!" Raynor made a sound of pure disgust. "I don't know why I'm talking to you about it at all, Nonie. You're a child, dear, an innocent, whatever you might like to say to the contrary. Why, do you know that just now you're blushing furiously even *talking* about a kiss? How could you possibly know how to interpret one when you quite evidently lack the experience even to discuss it without self-consciousness?"

"Is that one kiss all you have to base your supposition on?" Nonie asked quickly, wishing Raynor's eagle gaze would miss a trick or two just for once.

"No, of course it's not. I'm not as ingenuous as that," he told her drearily. "Look, Nonie, there was one occasion in particular, and it put me wise to the whole thing . . . after the accident when they thought I was still unconscious. I came round and there they were standing in the window bay in each other's arms. And that's God's truth I'm telling you."

"Well?" she prompted after a moment, for Raynor had stopped speaking and was gazing into space, his features drawn, his expression brooding, almost as if he had forgotten where he was.

He glanced up when she spoke, forced himself to go on. "I heard then what they were saying," he continued a little thickly. "There they were—embracing each other, remember, Nonie—and Jacey was saying very low, but I distinctly heard each word he was saying, 'Look, Ilse,' he said, 'if he comes round we mustn't tell him, not yet. If he's going to get better at all, you must carry on like you were as if nothing had happened, do you understand?' And she said, 'Oh, Jacey, I don't think I've the courage to *pretend* like that. Don't you think it best just to tell him? Maybe he'll actually suspect it anyway?' and my honorable brother—my *honorable* brother, mark you, Nonie—said, 'No, Ilse. Better to let him get stronger first although as you say, knowing Raynor, he might drop to it quicker than we think. He's pretty smart at summing up a situation, but it's better not to put it into words at this stage.' And then she buried her head against him and said she wondered how she could possibly carry it off, and he said she'd have to, just for a little while, to please him. And then he kissed her. That's when he kissed her."

There was silence after Raynor stopped speaking.

Marmalade came out from under the tankstand, mewed softly, picked up a crust of milk-soaked bread from the tin plate that Nonie had put there and disappeared into the darkness again.

"I still think it's all a mistake, Raynor," she said finally, stubbornly, *helplessly.* "It must be. Maybe you were delirious or something. Maybe you dreamed it. Drugs and things can have strange effects. I mean, the way Ilse *looks* at you—"

"Oh, she can pretend all right . . . quite a convincing act. I reckon Jacey just got me up here so that Ilse would be near him. Sometimes I just long to let her know that I know, but like the fool that I am I love her too much to actually do it. Even a little of her is better than nothing, you see, and as long as I'm tied to this blasted chair I suppose she'll stick to me through pity. That's how low I've sunk, Nonie, that I'll keep her with me through pity if

there's no other way. God, sometimes I wish I'd died in
that benighted hospital. I tried, you know. I tried to have
no will to live, but all the time Ilse was there, pulling me
back from the brink. That's what love can do, Nonie. It's
a damn fool sentiment, believe me. It can make a fool of a
man quicker than anything else on this earth."

Raynor scowled and Nonie remained silent. How could
one answer the unanswerable? What, after all, could she
say to this tortured and bitter man?

"Jacey knew Ilse before I did, you know, Nonie," Raynor informed her after a while, inconsequently. "You
didn't know that, did you?" He had been quick to spot
her unconcealed surprise. "Oh, yes, he did. It was Jacey
who met her first. I don't know whether he'd taken her
out before that time he brought her back to the house
we'd rented at the beach that year . . . probably he had, although people we'd met on the beach used to drift in and
out too and there were always plenty of women in Jacey's
life. You'd never know what he was thinking, even in
those days, or how serious he was about any of them, but
I knew the moment I saw Ilse how serious *I* was. I went
after her from the start—I couldn't help myself. It gradually seemed that we drew closer all the time, and while
the others still went in a sort of crowd to things, Ilse and I
would find ourselves coupled together. Eventually I asked
her to marry me and she said she would. And then, only
about a month after that, I was playing in a polo
match . . . and the rest you know. Oh, damn, damn,
damn!" Raynor struck the arm of his chair with his open
palm in sheer frustration. "I shouldn't have opened out to
you like this, child—I'm sorry, Nonie. There's no need to
look so stricken. Forget I ever spoke of it, will you? I wish
I could."

He swung the chair around deftly and sent it off at a furious speed, and Nonie, sighing briefly, got off the step
and went inside to help Hattie prepare the lunch.

Raynor seemed withdrawn, preoccupied for much of the meal, but Ilse, if she noticed, responded with her usual calm tranquillity. Nonie, meanwhile, did her best in the next few weeks to provide cheerful and diverting company for both Ilse and Raynor. That was what she had come here for, as far as Jacey was concerned, and she'd have to live up to her promise

She couldn't find it in herself to believe the things that his own brother had attributed to Jacey Lomax. He was autocratic, domineering in a way that roused her own spirited resentment, but...underhand? No.

And yet he had been with her, hadn't he, pretending all this time that he didn't know she was Dermot's daughter when all the time he *had* known it. Nonie found herself wondering how long he'd have let her go on playing out her forlorn little charade if Delphine hadn't surprised her into revealing her identity to him that day. Would he have bided his time, trapped her himself someday . . . intentionally? It was all too confusing to know with any certainty just what would have happened. She could only be thankful that Jacey had never referred to the matter again.

Unwillingly Nonie asked herself if he sometimes remembered that confrontation as she did. If he did, it was probably with the patronizing amusement that a man of his experience might bestow on a mere babe in arms. The memory of it, as always, was infuriating and filled her with an odd kind of despair. She found it difficult to conceal her awkwardness when Jacey was around these days and avoided him whenever she could.

Delphine was about a lot these days too, and speculation was in the air. One could almost feel it physically so tangible was it. Nonie and Hattie would often see the small yellow sports car weaving its way up the hill to the other homestead, where doubtless Jacey's own housekeeper would have a meal prepared for them. Nonie could imagine the two of them sitting together on the veranda, looking out over the valley and the winding creek below. She tried not to think along those lines though, Heaven knew why, except that the mental tableau gave her a feeling of vague unhappiness. Jacey had only taken her up to his new house the one time since she had come, and even then Delphine had been there. She had been quite charming to Nonie that day, as if she were in truth a mere visitor, a bare acquaintance, and Delphine herself the proper mistress of the house. In the subtlest of ways, her manner had indicated that she was in possession, and she even took it upon herself to show Nonie around the place almost as if it were her own.

Nonie had been somewhat aghast at the sheer luxury of it, the roominess, the size. The kitchen was lavishly appointed, air-conditioned, tiled. The bathrooms and showers had the latest chrome fittings and beautiful terrazzo floors. The verandas were columned with white pillars in the colonial style, and already colorful creepers that Jacey had had planted were beginning to twine their way up from their bases.

It made the old homestead seem more decrepit than ever by comparison, although Nonie and Ilse worked hard to restore it to some sort of order.

As Jacey had originally pointed out, what it really needed was a complete professional renovation, whereas the most that she and Ilse could do was to tidy up the place and scrape off some of the flaking paint, renewing it where they could. They were working their way through the rambling building gradually, room by room, but their efforts were only moderately successful. Whenever they put on new paint somewhere, all the rest looked worse by comparison. Nonie had a feeling that they were fighting a losing battle although she never said as much to Ilse. It would have been too disheartening actually putting her doubts into words ... and besides, it gave Ilse something o do when Raynor's moods were upon him, and it was a welcome escape when he was choosing to be particularly difficult.

In contrast to her elder sister, Pru was often up at the new place. Sometimes she called in there on Acorn on her way back from school and sometimes Jacey took her up himself. There was nothing the little girl liked more than to sit in the back of his Toyota truck with Jacey's two blue cattle dogs for company beside her and the breeze lifting her short brown hair into elfin spikes as they went along. He took her with him to some of the huts farther out too, putting out salt blocks for the stock to lick, cleaning bore drains, mending windmills, tightening fences.

It was on her return from one such excursion that Nonie, having lit the old heater and supervised the running of her sister's bath, was confronted with something of a problem—a minor one but embarrassing nevertheless.

As Nonie was sorting out the tumbled heap of clothes left on the floor by Pru before she stepped into the yellow water, the child's voice came conspiratorially from the bathtub.

"Nonie, I've got a secret."

"Mmm?" Nonie's mind was on other things.

"Well, a sort of secret. You an' me are the only ones that know. And Jacey will, of course," she added importantly.

That captured her sister's attention all right!

"Jacey?"

"We're going to give him a present."

Nonie regarded her, nonplussed.

"Darling, we can't do that. We haven't any money . . . well, not the sort that would buy someone like Jacey Lomax a present anyway. Whatever put that idea into your head?"

" 'Cos it's his birthday," Pru crowed triumphantly from the suds. "Two weeks today, exactly. Mrs. Parsons told me and she's going to make him a birthday cake, and I can come up and eat some. She said so."

"Is he having a party, then?"

"Well, sort of. Mrs. Parsons says we can all come if we like. But it was *my* idea."

"I see," Nonie said weakly. "And what do you suggest we give him, poppet? A yacht for the beach when he goes down to Sydney? Or another airplane? Or do you think he'd like a fabulous new bull, one of those prize pedigree ones?"

"Silly!" Pru couldn't restrain a giggle at the grand gestures Nonie was making as she suggested these various possibilities. "I *know* we haven't got the money for that sort of thing. I *know* we have to save it all up so we can buy this dear old house one day. But this won't take any money at all, hardly even a dollar."

"What won't?"

Pru put down the sponge she had been wielding and lolled back, a small smirk of satisfaction playing about her lips.

"What I've decided on."

"And what have you decided on, may I ask?"

"A sign, silly."

"A sign?"

"A nameplate thing, for the new house. A nice big wooden one. He hasn't got one and you can do them so beautifully, Nonie. It'll hardly cost a thing, see, because you've still got your brushes and stencils and paints and stuff, haven't you? He'll just *love* it," Pru said enthusiastically.

"I doubt it." Nonie gazed at her sister's ecstatic face helplessly. "I . . . I don't think I could, Pru. Not for Jacey."

"Why do you say that?" her sister demanded back, giving her a curious look. "Jacey said you wouldn't want to, as well."

Nonie was startled by this rather breathtaking revelation. "I thought you said it was a *secret?*" she remarked dubiously.

"So it is. I didn't tell him *what* it's going to be, stupid, only that I was going to get you to make him something for his birthday. Something special, that you're really good at."

"And what did he say to that?"

"Well, he did look sort of funny and doubtful, now I come to think of it. Then he said he didn't think you might want to, not for him. And he told me to forget about it, and I said I wouldn't forget about it, that I'd ask you anyway. I don't want to forget about it, Nonie. Honestly, I don't. I want to give it to him because he's given me such a lot of things, like the kittens for my own and the pony and, oh, heaps of things. Please say you will, Nonie, please! It's only a little thing and you've made them for heaps of people, so why not for Jacey? And I've *said* you're going to, so don't be a meanie."

Nonie didn't want to be a meanie and it looked as if Pru had taken the thing too far for her to be able possibly to retreat. If she refused and there was no gift forthcoming, Jacey would know she hadn't wanted to do it. And if she bought him some small, impersonal thing from them both, which she'd much prefer to do, he would realize that she'd been reluctant to make him something herself, and he would be as embarrassed as she was that Pru had sort of compromised them both. Whatever way one considered it, she was cornered.

Oh, dear, why did children have to land their elders in such difficult situations as this one?

Pru's hopeful face was still peeping over the towel she had enveloped herself in and that face looked so scrubbed and innocent that capitulation seemed inevitable.

Nonie sighed.

"Okay, Pru, just this once. But another time," she

warned sternly, "another time be sure to talk it over with
me first."

SHE WASN'T IN ANY GREAT HURRY to do the thing somehow, but with a week gone already since Pru had first
mentioned the project, she at last decided that she had
better get going. If she was to do it at all, she might as
well do it properly. Anyway, she had to admit that she enjoyed tackling anything creative like this, and as she went
to her room and searched out the necessary bits and
pieces of materials from her luggage, she found herself actually humming softly.

Four days later she produced her handiwork for Pru's
inspection.

"Yes, I *like* it," the latter murmured admiringly.
"What a lovely piece of wood!"

It was, too—a particularly attractive slab of Jacey's
own mulga, off his own property. Nonie had searched
hard before picking out a specimen of suitable shape, and
then she'd taken the thing into Tuckarimba township and
got one of the builders there to saw it flat across the grain
for her. The result was a most unusual, almost kidney-
shaped signboard, and she had further highlighted its engaging shape by following the outline with an edging of
pokerwork. The name itself—a simple *Tuckarimba*—
was in plain sloping print.

"Nonie, could you just put some gold on around the
edges of the letters, do you think, and then some more
black? You know how you do, so it looks as if they're all
turning sideways? I always love it when you do them that
way; it's as if the sun's sort of shining through it and there
are shadows at the back of the words."

"Well, I suppose I could. I like it plain, myself."

"I think me and Jacey might like it best turned sideways."

Nonie had to smile at that.

"Okay, have it your way." It was Pru's present after all.

It took her most of the rest of the afternoon to touch it up in the way Pru liked, the gilt edging first, for the thick strokes, and then the finest black outline again.

"How about that?" she asked at length, holding it up once more. "Careful, Pru. It's not dry yet."

"I think it's gorgeous, honest I do. And so will Jacey! Nonie, thanks for doing it. You really *are* clever—" and her little sister's sudden, impetuous hug was somehow ample reward for the pains that Nonie had taken over the work.

Jacey's birthday was on a school day, and when Pru had returned in the middle of the afternoon she found that her sister had her parcel already done up for her.

"Can you carry it on Acorn, do you think? I'm sure you can if I hand it up to you once you've got on."

"I've unsaddled him, Nonie, and turned him loose. I thought we'd walk up."

"We?"

"Well you're coming too, aren't you?"

"I wasn't going to, no."

"Oh, Nonie, *please!*" Pru's expression of anticipation had abruptly changed to one of plain and shattering disappointment. "Please. I mean, I've thought you'd come with me all along and Mrs. Parsons is expecting you. She's promised you a bit of birthday cake when we cut it. It's going to have blue icing and everything."

"You could bring me back a piece, darling."

"Nonie, it's not the *same!*" Pru's voice was a wail. "It won't be half as much fun if you're not there. You know we always share everything, we always have."

"Very well then, Pru, if you'll be so disappointed."

"I will be, Nonie, I will."

"Very well then. Wait a second till I go and get tidied a bit first."

When they got up to the new homestead a quarter of an hour later, Nonie found herself wishing that she had in fact taken even longer and tidied up a little bit more than she hurriedly had, for the sight of Delphine's yellow car filled her with dismay.

For two pins she'd have turned back, Pru or no Pru, but their approach had already obviously been observed by one person at least.

"Pru, is that you at last? School must've been late out today, surely? Come on, lasses, we've been waiting for you to show up before I put the tea through." So saying, Mrs. Parsons bustled off toward the kitchen around the side of the house and Nonie smoothed her palms a little nervously down the sides of her jeans and followed across the lawn as her small sister negotiated the front steps carefully with the brown paper parcel in her hands.

At the top the gauze door was thrown open. Pru put down the parcel unceremoniously and rushed right into Jacey's arms. They'd been held wide inviting her to do just that, and Nonie could see that as he hugged the child he wasn't bothering to hide the fact that he was pleased to see her.

"Thanks, scrap," he grinned in reply to her birthday wishes, adding a little ruefully, "Not that I'm as keen on marking my advancing years as you appear to be!"

"Many happy returns, Jacey." Nonie stepped forward awkwardly, put out her hand, aware of Delphine's mocking eyes upon her as she did so.

"Thank you, Nonie." Gravely he took the extended hand. "I see you've got involved in this affair too." A smile crinkled his eyes. "I'm beginning to wonder whose birthday it really is, your little sister's or mine."

Jacey pulled up a chair for her. Tea was set out on the table beside Delphine, and Mrs. Parsons must already have brought the pot in because there it was too, with a matching silver water jug steaming faintly at the spout.

Again Nonie wished she'd smartened up a bit more, Delphine made such a graceful picture presiding over the eapot. Her sleeveless dress of straw-colored tussore silk was superbly cut, and its matching jacket Delphine had placed over the back of the chair behind her head so that her wonderful auburn hair was foiled by the jacket's emerald lining. The combination was entrancing, and one could hardly blame Jacey Lomax for finding it so, as he obviously did. His eyes were resting appreciatively on Delphine's features—the beautifully tanned, absorbed face with its faint dusting of freckles and those unusual yellow green eyes.

"Thanks for pouring for us, Delphine. Scones and sandwiches to begin with, young 'un, and *then* I'll cut the cake," he told Pru, laughing at her expression as she somehow managed to drag her eyes away from the layered confection that Mrs. Parsons had made to mark the occasion, and instead took one of the proffered scones.

Jacey passed Nonie her cup, and only then did she register the fact that he too was dressed more formally than usual. No khaki bush shirt today, but a crisp white one, the sleeves rolled up to reveal his muscular brown forearms, a patterned tie at his throat. His trousers were narrow-cut, creased, evidently part of a tropic-weight suit, for he'd put the jacket over the back of his chair as Delphine had, except that his had been flung there rather more carelessly.

Delphine had seen Nonie's eyes on the jacket.

"Don't feel bad that you haven't dressed for the occasion, my dear," she said, quite kindly. "You're quite all right as you are. You see, it's not for *this* occasion that either of us is dressed at all." She smirked. "Actually Jacey's taking me for dinner in town tonight to celebrate his birthday. So when Pru wanted this little party first, we decided that we'd get ourselves ready beforehand, and then we wouldn't have to rush things quite so much. She was obviously terribly enthusiastic about there being a proper birthday tea, and we wouldn't have dreamed of disappointing her."

"Thank you, Delphine," Nonie replied as gratefully a
she could, for inwardly she was grinding her teeth at the
smug way in which the other girl could manage to pu
things across. "And I'm quite certain she's not a bit disap
pointed, are you, Pru? It's a really beautiful cake, isn't it
Jacey says you're to take some back for Ilse and Rayno
and Hattie afterward."

"And you've got to open your present now, Jacey. It'
from me and Nonie, and you've got to open it now anc
see what's inside."

To Nonie's secret dismay, her young sister had leapec
up with determination and was now lugging the ungainl
parcel across the floor from the place where they hac
propped it against the wall after they first came in.

"It doesn't look too breakable anyway," Jacey grinned
"not the way you're treating it. Careful, Pru," he addec
sharply, as she gave it a final nudge in his direction with
her foot.

"Oh, it won't break, don't worry. You'll see. Nothing
can break it, Jacey, except—well, something really *big*
could, I s'pose, but usually they last almost *forever*."

"*Forever?* That's a pretty long time. Whatever can i
be?"

Jacey's fingers were undoing the knots and he was tak
ing his time. He was doing it just to tease Pru, and as she
hovered around his shoulder he turned and winked at her.
When he unwound the wrapping and revealed the gift it
self his expression changed.

"Nonie made it. I told you she was going to make you
something. You see, Jacey, it is special, isn't it? Do you
like it?"

Jacey was studying his present with interest. He ran his
brown fingers over the smooth surface of the polished
mulga, inspecting the lettering and the way in which it was
done.

"Yes, it is special, Pru. And yes, I do like it. I like it

very much, thank you. Thank you *both*," he stressed, and just for an instant his eyes caught and held Nonie's.

"It was nothing," she mumbled awkwardly, acutely aware of Delphine's curiously still figure beside her. "Nothing. I did it for Pru."

"Yes, I know." Jacey's tone was suddenly bland. "Still, you put a great deal of work into it and the result is beautiful." Once again his eyes caught and captured hers, and this time there was some sort of message in them, a message that Nonie quite failed to translate.

"I mean that, Nonie. I shall treasure it."

There was such a sober honesty about the way Jacey added that that she heard herself say quickly, a little huskily, "*Do* cut your cake, Jacey. Pru is simply dying to have a bit."

"Yes, do, darling," Delphine interpolated, gracefully assuming charge of the operation again. "We'll all have a piece and then I shall ask Mrs. Parsons to wrap some up and the girls can take it back to the others. We shall need our time if we're going to look in at the club first, and I did promise I would, remember?" she reminded him, with just the right amount of hesitant apology in her tones.

After that, there wasn't much to do but eat one's piece of cake and depart with as little delay as possible, was there?

WALKING BACK in the semidarkness with Pru toward the old homestead at the bottom of the valley, Nonie had to admit to herself that she hadn't enjoyed it much. In fact, the whole afternoon had been a bit of an ordeal from start to finish. The only warming thing had been the sincerity of Jacey's appreciation, his kindness toward them both. That hadn't been in any doubt, and yet, probably because it had been directed toward her as well as Pru, Nonie found it intensely embarrassing although she wouldn't for

the world have said so to Pru, who was busy enthusing al
the way home. The whole setup had been made even
more uncomfortable by the very presence there of Del
phine Simpson. Not that she, too, hadn't been kind, even
gracious in an offhand sort of way, but at the end Nonie
had sensed an alienation between her and Delphine, a
hostility that was almost a physical current passing from
one woman to the other, from Delphine over to her
Maybe she had imagined it but she didn't think so.

Yet she could be wrong, because as they'd left Del
phine had waved a languid hand in her direction and said
quite sweetly really, "Goodbye for now, Nonie. And you
must come into town and see me sometime so that we can
get to know one another a little better."

Nonie hadn't known quite what to say to that if she
were to be honest, so she had simply smiled and returned
the wave somewhat unconvincingly. Delphine always
made her feel ungroomed, gauche and incredibly—
well—*young*. A child, in fact. A child, as Jacey and in
deed Raynor had already defined her to her own face. I
was galling to be thought of in that way when you'd been
a fully responsible guardian for years and years and when
at times you felt about a hundred years old.

Anyway, as it turned out Delphine was as good as he
word about arranging to see her again, and only a few
days later she issued an invitation that Nonie would have
felt churlish in refusing.

It was Ilse who had taken the telephone call.

"By the way, Nonie, Delphine rang and asked for you
but you were out at the chickens or somewhere and
couldn't seem to find you. She was in a hurry so she left a
message. She wondered if you'd be kind enough to help
her on one of the Country Women's Association stalls a
the sale on Friday. Janet Daniels who was to be on it with
her has gone sick so I said I was sure you would not mind
helping out."

"What would I have to do, Ilse?"

"They're on produce so it'll be as simple as pie. You'll need to go in early to help price everything as it comes in, and once the sale's open it's just a case of selling the stuff and doling out the right change. It will be a nice break for you and you'll get a chance to meet some of the other country people from the stations farther out. They all come in for it. And you can take my car, Nonie; I told Delphine not to bother to collect you. I'll be here for Pru coming home from school so there's nothing to worry about at this end."

They seemed between them to have it all arranged.

"Okay," she agreed a little faintly. "I suppose I'd better."

"Of course you will! It'll do you good. Jacey was saying only the other day that you're still looking a little bit off color and strained, and I felt quite guilty because I knew how hard I've been working you with all that painting and scraping that we've been doing."

"Nonsense, Ilse, I've enjoyed it. We'll clean out the store next week, shall we? I know you've been wanting to go through all that junk that he more or less threw in there out of sight when he came here."

"Mmm, yes. It may be out of sight, out of mind with Jacey, but I can't feel that way, I'm afraid. Whenever I look in the door I nearly have a fit. I'm sure we can at least tidy it up anyway, if not get rid of quite a lot of it."

"Ilse, I . . . I hope I won't meet any of the customers from the Pink Pelican when I'm on the stall," Nonie ventured shyly. The thought had been worrying her not a little ever since Ilse had brought up the matter. "I mean, Delphine is so . . . so fastidious and refined, isn't she, and they were a pretty lewd bunch, you know. I would hate to be the means of embarrassing or offending her."

Ilse put back her head and laughed.

"My dear Nonie, I can see just what you mean. I'd forgotten your shady and suspect past! But don't worry on that score. It'll be almost exclusively a women's thing, I should think. I doubt if there'll be a man in sight . . . and certainly not the kind who frequent the Pink Pelican. They'd want something a little stronger than a C.W.A. cuppa and a lemonade, which is about all there'll be."

Thus reassured, Nonie went off to string some beans for Hattie.

When Friday came she got up early to light the heater and wash her hair. It was almost dry and becoming fairer every minute as the dampness went out of it by the time she went to get out Ilse's old blue Chev.

She was reasonably pleased with her navy linen shirt-waist, too. It looked businesslike and yet feminine, and to boost her own confidence while in Delphine's elegant company, Nonie had made up her face with more care than usual, using a soft rosepink lipstick and mascara on her abundant lashes.

"Would you like to borrow these? The sun's quite strong." Ilse, looking over with approval, handed her her own blue-framed sunglasses. "Yes, you look good, Nonie. I've never seen you all dressed up before."

"Neither have I, young 'un, and yes you do look rather good. Simple but stunning . . . or should I say 'simply stunning?' " Raynor had wheeled himself over to join Ilse in a final inspection. He was in one of his more amiable, faintly bantering moods. "See you stand at the back of the counter or they might put you up for the raffle."

"You make me sound like a cellophane-wrapped chicken! Well, I'll see you both later."

Nonie let in the clutch and reversed away from them with care, waved again and finally bounced sedately down the trace to the main road.

The sale was out at the pavilion at the showground. When Nonie got there, there were already a number of cars parked under the gums near the entrance. They mostly belonged to the stallholders who had come early to arrange their wares, but cars came and went right up to the time of the official opening, and Nonie found that she was kept busy accepting goods, discussing what should be charged for them, and finally labeling them with the little price stickers that Delphine had given her for the purpose. Delphine herself worked surprisingly hard and competently, arranging boxes of tomatoes, eggs, and jars of honey, lining up jams and fruit and pickles, stacking mountains of green speckled watermelons, succulent palest green cucumbers, prickly chokoes, gray-green pumpkins and attractive little round rockmelons with lacy skins that looked as if they'd been dipped in cobwebs.

"Will we ever manage to dispose of it all?" asked Nonie, surveying the growing pile dubiously.

"You wait and see," replied Delphine obscurely ... and to Nonie's amazement they did. Almost all of it anyway.

As they were clearing up the debris at the end, there only remained a couple of pumpkins and a longish yellow-striped melon or two.

"Those ones are jam ones, that's why." Delphine looked up from where she was placing the money into neat little piles prior to making a final count. "Not everyone can be bothered going to all the fuss involved in melon jam, though. It's quite a palaver really. Leave them there, Nonie, and I'll take them myself. How much are they marked at? I'll take them out to Mrs. Parsons and she'll know what to do with them. Jacey's particularly fond of melon jam." A pause, during which Delphine reached for her handbag and took out a small leather purse. Having placed the price of the melons carefully in the kitty with the rest of the day's takings, she snapped the little purse shut again and put it back inside the larger handbag. "By the way, Nonie, I feel I must just say a word or two to you about that."

"About what?" Nonie looked over startled by the other's clearly determined manner.

"About Tuckarimba in general." Delphine made a small move with her pretty red lips, spread her manicured fingers a little deprecatingly. "It's for your own good, my dear, believe me. I hesitate to speak of it, I don't particularly *want* to speak of it but after the other day, after Jacey's birthday, I realized that I must."

"Go on." Nonie was beginning to feel curiously apprehensive. She wished that Delphine would get to the point.

"I think you will have to remember," Delphine continued with clarity and a definite air of purpose, "that you are an employee out at Tuckarimba, and it would not be wise for you to try to step outside that role."

"I . . . don't understand."

"My dear Nonie, I think you do. Don't you think, for instance, that it was a little presumptuous of you to make Jacey *quite* such a personal gift for his birthday . . . or indeed to give him a birthday present at all? It was obvious that you had spent a vast amount of time and thought and attention upon it, wasn't it. I mean, if it were to be something from Pru, a small box of chocolates would have been appropriate. The whole thing was so obviously *your* notion." Another pause. "I think you made—shall we put it charitably—an error of judgment. It was an unwise choice, my dear, too personal, too intimate, and therefore in bad taste. I shall be grateful if, as an employee, you in future show a little more care and circumspection in your actions. That's all."

She made a dismissive gesture and would have returned to her counting, but Nonie, her face aflame, somehow stood her ground.

"Aren't you being a bit presumptuous yourself, Delphine? I don't quite see where *you* come in. What right have you to reproach me like this over something that can't concern you?"

"But it does concern me, Nonie," corrected Delphine coldly. "It concerns me very much, as Jacey's future wife. As the future mistress of Tuckarimba."

Nonie gaped. She felt dazed, a little breathless, as if she'd been dealt an actual blow.

"You . . . are you *engaged* to Jacey Lomax?" she insisted hardily because now she was recalling Raynor's bitter face, his persistent misery, his unhappiness in the fixation he had that Jacey loved Ilse Bjornig.

Her eyes sought Delphine's ringless left hand, and Delphine's own eyes followed them.

"One doesn't rush a man like Jacey Lomax, my dear. He prefers to make the running and take his own time. I don't need a ring to prove his affection for me, but I'm beginning to think it might be wise to display one all the same, just to clear up any possible misconceptions. Believe me," she stressed, taking Nonie's dubious expression, "there is a very clear understanding between Jacey and myself. Further than that I am not prepared to elaborate. Why should I, and to *you*, a mere servant . . . although I'm not too sure that you'll remain one for very long once I'm in charge out there. There can be too many women about the place unless their roles are very clearly defined. It can make for complications, I often think. Just remember your position out there in the meantime, will you, and the reason Jacey took you on at all."

Delphine turned back to the piles of notes and change and Nonie went on clearing up mechanically. When she had carried the last remaining cartons to the trunk of Delphine's car, she came back again, said tonelessly, "That's it then, Delphine. I think I'd better be going back now."

Delphine glanced up.

"Do you know how much we've cleared? A hundred and eighty-four dollars, sixteen cents. Not a bad day's work, after all. Tell Ilse that figure, will you, and thank her for lending me your services for the afternoon. You were a great help, Nonie."

Nonie mumbled as gracious a reply as she could muster and took her leave, thankful to at last be able to get away.

How ghastly it had all been, that ticking off of Delphine's! She wanted to nurse her embarrassment to herself, to lick her wounds in private. Although why that particular expression should come to mind right now, it was beyond her to think. What wounds had she to lick, for heaven's sake?

She scrambled into the old blue Chev and rattled off around the white-railed arc of the racecourse out onto the Tucka road. Her mind was a jumble of incoherent thoughts and emotions, and she felt sore and bruised and confused.

It was only when she was halfway home and the soreness exploded into a great tide of pain that Nonie knew with clarity, the answer.

She was in love with Jacey Lomax herself.

CHAPTER SEVEN

IT DIDN'T HELP MATTERS MUCH on arriving home to find Jacey there himself. He and Ilse and Raynor were sitting having a drink on the veranda when she came through the gauze door.

"Hello, there," Raynor called immediately. "Come and join us. How did things go?" Then, as she came nearer, "Good lord, what did they do? Run over you with a steamroller? You look all in."

She managed a pale smile. "It was a longish day," she admitted briefly, accepting the drink that Jacey had poured for her. "I guess I'm not used to that sort of thing—the people and the standing."

It must have sounded lame. Jacey thought so anyway.

"I'd say you were more than used to it," he contradicted, giving her one of those long, shrewd looks. "You'd plenty of it at the Pink Pelican, under much more strenuous circumstances than a mere women's get-together at a country fete."

"Maybe so." Nonie was not prepared to argue. She compressed her lips and wondered that it showed so much. Certainly she felt different, so maybe she looked it too. As long as nobody guessed the *reason*—

"The wringer, not the steamroller," she corrected Raynor, grinning gamely and ignoring his brother's nearness as best she could. "I feel a bit wrung out rather than flattened. The heat was wilting and the sun was right on our particular stall for the whole afternoon, although some of them were more under the trees and got some shade. Thank you for the glasses, Ilse, they really were a necessity, as you'd guessed."

"They suited you." Ilse smiled gently. "How did the actual sale go?"

Nonie related the day's total.

"We had masses to sell. Rather many preserves and eggs, but we got rid of them all in the end. We had fun, really."

"Yes, it *looks* as if you'd had fun." Jacey's voice, deep and sarcastic, sounded in her ear as he leaned over and prized her fingers from the stem of her glass. "If you hold onto that any tighter it'll crack in two under the strain. Why so tense?"

"Just leave me alone, will you, Jacey?" she snapped, more irritably than she intended. His nearness, her awareness of it, were almost intolerable. She had no idea that discovering oneself to be in love could be such a traumatic business.

His mouth took on an unpleasant twist, the gray eyes narrowed.

"Take a sip of that drink, little one," he bade her, handing back the glass. "It might help to sweeten you up a bit."

"I'm not aware that I need sweetening up, thank you," she retorted coldly.

"Nonsense. There's a certain acrimony about your approach that wasn't there before. If it's tiredness that's caused it, the sooner you hit the hay tonight the better." A pause. "Were there just the two of you on that stall? You and Delphine?"

"That's right."

"Did she work you too hard?"

"I'm not complaining, am I? She worked darned hard herself too. As I said, it was a successful day. Well, if you'll excuse me– ·" she put down her drink almost untouched "—I think I'll go and . . . and have a wash and change out of this dress."

"Take your time Nonie," Ilse said kindly. "We can always have our meal a little later than usual. You'll stay, Jacey, and have a bite with us?"

"Not tonight, thanks, Ilse," he replied tightly, reaching for his hat and getting to his feet. "I don't think the vibrations around here are too friendly at the moment, certainly not sufficiently to persuade me that my presence at your table would be unanimously welcomed."

Nonie, already at the entrance to the hall, couldn't miss the bite in his deep voice, and a quirked brow in her direction left her in no doubt that the remark was aimed at her. She was thankful to escape before he could discern the painful color that crept into her cheeks, even though there was a certain temptation to stay and answer back. Even now she couldn't take that domineering manner without wanting to fight back. In fact, more than ever now, she'd have to fight back when Jacey tried to dictate, wouldn't she? More than ever now she'd need to assert her independence, steer clear of involvement, emotional or otherwise. It would never do to succumb to his autocratic charm, although when you loved a man with the steady, constant ache that was beginning to plague Nonie it would have been the easiest thing in the world to succumb.

She managed in the next couple of weeks and by sheer dint of willpower to adjust to the discovery she had made about herself. The utter hopelessness of it forced her to a sort of compromise so that she could go about her everyday tasks with a reasonable semblance of normality. It seemed to her that she had been fighting against hopeless situations most of her life and therefore it was nothing new to have to do it once more.

Together she and Ilse got down to the last of the scraping and repainting that they'd been doing, and after that they moved on to the store. It was a long, narrow room at the rear of the main wing, lit by a single electric bulb. To increase the light in the corners, Nonie had removed the shade, but even then she found they needed a torch apiece to play along the dusty shelves and into the cobwebby cupboards so that they could see exactly what was there.

Never had Nonie come across such a conglomeration. Stacks of old crockery, none of it matching, pots and pans minus handles or lids, saddlery and harness, bolts of calico, piles of gray blankets half-eaten by mice. Nonie could remember those blankets. They were the ones that were used each year for the shearers when they came, and she had often helped her mother to fold them up and put them away when the shearing contractor and his team had moved on to the next shed.

It was a somewhat eerie experience, recalling that.

She bit her lip. "What shall we do with them, Ilse?"

"Burn them, I should think. The mice have really been making merry with them, haven't they? This calico is quite good though, and there's a set of curtains here that could be quite nice if we washed and starched them up a bit. I think we'll stack all that harness at one end and get Jacey to give his opinion on it. Some of it looks all right if it was done over with neat's-foot to make it supple again, although I don't suppose there's a draft horse within miles to wear it."

"And what on earth's that?" Nonie had pulled a large flat sieve out from under the horsecollars and blinkers.

"A prospector's pan?" Ilse shrugged. "There were a lot of diggings around here at one time, I believe." She inspected it more closely. "It's no use though. See, it's all gone on the bottom. Out it goes," and it joined the mounting pile of junk outside the doorway.

Nonie shone her torch into the corner again, stirring the pile gingerly. An item had caught her eye, something else she recognized, even though the luster of the grained walnut case was obliterated by a thick coating of dust. It was the old carriage clock that had always stood on the mantelpiece in the front hall. It had an ornate brass face with black enameled numerals and hands, and at the top there was an antique brass handle for lifting it. Every week of her life her mother used to wind that clock. Every Monday morning on washday while she was waiting for the water to boil.

Nonie brushed away some of the dust with the palm of her hand. Then she stepped under the light, slipped the catch at the back and pulled it open to get the key to wind it up. Perhaps it still went. Her fingers found the key, and something else as well. A folded piece of paper. It had her mother's name written across it, back and front.

Nonie gazed at it awestruck for fully a minute. Then she put the key in its place, snapped the back shut and set the clock down at her feet. Carefully, with fingers that were suddenly clumsy, she unfolded the paper.

It was a written sheet, and although the ink was a little faded and the paper creamy with age, the words were completely legible. Instinct, rather than familiarity with her father's handwriting, told Nonie that it would be his. The signature—Dermot—at the bottom confirmed the fact. She read:

My darling, I am more sorry than you will ever know to have to inflict this pain upon you, whom I love more than anything or anyone in this world. By the time you find this I shall have left you, but you will have Wenona and must be strong for her sake. I've made a lot of wrong decisions for both of us, my darling Alice, but somehow I know that this is the right one. I couldn't tell you because things were already going so badly on the property anyway, but my last two trips to the city were not to visit the bank's head office at all. The doctor I saw last time said I've a condition for which there's no hope of a cure at this stage, and the specialist in Sydney confirmed it. Six months at the most. That's not long enough to get us out of the mess I've made, and the only thing I can now spare you and little Nonie is the suffering of watching me getting worse day by day, probably irritable and changed because of the drugs I shall need, and saying and doing things that aren't in my character and that the child would not comprehend. I'd rather be remembered by you both as I am now, but above every other consideration there's the expense. You will both need what little money we have left, Alice; it would be even further folly on my part to allow it to be squandered on a lost cause. Goodbye darling, and I pray that you will understand my reasons for taking the step that I am about to take. It will be better this way. God bless you both. I shall love you always.

                                                    Dermot

"What's the matter, Nonie? You look as if you've seen a ghost."

Nonie folded the piece of paper and put it into the pocket of her jeans, groped her way to the door. She felt that she was going to suffocate.

Outside the sun was getting low in the west. It cast long shadows over the gulleys and through the timber as she made her way, slowly because she was very tired, up the hill and along the driveway with its avenue of small new trees in their netted enclosures to the new homestead.

"Nonie! Good gracious, you're as white as a sheet, do you know that? What is it?"

"Is Jacey in, Mrs. Parsons?"

"No, he's not. He shouldn't be long though. You do look a little under the weather, dear. Are you really feeling all right? How about a cup of tea?"

"I don't think I'll wait." Nonie felt helpless. She couldn't think properly, wasn't even sure why she was here now.

"Just a quick cuppa and then you can go," said the motherly Mrs. Parsons firmly.

"Yes, very well then. Thank you."

She drank the tea when it came with gratitude. It wasn't too hot, but sweet and strong. She put the cup down again.

"Thanks, Mrs. P., that was lovely."

"You won't wait for Jacey?"

"No, it doesn't matter. It was nothing really."

Nonie got up and left the kitchen by the side door. She had walked along the veranda and was crossing the lawn when she heard Jacey's voice. Mrs. Parsons was there too.

"Which way did she go?"

"I don't know, Jacey. Down the drive, I suppose. It was only moments ago that she left."

"She didn't say why she'd come?"

"She said it didn't matter."

"Thanks, Mrs. Parsons. I'll have a scout around. Maybe I'll catch up with her."

Nonie heard the quick, staccato sound of Jacey's elastic-sided boots as they crossed the veranda, and the gauze door creaked as he opened it and closed it after him. Then he came down the front steps and over the lawn toward her.

"Nonie? You wanted to see me?" He peered into her face in the fading light. "Did you want to see me about something?" he repeated.

She returned his stare a little woodenly.

"It was nothing," she told him, trying her best to keep that awful weariness out of her voice. "It doesn't matter, Jacey."

His hand on her arm prevented her from continuing on her way.

"I think it does," he contradicted her quietly, his eyes sharpening. "Come on. We're going back to the house.

He led her back over the lawn, up the steps again and through the lounge to a room she couldn't remember having been shown by Delphine on their rounds of the house. It must be his office, of deep leather chairs and an enormous rolltop desk with a calendar sitting on the top. There were maps all over the walls. Jacey pushed her gently down into one of the chairs and Nonie gazed up at him a little blankly.

"I shouldn't have come, Jacey," she told him defensively. "I don't know why I did. It was silly."

"I'll be the judge of that," said Jacey, and she couldn't help a faint smile at the old, autocratic brusqueness back again. "I'll get you a drink. You look as if you could do with one."

"No, thanks—truly. Mrs. P. made me a cup of tea."

"So she said. What did you want to see me about, then? Is it Pru?" Jaceylike, he came straight to the point.

Nonie fished the note out of her pocket and handed it to him. She fumbled it into his hands with fingers that were surprisingly stiff and cold in spite of the warmth of the evening.

"I found it when Ilse and I were doing out the store," she heard herself explaining flatly. "In the back of an old clock. *Our* old clock."

Jacey took the note and unfolded it, scanned the message quickly. As he read, his expression altered subtly, and he went over the contents again more thoroughly. Finally he folded up the note again and put it on the top of the desk. Nonie, waiting, thought she could hardly bear the compassion that was in Jacey's eyes as he turned back from the desk.

"I'm sorry, Nonie," he said slowly, and his voice was very deep, just a bit gruff. "And I'm sorry I wasn't here when you came up looking for me."

And that was the point at which something inside Nonie just seemed to give way. He'd never be there—not for her, anyway—and she'd had no business, no right, to come looking for him, either. Nonie put her head down on the side of Jacey's great padded leather armchair and wept. And once she began, she couldn't seem to stop. She wept for her father, for his illness, his loneliness in the secret knowledge of it, his despair. She wept for her mother and the note she'd never got, and for little Pru and poor faithful Stroud who'd done his best to be all a father should and for patient Ilse and bitter, crippled Raynor and herself and... and...oh, *everything*.

She cried and cried, with her head buried on her arm.

All the time she wept, Jacey Lomas was squatting down beside her. He made no attempt to stop her or to touch her, except that just once she felt the roughness of his fingers caressing the soft skin at the nape of her neck. That was the only way she knew he was there at all, until his voice sounded almost in her ear.

"That's right, little one, you have a good cry," he told her soothingly. "I reckon you should have done that a long time ago."

Perversely, when Jacey Lomax told her to do something, she wanted to do exactly the opposite. She seemed to have sobbed herself to a standstill anyway. She felt drained of emotion, yet somehow relieved too.

"Here, take mine." Nonie, searching unsuccessfully for her handkerchief, found Jacey's pressed into her hand. When she finally straightened up and pushed back her hair, he abandoned his squatting position and stood up again.

"Still no drink?" She shook her head mutely. "Cigarette?"

When Nonie shook her head again, he helped himself to a tailor-made one from the box on top of his desk, hitched his trousers and took the other chair. There was silence while his lighter flared.

Jacey drew on his cigarette soberly for a moment or two and then spoke again.

"I think you'll feel better when you think about it a from now on, Nonie. I mean later of course. Just no you've had a pretty tough shock."

She sighed. "My mother never found the note, Jacey She couldn't have bothered to wind the clock every wee afterward like she did before my father . . . went. I sup pose the heart just went out of her. It's a pity. It will a ways be a pity that she didn't know why."

"I think she probably had a fair idea, Nonie. When man and a woman love each other they become ver close. They often know things though they may not pu them into words, even to each other. They're part of th unspoken, shared experience that comes with living to gether and loving one another over a period of years. think, in fact I'm sure, that your mother knew more tha she was able to communicate to you. Remember yo were only a child. What, eight years old? Pru's age, n more."

"I suppose you're right."

"You think about it. I'm glad you found that note. Yo can know, can't you, that your father had his own particu lar brand of courage after all."

"I'm grateful to you for saying that, Jacey." Sh glanced up at him, at the stern set of his jaw in the brown craggy face and the level mouth that, surprisingly, wasn' pronouncing judgment. "*You* wouldn't have taken tha way out, though, would you?"

The broad shoulders shrugged. "I might have."

"No. I just know you *wouldn't*." Her voice threatened to crumble again.

"Who can possibly say with honesty what he would d unless he's confronted with an identical set of circum stances? It took guts to do it. We all have decisions t make and they can't all be the right ones. We've just go to do what we think best. The important thing is to *mak* them, to *take* decisions."

"Yes, I know. One has to *make* them." Nonie took a deep breath. "I'm leaving here as soon as ever Ilse and Raynor can get along without me, Jacey. Pru and I. Perhaps you can find another sort of companion for them to take my place."

Surprise flickered in Jacey's eyes. She could see that somehow she had caught him unawares. Just for a moment he seemed to hold his breath. There was a complete stillness about his stance and the way he held the cigarette in midair and allowed the smoke to curl in little spirals through his fingers without even moving them that told her he was making one of those lightning assessments of his. He was watching her all the time he was making it.

"Why did you come up here just now, Nonie? Why to *me*, in particular?"

She shrugged. "I hardly know why; I just know I shouldn't have. I expect it was because I knew you were the only other person around who actually knew about my relationship to Dermot."

"Is that the only reason?"

"I just had to tell *somebody*."

"I don't think this is the time to be making decisions of that sort, Nonie. Not just now. You're overwrought; you know that."

"No, I'm not. I decided it a while ago. It's not a . . . a . . . sudden idea. I've thought it over carefully from every angle."

Especially from the angle of Delphine Simpson, she could have told him. Delphine and Jacey. How could she possibly stay on there in the house right beneath them when even his nearness just now was a form of torture?

"Self-inflicted punishment," she muttered miserably.

"*What* did you say?" His eyes sharpened.

"Nothing, really. I was thinking aloud. But I mean it, Jacey . . . every word."

"And what about Pru? You'll be taking her away from everything she has grown to love."

She shrugged again. "She'll get over it in time. She's young enough to adapt again."

"So." He was quick to pounce, as she might have known he would. He'd been edging her around to this, into a trap. "It's not Pru who wants to go; it's only you. Why?"

"There's nothing for me here," she told him dully.

Jacey took her hands and pulled her to her feet to confront him.

"There is, Nonie, you've said so yourself. You're Dermot's daughter, aren't you? Come on, where's that spunk? It can't just have gone, disappeared into thin air? You're going to make a market garden, remember, and renovate the house. You're going to show them all that you can do it." A pause, because his words didn't seem to be having the effect he'd obviously desired. "You don't have to buy that old place, Nonie. I don't think I want to sell it after all. A simple lease for a nominal sum is all I need. It'll give you the same security without the big outlay of capital in an outright purchase. I'll see that your interests are protected when we draw up the lease; you needn't worry about it. Just leave it to me."

She shook her head. This was almost unbearable, especially now that Jacey was in one of his *persuasive* moods.

"It's very kind of you, Jacey, but no," she said firmly, staring numbly at the middle button of his shirt just about level with her forehead.

Jacey's fingers tipped her chin, took in her widening eyes.

"Don't be frightened of me, Nonie, please," he ordered crisply. "You aren't being honest with me, are you? You were really keen on the whole idea not so long ago, and now you're not, even though Pru is settled and happy and it would be the very thing she'd like to happen. What's made you alter your plan so radically? What's changed?"

Nonie's eyes were locked with his. She couldn't seem to drag hers away from Jacey's gray ones, which had gone dark and penetrating and insistent.

"*I've* changed, Jacey, that's what. *I* have." In spite of her intentions, her composure disintegrated. "*Please*," she begged brokenly. "Please don't argue about it, please, Jacey. I...I can't take much more."

"We'll leave it for now," he agreed unexpectedly.

"Not just for *now*. For *good*," she pleaded shakily.

"We'll see," he would only compromise, gently. "Come on, Nonie. I'm going to take you home."

AFTER THAT SHE SAW LITTLE or nothing of him. Whether he was being tactful, giving her time to recover her balance or whether she had simply gone right out of his mind Nonie had no way of telling, but she was grateful that he hadn't sought her out and raised the matter again.

During the rest of that week and into the next, she and Ilse completed their cleanup operations in the store. They burned the rest of the blankets, threw out everything that was too cracked, old or broken to be of use and restored as much of the harness as they could, soaking oil into the parched leather and polishing up the tarnished buckles and trappings.

"Some of it's really lovely, isn't it, Ilse?" remarked Nonie a little wistfully. "Just look at the way this brass has come up. It's so beautifully substantial looking."

"Mmm, those were the days right enough. They really made things to last. These are greatly prized now, you know. They've suddenly become much sought after for their antique value, like those old Victorian brass bedsteads that we used to think were so awful, and old commodes and the rest."

"I couldn't collect things just for their rarity though, could you? I'd have to really like them and want to look at them. I adore these horse brasses, though. I'd love to have a room, a proper harness room like they did in the old days with all these brasses and collars and blinkers hanging up around the walls, and all the different sizes of horseshoes, the hand-turned kind that the blacksmith used to make himself, and old sulky wheels and snaffles and wooden yokes and maybe even a bellows in the corner, if I could get one, one of those truly huge ones that used to blow up the forge, and . . . oh, lots of other things."

Nonie's eyes had gone dreamy. She caught herself up with difficulty.

"Do you smell anything, Ilse?" she asked suddenly, sniffing the air.

"Should I?" Ilse looked up from the top step of the veranda, upon which they had spread out the leather articles on old bits of paper while the oil was soaking in. "All I can smell is this revolting oil, I'm afraid."

Nonie wrinkled her nose, stood up.

"I think it's smoke," she said uncertainly. "In fact, I'd swear it is."

At that precise moment the phone rang and Ilse went off to answer it. When she came back her face was unusually troubled.

"That was Jacey and, yes, it's smoke. There's a fire out on the plains to the west of the town and he's got to go with the other men to get it under control."

Nonie's eyes were round.

"Will that be possible, Ilse? It must be a pretty big one for us to be able to smell it from here."

"It will be possible if they can get it controlled before it gets to the timber country and if this breeze doesn't get stronger." Already Ilse had screwed the cap back on the oilcan and was wiping her hands on one of the rags. "Jacey has phoned the school. The children will be quite safe there, Nonie. It's got really wide firebreaks plowed around it just like he has up there at the new house. The teacher will keep the children there unless it's quite safe to let them go by the time school's out, and Pru is to go up to Jacey's house. Hattie will be up there with Mrs. Parsons anyway, to man the telephone while Jacey's away and prepare supplies for the beaters."

"And what about here?" Nonie asked dubiously, glancing around at the decaying weatherboards and ant-eaten veranda posts.

Ilse pulled a wry face.

"I've told Jacey we'll stay meantime. The way its heading now, it's almost parallel with the creek and so we could just be lucky. He says we're not to leave it too late, though. If the worst happens, I'm to have the car out so we can go up to his place if we need to."

"I see. Is there anything else we can do?"

Ilse shook her head.

"Not really, unless I were to take Raynor up to Jacey's house and leave him there with the women and children. And I can't do that to him, Nonie. At least he feels he's in charge here and that he has some sort of useful role to play. You can imagine how miserably frustrated he is knowing perfectly well that all the other men, the ablebodied ones, have gone off to the fire."

Yes, she could imagine how he must feel, thought Nonie, as she went to collect the eggs from the hen run. She felt helpless enough herself, but glad of the few small duties she could think of to do.

The waiting was the worst. Cinders drifted past on the breeze and as the morning wore on they became thicker, larger, and smell of burning increased.

They ate a salad lunch almost in silence, all three aware of a sense of strain. The surrounding bush was almost lost in a blue haze that intensified in the early afternoon. The heightening breeze lifted it past the house in everchanging density.

When Nonie climbed to the top of the tankstand she

could now see a great orange cloud in the sky on the othe
side of the scrub. One could only conjecture the hold tha
the fire must have to make such a widespread glow a
that, and her heart went out to the teams of men who
were fighting the battle to deflect it from its path toward
the timber. To Jacey and the others.

Now she could catch the roar of it above the trees and
even as she looked a tongue of flame leaped high into the
air and then another. The roar was louder, a background
now to the staccato crackle of burning wood and leaves
The fire must have eaten up the big body of grass out on
the plain; it was licking into the scrub. The timber had
caught.

Nonie scrambled down the iron ladder on the side of
the water tank and hurried around the side of the house.

Ilse and Raynor were watching from the lawn.

"It's come," she said. "It's into the trees."

"Yes, it's caught," repeated Raynor fiercely, helplessly. "God, if only I wasn't so blasted *useless*, tied to this
damn contraption. Nonie, get me the hose and connect i
to that tap, will you?"

"What are you going to do?"

"I'll soak the veranda boards and uprights. It's worth
chance."

"But it won't touch the *house*, will it?"

"With the wind where it is, it could," he replied grimly.
"Get going, girl. We won't let the old place go without at
least the semblance of a fight."

She ran then to do as he had asked her, watched as he
started to wheel himself up and down, playing the jet o
water over the perimeter of the rambling structure.

"It *is* heading this way, Raynor," she told him breathlessly after another scramble up and down the tankstand.
"What can we do, Ilse and I? We can't just stand there
and...and let it come."

"We may have to yet. You can get a ladder and block

ip the downpipes, Nonie. Go right around the house.
Use those old tennis balls in the chest in the hall, or stuff
them with wads of cloths, anything. Ilse, fill as many
buckets of water as you can and bring them out and pass
them up to Nonie. We'll run water into as much of the
guttering as we've time for. It could just stop the building
catching."

"Yes, Raynor."

They worked like beavers, breathlessly, in silence. Nonie was glad of the intense activity. The heat was now oppressive, and each roar of flame and crash of branches
was followed by a bursting shower of sparks sent skyward.

"That's it, Raynor," Ilse was gasping, her face flame
colored itself. "What else?"

"It's all we can do, Ilse, but wait." His voice was taut.
"We could still be lucky."

"I think I should get you into the car, Ray."

"No, we'll wait a bit yet. Jacey was right. It's running
parallel to the creek. If it misses the house, we'll need to
be here anyway to put out any sidespread that could still
threaten it. There's always the water to retreat to, anyway."

"Ray, Jacey *said*."

"You *hear* me, Ilse," barked Raynor with a good hint
of the old Lomax bossiness.

They waited and watched, too tense to speak again.
Nonie never knew afterward how long they waited before
Raynor said on a note of elation. "We're going to be in
the clear. The wind has veered a little, look. It's taking it
away a bit. By God, it's like a miracle!"

But the miracle was short-lived. As the top of one of
the lofty, blazing ironbarks broke off, it fell through the
air in a veritable shower of sparks and crackling twigs and
the next moment the old wattletree was alight. From
there on it was almost inevitable that the homestead's
frail timber, so close, so very close, would be next.

"Raynor, *no!*" Nonie was hardly aware that the ago-nized shriek of protest was hers.

"That's it, Nonie, I'm afraid. It's going to rip through there like lightning now."

Nonie ran up the steps and along the veranda.

The west wing was well alight. She could hear the steamy hissing of the flames licking the wetness out of the wood that Raynor had spent so much effort in soaking. They had taken a proper grip and the water had evapo-rated altogether in the intense heat by the time she dragged her old tin trunk outside and dumped it on the lawn. On her way back past the piles of harness that she and Ilse had been working on, she stopped to fling all that out over the veranda rail too, piece by piece . . . and then the heat was too much and she was forced back down the steps again.

"Come out of that, Nonie, for heaven's sake! Do you want to be burned alive?" Raynor shouted in some irrita-tion.

Nonie came back obediently to Ilse and Raynor to find that Delphine had joined them. Beside their own grimy persons she seemed like a creature from another planet, fresh and clean in a buttercup-yellow linen dress. Except for the fact that some of the flying cinders had settled on her hair and shoulders and that her feet were bare and a little slimy because she had waded across the shallowest bit of the creek, she was dressed for a stroll down Martin Place.

"I left my car on the other side of the water," she ex-plained, flicking off some of the smuts from the yellow linen and slipping with a small grimace of distaste into the white sandals she had been carrying in her hand. "Hadn't you better come up to the other house now? Those were Jacey's clear instructions as I understand it."

"We're safe enough here, Delphine. The wind is taking the fire away from us now. We're behind it here, or as good as. There's nothing more we can do though. Things just didn't go our way, that's all."

The defeated twist to Raynor's mouth, the bitter frustration in his voice were too much for Nonie to bear. She couldn't just stand there like the others, watching Raynor watching the house burning. Anything was better than that!

She slipped away with a couple of the buckets, the ones that she and Ilse had been using earlier to run water into the gutters and took them down to the creek to fill, intending to douse the few spoils she had salvaged on the side lawn. The tin trunk should survive all right but the harness would stand a better chance to withstand small flying bits of burning wood if she covered it with some wetted sacks. One or two good-sized sparks could easily set the thick checked felt padding on those old horsecollars and saddles alight. She might as well do her best for them seeing that she had thrown them there.

Nonie clambered down the steepest part of the bank and let each pail sink slowly into the water until it was full to the brim. Then she began to carry them back, but this time up the proper pathway because the gradient was easier and she had a fair load. Every now and then the water slopped out over her legs so there was no point in hurrying too much with them. When she reached the top again and came into full view of the blazing house, Nonie put down the buckets and stared. She stared in a sort of mesmerized horror because she thought she must be having a nightmare.

Delphine and Ilse were still standing on the lawn, and they were looking toward the house, and there, coming out of the house, framed for an instant in the burning doorway, were Raynor and Jacey.

It could only be Jacey. Nonie knew so well the set of his shoulders, his narrow-hipped, tall figure in the khaki bush shirt and that awful old hat. And Raynor beside him, al-

most as tall, nearly as broad, was propping Jacey up as
they came clumsily down the steps and back over the
grass.

Raynor was propping *Jacey* up?

Raynor was *walking?*

Nonie rubbed her eyes to see if the vision would disappear. It didn't. Like a slow-motion movie the two men
crossed the lawn clutching each other, and when they
reached the foot of the box-gum at the edge of the grass
Raynor put one hand against its stout bole and allowed
Jacey to sink gently down at his feet.

Nonie picked up the pails again and ran abandonedly
with water spilling and slopping as she went. By the time
she got there Ilse and Delphine were already kneeling beside Jacey. Raynor was still leaning against the trunk of
the tree at whose base his brother was slumped. He was
breathing heavily. In answer to Nonie's agonzied, unspoken question, he gasped.

"He's okay. Nonie . . . he thought you were . . . *in* there.
Didn't . . . even . . . ask. . . ."

She put her arms around him and hugged him, her eyes
brimming with tears that didn't actually fall because she
was too full of wonder even to think of crying just then.

"Raynor, you're walking! Don't you realize what
you've done? You're *walking!* Ray, we've got our miracle
after all!"

Raynor had regained his breath. His gaunt features
split in a rueful grin.

"And it'll be another miracle if I ever get away from
this tree. I reckon I'm pretty well wedded to the damn
thing. Here, give us a hand, will you, Nonie. I've a feeling
that if I let go I might fall over."

She placed her arm firmly about his waist. "No, you
won't Raynor," she asserted confidently. "There's no going back now. You've got it made. Let's go now."

Together they walked a few steps jubilantly.

"Nonie?" That was Ilse, Ilse was calling to her from where she was kneeling beside Jacey's recumbent form. "Please Nonie, could you come?" she called softly, but with an underlying sense of urgency that caused Raynor to turn around and meet her eyes. There was no mistaking the message in those beautiful blue eyes of Ilse's. The message was for Raynor alone and even Raynor couldn't mistake it this time. As Nonie dropped down beside Jacey, Raynor took Ilse into his arms and embraced her quietly. Then they walked slowly away together, and each painful step seemed to Nonie to be a step of triumph.

Jacey's face, when Nonie looked down at him, was almost unrecognizable. Her heart gave a lurch. His eyes were closed and even the lids looked red and sore. His forehead and cheeks were blackened, his neck was smothered in soot and cinders and the bush shirt was spattered with masses of ragged holes. There was an angry burn up his left forearm from wrist to elbow and behind his left ear a small trickle of blood was already congealing.

Nonie gazed at it in awe.

"I thought Ray said he was *all right?*" she said to Delphine in a strangled voice that she could scarcely recognize.

"He will be, Nonie, though why you had to disappear like that and send him looking for you goodness only knows. Now look what you've done!" She relented at the sight of Nonie's stricken expression. "He was conscious when Raynor and he came out," she told her grudgingly. "A falling beam caught him on the side of the head just before they got through the doorway."

"What can we do?"

"The doctor will be here shortly. Jacey had phoned for him and an ambulance from his house before he came down. He expected to find you all up there, and when he didn't and saw the place ablaze as well, he thought something must have gone badly wrong. You knew well enough what his instructions were."

Oh, Jacey. Darling Jacey. What had she done? What had they *all* done?

Nonie stood up, rubbed the grass from her knees and carried over the water she had brought. Then she took her handkerchief and dipped it in and began very gently, to wash away the soot and grime from Jacey's face. It was a pitifully small scrap of handkerchief but it served the purpose not too badly. The pallor that was revealed by her ministrations smote Nonie afresh. The color that normally ran healthily beneath Jacey's heavy tan had drained away, leaving his complexion a ghostly, ghastly yellow.

It was all their fault—hers, especially—for not doing what he had ordered in the first place!

Nonie got the other bucket of water and eased Jacey's burned arm into it, running the water through the small piece of cloth she had to the place where the water couldn't quite reach up near his elbow.

"I hope you know what you're doing?" remarked Delphine with some asperity. She had thus far watched in complete silence.

"I think so. I read it somewhere."

The coolness of the water on his burning arm seemed to waken Jacey. He opened his eyes and gazed up at Nonie with an expression that was quite blank at first and then with returning recollection somewhat sharper.

"Where's Raynor?" he asked faintly.

"With Ilse, walking. They went down to the creek."

"Good."

He closed his eyes again, then opened them as another thought seemed to occur to him. He raised his head a little, reached out with his good hand and took Nonie's wet one in a firm grasp.

"Don't run out on me just when I need you, will you?" he said, and although his voice was still faded and hoarse and not like Jacey's at all the words themselves were quite distinct.

"No, Jacey, I won't," she promised, but it was doubtful
if he heard her because already his grasp had slackened as
he slid into unconsciousness again.

"I wish the doctor would hurry up," said Delphine impatiently. "I think Jacey's out of his mind with that blow
on the head. Concussion, probably."

"I think so, too," agreed Nonie.

And it was the only point upon which she had seemed
to have agreed with Delphine Simpson during their entire
acquaintance!

CHAPTER EIGHT

THE SOUND OF VOICES and footsteps making their way up the bank aroused Jacey once more. By the time the doctor arrived at his side, followed by two ambulance men carrying a stretcher, his eyes were open again and he lifted his head and tried to sit up.

"Lie back, Jacey, and let me look you over, you mutt," the doctor told him with what seemed to Nonie a total lack of respect. He gave his patient a little push that sent him flat again and chuckled. "I must say this is the first time a feller has ever phoned and sent for me before he's even *had* his accident. Warning in advance, so to speak. You must be psychic!"

Jacey grinned sheepishly. "Far from psychic," he replied with a certain quiet irony. "There wasn't anyone in there as it turned out!"

The doctor was checking his eyes and the bruised swelling on the side of his head. Finally he sat back on his heels.

"You've most certainly had a fair wallop there, Jacey. You must have a skull of cast iron. I can't detect any signs of concussion but that's not to say it mightn't be delayed though. We'll take you in anyway and keep an eye on you for a bit." He was snipping away at the armhole of the tattered shirt while he was speaking, pulling the cloth aside as he cut it. "This will need attention too."

"You can do it up at the house, can't you? I'm not going in just now."

"You'd better."

"I'm not. I've things to see to." Jacey struggled to a sitting position.

The doctor sighed. "Have it your way, Jacey. I know you too well to waste time in arguing. At least let these blokes take you up there, just to prove to themselves if to no one else that their journey was really necessary. You're in a shocked condition so you might as well let them save you a little unnecessary exertion. And you needn't try to pretend that you're feeling any too great. You can't be."

Jacey gave a wan smile. He was even paler than he'd been before, now that he was sitting up.

"See what I mean?" The doctor pressed home his advantage. "Anyway, why should we *all* get our feet wet? We're over the other side of the creek, so you'd need to wade it. The fire's burning out by the way, Jacey. Your own firebreaks have it cornered, but there was still too much smoke around to chance the main road."

"You kept to the other side of the water?"

"We did."

"I see." He considered a moment. "Where's your car, Delphine?"

"It's over there too. I'll take it up to the house."

"You might give Nonie here a lift up with you," Jacey said to the doctor as he allowed the men to move him on to the stretcher with a reasonably good grace. "Where's my hat?" he asked in afterthought from his supine position.

"If you mean this—" The doctor picked it up with an expression of disgust.

"That's it."

"It's sopping wet. What did they do, pour a bucket of water over you to bring you round?"

Jacey's lips quirked.

"I dipped it in the horse trough on my way down. Part of the old fire drill. Habit dies hard."

"Hmm. Maybe it's a good thing it does. It no doubt helped deflect that rafter a bit when it hit you."

"That's right," agreed Jacey calmly, placing the ha
over his eyes to keep out the glare from the sky. "Every
thing's jake now. I can't think straight if I haven't got m
hat. As I said, habit dies hard."

"Let's go, then."

They moved in slow procession over the grass and
down the path to the shallow part of the creek. On the
other side the men put Jacey into the ambulance and
drove off. Delphine following in her yellow Lotus. Noni
and the doctor brought up the rear.

"So you're Nonie, eh?" He reached across her to pul
the passenger door shut. "I was wondering when I'd be
meeting you. I've heard a lot about you from Jacey."

"What?" Nonie looked at him, startled.

"Nothing bad, don't worry! Nor am I speaking profes
sionally now when I say that, but as a friend of the
Lomaxes—a personal friend. We're good mates, Jacey
and I. I've known him for more years than I care to re
member."

"Oh, I see." Nonie opened her palm to find her white
handkerchief still clutched in her hand—a tepid, sodder
little ball of cloth, and not white anymore either. She
gazed down at it a moment and then began to unfold it
spreading it out carefully upon one knee as they drove
"Will he really be all right?"

"Who? Jacey?" He sensed her need for reassurance
"He's as tough as they come; you must have seen that for
yourself. We'll keep him in bed for twenty-four hours
just in case of concussion. The burns will take longer to
get right, of course. One's fairly major and I've no doub
it's giving him hell, although he'd be the last to admit it."

"I feel it's mostly my fault that it happened."

"You mustn't feel that." He glanced over, took in the
strain in her voice, the tenseness as she sat there smooth-
ing the edges of the little hankie with unnecessary attention. "You've no need to feel that way; it's the very last

thing Jacey would want. And anyway," he added bracingly, "look at the good that's come out of it. Raynor is walking."

"Yes, that at least is wonderful."

"I've had the idea for a long time that there was some emotional block to his total recovery, some mental reason rather than a medical one for his progress being arrested. It took something big to shake him out of it, and Jacey unwittingly provided it."

"I still don't know what happened."

"I do, or the bare bones of it anyway. I met Raynor and Ilse on their way up to the other house. I couldn't believe my eyes when I saw Raynor was actually walking, but I couldn't spare the time to stop and yarn about it beyond telling him he'd done enough for one day. He told me about Jacey, seemed pretty shattered by the whole experience. He said Jacey came around the corner of the house. He was looking over to where they were all standing and then he just plunged inside. It was only when Raynor heard him shouting your name that he looked around and saw you weren't standing with them any longer. He knew you weren't inside the house, wherever else you might be, but Jacey obviously thought you were so he had to act fast. He said he doesn't even remember getting out of the chair and going after him, but he got the message across inside and they were just coming out again when Jacey got clobbered by that falling beam."

"It really *was* my fault, then, but I'm glad about Raynor and so will Jacey be. He'll think it was worth it."

"Yes, I'm sure he will," agreed the man beside her comfortingly. "I'll see you later, then," he added, for they had drawn up at the front of the new homestead and the men were carrying Jacey inside.

The doctor followed them into the hallway and through to the bedroom, and Nonie found herself left on the side veranda with Delphine.

"Excuse me a moment, I must go and wash my feet. These sandals will be quite ruined, I'm afraid." Delphine regarded them fastidiously. "Don't go away before I come back will you, though, Nonie. I want a word with you."

Left alone on the veranda, Nonie wondered where Delphine thought she would be likely to go away *to* right now anyway.

From here she could see the smoldering ruins of the old house down below her. Every now and then a flame wriggled out of the smoking heaps of rubble that were all that were now left of the place. Ironically, the outbuildings were still intact. The engine shed, the chicken yards hadn't been touched by the fire at all. The wind had veered enough to save them at the last moment . . . the house, too, if it hadn't been for the old wattle tree catching alight like that.

Nonie sat back with her eyes closed, thinking. She was still reliving the horrible moment when they'd known the old building was finally doomed. She could still hear the roar as the flames took hold, and her nostrils still stung with the acrid fumes of the smoke that had billowed up in such great, dense gusts.

A sound brought her back to the present.

"That's better." Delphine had returned. "I couldn't wait to get that mud off. I didn't bother putting my sandals back on though. I shall throw them away when I get home. I happened to have a pair of driving shoes in the car, so I've put them on instead." She stretched out a shapely leg to inspect her neatly shod foot.

"I've been thinking while you were off just now. It's wonderful about Raynor, isn't it?" Nonie said a little shyly. She always found herself ill at ease when she was alone with Delphine. "It was strange the way it happened, the way it all worked out."

"Yes. That's partly what I wanted to speak to you

about," Delphine replied matter-of-factly. "Now that Raynor is walking again, there's no need for you to remain, is there? Your services can be dispensed with after this."

"Yes, I expect that's so."

"And they've nowhere even to put you up, with the house burned from under their feet. You'll be something of an embarrassment to them in the circumstances—you and the child."

"Yes, I realize that too, Delphine." Nonie was beginning to feel a hot, uncomfortable flush seeping into her cheeks. "I'm as aware of it as you are, I can assure you. I've no intention that we should embarrass them, though. I'll make arrangements to relieve them of our presence just as soon as I can."

"Good. I'm glad you regard the situation in such a sensible light, Nonie." Delphine paused. "As a matter of fact, I'd like to help. I can give you a lift back into town right now."

"Oh, you mustn't think of doing that."

"Nonsense, it will be a pleasure. My car is here anyway. If you get the child we can go right now, and we'll collect that old trunk you rescued on the way. That's another thing—and I don't want you to be hurt or offended at my mentioning it. You won't have much left in the way of clothes, either of you, will you? I can give you some of mine when we get to town, and I'd like to buy you some more to set you off again. And for Pru, of course."

"Why would you want to do that?" Nonie couldn't help asking in some surprise. She had never found Delphine quite so friendly or sympathetic before!

"One wants to be neighborly, doesn't one? It could just as easily have been me and my things that were affected in a fire." Delphine shrugged. "If it had been, I'd be appreciative if someone offered to do the same for me."

"No, I couldn't allow you to do *that*, thank you, Del-

phine." Nonie sounded quite shocked. "I have enough
money in the bank to take care of both of us, although of
course I'll have to be sparing with it. I hadn't counted on
a disaster of this sort exactly. We don't need a lot of
clothes though. I'll get us the bare minimum in the meantime. I prefer to be independent, but I do thank you all
the same."

"Well, at least you'll allow me to pay your fares down
to Sydney or wherever it is you'll be going. We can get
you onto the plane or the train, whichever you prefer.
Tonight, if you like, if it's the train. You must see for
yourself that there are far too many people in this house
already just now—Ilse and Raynor, and Mrs. Parsons
and Hattie. We're simply not needed, you and I, and as
for Pru, children are in the way at a time like this. In fact
I'm even feeling a little bit *de trop* myself at present.
There can be too many women around, all getting under
each other's feet, don't you agree?"

She stood up, smoothed the yellow linen down over her
hips and seat.

"Come then, Nonie. I shall drive you both into town."

Nonie hesitated.

"I'd like to say goodbye to Jacey first, Delphine. He's
been . . . well, kind. I'd just *like* to say it, if you don't
mind?" Her voice thickened, because there seemed to be
a lump in her throat that prevented the words from coming out properly. She knew they had to go—she'd known
it for weeks now—so the sooner the better. She dreaded
having to see Jacey again. She wondered how she could
bear it, actually *saying* goodbye, but it had to be done and
she'd manage it somehow, just as she'd always managed
to do things that had to be done. It was the only
honorable way, even though it would be for her the most
difficult and painful task of her entire life.

Delphine seemed to sense the struggle that Nonie was
having with herself.

"You don't have to see him at all, Nonie. What nonsense! You can always write and thank him. I shall personally see that any salary due to you is forwarded on. Indeed I shall pay you what is owing to you, with a comfortable margin, before I see you off. If you don't hurry we shall miss the train." She was beginning to sound impatient.

"I promised." Nonie's eyes were full of tears. They blurred her vision and made Delphine's figure just a fuzzy yellow shape in front of her.

"Come *at once*, do you hear me?" Delphine's voice rose peremptorily. "Come now, and get the child too. As usual you quite overrate your importance, Nonie, and forget that you're a mere employee. Goodbyes are quite unnecessary, so forget that rubbish and get a move on."

"Indeed, goodbyes are unnecessary, because there aren't going to be any."

Jacey's voice, deep, a little hoarse but slow and clear, sounded from somewhere behind them. He was propping himself up in the doorway, and save for his unearthly pallor he appeared to be the old Jacey back again—in a clean shirt and trousers, sporting a heavy white bandage right up his left arm, which was supported in a neat calico sling. The doctor was hovering behind him as he stepped out onto the veranda.

"Jacey!" Delphine swung around. "How long have you been there?"

"Long enough." He sounded—and looked—unbelievably grim. "Come here, Nonie.

"Jacey?"

"Come here, Nonie. Just do as I say. You are *not* going to say goodbye, do you hear me? You are *not* going to town with Delphine. You are *not* going to run away, or even try to. You are going to remain here. You are going to stay here with me and do me the honor of becoming my wife."

"Your wife?" echoed Nonie in the very faintest o voices.

"My wife," repeated Jacey firmly. "Come here."

He put out his hand imperiously and Nonie found her self obeying him wordlessly. His fingers closed over her in a warm, commanding clasp.

Delphine shrugged from the doorway.

"If and when you recover your senses, Jacey, give me a ring, will you?" she managed in acid tones.

"Thank you, Delphine, but I'm perfectly in command of my senses, never more so."

For the first time, at the sober firmness of his voice and expression, she faltered just a little. "Then there's nothing more to be said, is there?"

"Not as far as you're concerned," he replied with uncompromising politeness.

"Then I'll wish you all the luck in the world, darling... and I think you'll need it," she couldn't resist adding spitefully. "Remember you'll be taking on that kid as well."

"I'm well aware of what I intend taking on, thanks Delphine. Now please go."

And she did, with a furious slamming of the gauze door as she ran down the steps. Seconds later, the Lotus revved wildly and in a shower of flying gravel went spurting off down the drive.

Jacey let go of Nonie's hand and sat down heavily in the nearest chair. There were beads of sweat on his forehead and his breathing was noticeably uneven, but as the doctor leaned over him in concern he actually grinned, and the doctor started to laugh.

"That was more of a statement than a proposal, Jacey I reckon, but may I be the first to wish you every happiness, *and* mean it?" He gave a mock whistle. "Phew! What a virago Delpine can be when she gets going! I can quite see why you insisted on staying on your feet till

ou'd got the thing sorted out to your satisfaction, old
chap, but *now* will you let me get you into bed and give
you a shot of something for that arm? For a prospective
bridegroom you're in abominable shape." He turned to
Nonie, still standing there in a frozen state with a wide-
eyed look about her. "You aren't going to turn him down
now, I suppose, at this stage? You won't *really* run out on
him, like he's kept saying you would?"

She shook her head stupidly, trying to bring herself
back to reality.

"I won't run out."

"Good girl! Then give me ten minutes with him, Nonie,
and after that he's all yours."

The doctor hauled Jacey to his feet again and would
have propelled him toward the bedroom except that Jacey
stopped once more when he was passing Nonie.

"It wasn't much of a proposal, Nonie," he told her in
an unabashed, husky voice, and passion blazed quite
shamelessly in his eyes as he looked down at her for a moment. "We'll have to regard it as a trial run. I'll do better
the second time round, when we're alone."

She nodded, felt his lips just brush her forehead before
he went inside.

The doctor was more than ten minutes with Jacey but
when he came back he seemed well pleased.

"I've given him something for the pain from those
burns, and he should be asleep shortly, so make it snappy
if you want to get some sense out of him."

"I will." She hesitated. "I won't know what to say to
him," she confessed shyly. "I mean, I never dreamed...I
didn't know...I thought that he and Delphine...."

He looked at her sharply.

"Delphine? Nonsense! He's been in love with you for
months; I've known that by the way he spoke about you.
I'm not wrong, believe me. I know Jacey Lomax better
than most people do and it's the first time I've seen him

uncertain how to handle a situation. He must be slip
ping!" He couldn't resist a chuckle. "He had this notion
that you didn't like him. Said something about having to
buy some time to work you around to the idea. I think
you're going to be good for Jacey, do you know that?" He
patted her kindly on the shoulder. "Go on in there and
cheer him up. He keeps thinking you're going to do a dis
appearing act, so he can't be too sure of you even yet. I'll
see you both tomorrow. I'll have to go and find Raynor
now."

When Nonie went into Jacey's room, she was surprised
to find that he wasn't in bed at all, but merely stretched
out on top of the counterpane with a couple of pillows
slung behind his head.

Lying there in his open-necked shirt and pale drill trousers, with the dressing on the side of his head and his eyes
closed, he appeared boyish and—in a way that Nonie
could not have explained—vulnerable.

At the sound of her step, Jacey opened his eyes and invited her to come in. She advanced timidly.

"I thought you'd be in bed, Jacey—properly, I mean.
Shouldn't you be?"

"I'm resting, so it amounts to the same thing. There are
a few things I want to see to later and I've a couple of
phone calls to make. I didn't intend to opt out of the fire-
fighting activities quite so suddenly." He smiled. A rather
pale and weary smile it was, and his mouth lifted somewhat satirically at one corner as he looked across at her.
"It wasn't a very dignified exit, was it?"

"Not very. It was a brave thing to do, Jacey. Just what
one would expect of *you*, but foolish too. And all my
fault," she added bitterly.

"Come here, Nonie, and sit on the bed beside me."

As she obeyed, Jacey put his good arm around her and
drew her against him, pressing her head against his shirt.
She could feel his breath on her brow, his lips near her
cheek.

"I thought you were in there." He murmured the words into her hair in a voice so deep and full of despair that what he was saying was barely distinguishable. "I thought you were in there. I thought you were *in* there." He seemed to be torturing himself by saying it aloud.

"I know, Jacey. I'm sorry. If anything had happened to you because of me—" She stopped, unable to continue.

He put her away from him, studying her face intently.

"Would you have cared, Nonie? Would you?"

Jacey's eyes held a strange searching glitter.

"Of course I'd have cared. How can you even ask such a thing?"

"I find I can ask it with some justification," he replied, inscrutability returning. "You'd have gone, wouldn't you, there with Delphine just now? *Wouldn't* you?"

"Yes," she admitted lamely, dropping her eyes.

"Why?"

"Jacey, please. Can't we leave it, for now at least? You're supposed to be quiet. You're supposed to be asleep."

"And while I'm asleep you'll doubtless be thinking of all sorts of evasions and half-truths to fob me off with."

"I *won't*. I don't *want* to fob you off." Nonie blushed fierily.

"I want the truth, Nonie, and I want it now." Jacey's tone was relentless. "Why would you have gone with Delphine?"

"Because I thought . . . I thought . . . ."

"What did you think?"

"That you and Delphine . . . that you . . . ." She searched for the right words but it was impossible to find them.

"That we . . . ?" He waited, and when he saw that she wasn't going to continue he actually said it for her. "That there was some sort of understanding between us, was that it?"

She nodded miserably. "Yes, that was it. *I* knew it all

along. I knew it was Delphine, even though Raynor said it wasn't. *He* said it was Ilse."

"Ilse? Ilse!" Jacey exclaimed, startled into a sitting position on the bed. "Good God, who am I supposed to be? Don Juan and Casanova rolled into one?" He ran frenzied fingers through his hair and swung his legs over the edge of the bed. "What the hell do you mean, *Ilse?*" he demanded agitatedly in supreme exasperation.

"Jacey, *please*. Lie down, please."

"Not till you explain, I won't. Ilse! Dear Lord in heaven!" he muttered perplexedly.

"Lie down, Jacey."

"I can't, not till I know. What the devil have you all been hatching up?"

"I've no intention of explaining until you lie down again, Jacey Lomax," Nonie told him with a calm that she wasn't actually feeling.

Finally, seeing that she truly meant it, he lay back against the pillows again with a sigh of resignation.

"I don't think that all this discussion is good for you," she offered uncertainly, taking in his drawn appearance and the fact that he had closed his eyes again.

He brushed that aside impatiently.

"Never mind whether it's good or bad. We'd better get the record straight while we're at it. Get on with it, Nonie. What about Ilse?"

So Nonie told him. She repeated word for word the conversation that Raynor had overheard and had related in turn to her.

"I'm beginning to see," said Jacey thoughtfully when she had finished. "That poor devil of a brother of mine! Poor Ray. If only he'd *said* something, brought it out into the open. Do you know what we were actually talking about, Nonie?"

She shook her head.

"We were talking about the fact that he probably

wouldn't walk again. At that time, you see, the doctors thought the outlook was hopeless. It was many weeks afterward before they concluded that the problem was now an emotional one because in other directions he had made unexpectedly favorable progress. One didn't know *when* to tell him or *what* to tell him but in the early days the situation was quite clear-cut—they thought the shock of knowing that his legs were possibly permanently damaged might set him back irreparably. He was in no condition for the truth. I had to beg Ilse to try to pretend somehow that all was well, that things were just the same as before. For his sake, we waited till they deemed him fit enough to hear it."

"There was something else too."

"Was there?" Jacey's gray eyes had sharpened. "What else, Nonie?"

She traced the checked pattern on the bedcover with one finger, gazing at it.

"You kissed Ilse then too, Jacey. You had your arms around her and you were kissing her and Raynor saw that too."

"Yes, I believe I did. I *kissed* her; I wasn't *kissing* her. There's a difference, Nonie. I was comforting her, nothing more. I'll have to have a yarn with Ray about it sometime."

"He'll understand, Jacey. I told him there'd be an explanation if only he could bring himself to seek one from you."

"It was a kiss of comfort, of consolation, nothing more. I hoped that Ilse could draw some strength, some encouragement from a little brotherly support."

"Yes, I know. I *told* Raynor it'd be that sort of kiss."

His lips twitched although he still lay there with his eyes shut.

"You certainly seem to have discussed some surprising topics with brother Raynor. You sound quite an authority on kisses, too," he murmured drowsily.

She flushed. "Well, I know there are different sorts, for different reasons."

The flush deepened painfully as she remembered the kiss *she* had once received from Jacey too.

With uncanny perception he seemed to have read her mind.

"Yes, Nonie," he said, and his voice was a very soft, deep murmur, nothing more. "There are different sorts, for different reasons."

Jacey still had his eyes shut but he was drawing her toward him again inexorably and there was a slow, delicious anticipation about the way he did it that set Nonie's heart racing. When he opened his eyes and looked at her, there was no anger in Jacey's darkening gaze, not like that other time, and when his lips found hers they were gentle, fleeting. It was the merest butterfly of a kiss, right on her mouth.

"I'm sorry about that other time, Nonie," he murmured, his lips at her temple. "I was so angry. How can I ever make you understand? I was angry that you didn't trust me enough to confide in me who you really were. I knew, sure, but I still hoped that *you* would tell me yourself. I've loved you almost since the first time I saw you when you and Pru were standing there in the half-dark by the old wattle tree looking like a couple of lost and frightened kids. If you only knew how many times I've longed to take you in my arms and kiss you and transfer all those worries and troubles of yours into *my* care and *my* keeping."

"Jacey, I didn't know." Nonie gazed at him, a mixture of incredulity and astonishment. She was longing to believe what he was telling her right now. Longing to but hardly daring to.

"I just couldn't seem to get through to you. You were so independent I just got nowhere and I thought I'd go crazy with the sheer frustration of it."

"But, Jacey, I didn't know. How could I *know*?"

"We always seemed to be striking sparks off each other and the situation never seemed right for telling you how I felt. And then you said you were going to leave as soon as Raynor and Ilse could get along without you, and I knew then that you would never feel for me the way I was feeling about you."

"But I did, Jacey. I do. I love you, I love you."

"I reckoned, though that if I could somehow buy some more time, I'd *make* you care, I'd *make* you love me, just a little bit. Goodness knows how I was going to do it but I certainly had to keep you here somehow."

"Jacey, *darling* Jacey, you didn't have to *make* me."

"No? 'There's nothing for me here,' you said. Those were your very own words, Nonie."

"*Because* I cared," she told him urgently. "*Because* I loved you. I couldn't stay down there at the bottom of the valley with you and Delphine up here, not possibly. How could I, loving you as I do? I knew I'd have to go when I . . . when she . . . well, I just knew I'd have to, because life would have been too unbearable being so close to you and unable to share things with you, having to watch you sharing your life with someone else and unable ever to let you suspect in the smallest degree how I felt."

"She said something to you, didn't she? Delphine? Something pretty positive, it must have been, to make you so unswerving in your decision to go. You don't have to answer if you don't want to, Nonie. I *know* she did, and I heard enough out there on the veranda to make doubly sure that my suspicions weren't unfounded. Dear heaven! I wish I could think straight." He passed a weary hand over his eyes. "That damned drug of Trevor's just adds to the muddle. Look here, Nonie, it seems to me, if I hadn't gone out there to the veranda just now and stopped you, you'd have walked right out of my life."

"Only because I loved you. Only because I didn't *know*."

"Hmm. And where would you have gone, fo interest?"

"I don't know. I hadn't really thought about where."

"Well, wherever it was I'd have found you. I'd hav tracked you down and brought you back and made yo learn how to love me."

"I love you already, Jacey, I don't have to learn how. couldn't love you more than I do. It's the most tender wonderful, painful thing that's ever happened to me. Th only greater pain would be leaving you."

"You won't, will you, Nonie? You *will* marry me, b my wife? Trevor was right; it was one hell of a strange proposal out there on the veranda. I muffed the thing bit but I had to stop you leaving at all costs and I hadn' time to consider any finesse. There were too many people around and anyhow, I didn't know then how *you* felt ei ther. I just had to take a chance on it. Will you be m wife, please, Nonie?"

"If that's what you really want."

"Want? Good Lord, what does one do to convince you?" He kissed her then, long and tenderly and wonder fully, with a quiet, possessive skill that caused Nonie to cling to him in a way that she wouldn't have dared ever hours ago and to return his kiss with an almost instinctive passion.

"By God, you do love me, after all, you deceiving little minx," he told her thickly when they finally drew apart. "We'll get married as soon as we can arrange it. A big wedding if you like, or a small one, just whatever way you want it to be, my darling."

"A small one, please, Jacey. Raynor could . . . could give me away, couldn't he? I'd like it in a church, though."

"And we'll have Pru for our little attendant and Trevor will be my best man."

"Trevor? Is that the doctor? He's really sweet, and I don't even know his other name."

"Trevor Kendrick. I owe him a lot."

"So do I," said Nonie, with a sudden mischievous smile. "He gave me the courage to come in to see you just now. He said you loved me, and he told me to come in here and cheer you up. If he hadn't been so convincing about it, I don't think I'd have dared. I couldn't believe it."

"He's been in my confidence for a long time, and of course I've seen him pretty frequently on Raynor's behalf too. He says he wants to get Ray into hospital for some tests tomorrow but more to confirm what he already knows than because he's worried that he'll slip back at this stage. Where is he now?"

"Raynor? He's with Ilse on the front veranda, I think. Hattie was helping Mrs. Parsons to make up some beds."

"I'll have to see him after I've had a bit of a nap to get my mind clear. Among other things I want to thank him for coming in and helping me out of that hellhole. When I saw your trunk and all those things you'd been cleaning with Ilse piled up on the side lawn and then looked and saw you weren't with the others, I was so *sure* you were in there—"

"Don't think about it," Nonie said quickly, sensing the anguish that this line of thought was recapturing.

"No, I'll think about you instead. About *us*. I'm sorry about the house, though, Nonie. It meant a lot to you, didn't it?"

"Only because I'd built up a lot of foolish sentiment around it. Dear old Tuckarimba. It served its purpose by bringing us together, didn't it, and helping Raynor to walk again? I'll always remember it with love and gratitude, but I'm not looking back anymore, Jacey. Only forward to when you and I can be really together as man and wife."

"Mrs. J.C. Lomax." Jacey's hand sought hers. "Nonie?"

"Yes, Jacey."

"Nonie, if I go to sleep right now, will you still be ther when I wake up?"

"Yes, my darling, I'll be here."

"You're quite sure about that?"

"Quite sure," she replied softly. "I'll always be here for as long as you need me."

"For a lifetime, then," said Jacey firmly, and his brow fingers tightened over hers, making quite certain that sh would stay right there beside him as he drifted off t sleep.

HOLD ME CAPTIVE

Hold Me Captive

Margaret Pargeter

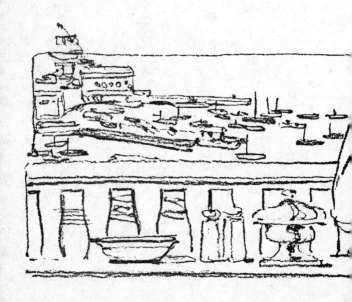

Veronica had gone too far this time! Amanda wouldn't stay and be insulted! She packed her bags and left her sister's apartment, flight uppermost in her mind and sensible planning taking a back seat.

She'd go to her father's house in Dartmoor. Amanda could stay there alone until her father and stepmother returned. But she arrived wishing she hadn't acted so hastily: the house was locked tight and a blizzard was beginning to rage.

So, totally snowbound, Amanda found herself under the roof of one Jason Meade – the most arrogantly disturbing man she'd ever met! Enforced intimacy with such a man threatened to play havoc with her heart – and did.

CHAPTER ONE

AMANDA TRENT had just had a bath. Relaxed and smelling sweetly of her favorite bath essence, she was anything but prepared for the sound of stealthy footsteps on the corridor outside. So far as she knew she was entirely alone in the flat. Head flung back, sapphire blue eyes startled, she listened. There was, along the corridor, a loose board that creaked when trodden on, and it was definitely creaking now!

"Is anyone there?" she called loudly, suddenly finding her voice, her frantic cry as she grabbed her white bathrobe a mixture of bewilderment and fear.

The lock on the bathroom door hadn't been entirely reliable for some time, but when two girls occupied a flat such a matter was not of paramount importance. Usually the tightly closed door was enough to indicate that the small room was occupied. In fact Amanda, since returning from America three weeks ago, had forgotten that the lock gave beneath the slightest push. And if she had remembered she would only have shrugged and said it didn't matter. The flat was leased, and the lease was not to be renewed. One faulty lock was neither here nor there. There was only her sister, Veronica, and Veronica's new husband, Herman, and they would be the last people on earth to intrude.

To Amanda's dismay the footsteps drew nearer, halting abruptly directly outside the door. Nervously fascinated, quite unable to look away, she stared, now feeling trapped and utterly frightened. Veronica and Herman had not intended coming home for dinner this evening.

They'd arranged to meet in the West End after work an have a meal out. Yet who else could it be but Veronica She must have returned for something. It wasn't impossi ble. Amanda's mind reeled, clinging in thought to her sis ter. No one had answered her short, sharp query, bu surely it must be she who was there?

Only three months ago Veronica had married Herma Allen from the American embassy. Veronica, at thirty five, was fifteen years older than Amanda, and Herma was her second husband. Her first marriage had ended i divorce. Amanda's mother had died when she was born leaving her to be brought up by a somewhat elderly rela tion who hadn't really cared very much. But since their fa ther had married again when Amanda was sixteen she ha lived with Veronica in this flat, apart from the time sh had spent abroad.

During the past two years, while she had been away Amanda had been almost too busy to acquire so much a a boyfriend; nevertheless she was happy for Veronica even if she had reservations about Herman. In the shor time she had known him she had found him amiable somewhat lacking in purpose. Moreover, he had raised no objections when Veronica had asked that Amanda be al lowed to accompany them back to America. Veronic had pleaded and Amanda, until this moment, when the bathroom door jerked suddenly open, had been quite willing. But not now. Certainly not now!

Amanda knew it would be impossible as soon as Her man stepped over the threshold, a wide, facetious gri stuck on his oversmooth, over-cared-for face, lookin very much like a fox trying to fool an unsuspecting chick en. Her momentary relief faded as the thought pierce sharply and she shivered in spite of the heat of the room eyeing him warily, yet not willing, even at this stage, t jump to the wrong conclusions. There could be some sim ple explanation.

The bathrobe didn't cover her neatly. It caught and clung to one damp shoulder, for an instant exposing a whiteness of skin, a glimpse of enticing curves that were partly responsible for the sex appeal she didn't know she possessed but which Herman was hard put to it to resist. One quick, impatient tug wrapped her safely within the ample coverage of soft toweling, and her voice was tinged with the same impatience as she asked shortly, "Did you want something, Herman? I did shout, and you must have heard me?"

He was unperturbed; the facetious grin broadened into something slightly different. For a second he halted, his eyes lifting to Amanda's face, around which her short dark hair was a shining cap, his gaze lingering on the satiny texture of her cheeks, her eyes fringed with thick, silky lashes. That her sensitively shaped mouth with its short upper lip was in no way relaxed, he didn't appear to notice. "Veronica is out," he muttered thickly.

"Of course she is—you arranged to meet her, and you must know you shouldn't be here," Amanda retorted sharply, all in one breath, while her senses, screaming in protest, flashed red. Apprehension tore along her nerves, yet she knew she must try to handle this with delicacy. Otherwise the whole silly thing could explode into a nightmare. Never had she experienced anything like this before, but there must be ways and means, if she kept her head. Staring at him coolly, she forced a slight smile. "If you'll kindly remove yourself, Herman, I'll join you in a moment. Then, if there's anything I can do...?"

It seemed inevitable that her tactics failed. "There's a whole lot you can do, honey!" He moved nearer, his eyes fixed on her figure, his tone heavily suggestive.

In fright, suddenly devastating, Amanda took notice of her built-in radar. She forgot about being tactful. Her voice rose an octave and came clearer. "Herman, you're being ridiculous! I told you to wait outside."

"And just supposing I don't want to?" Herman's fa
lower lip stuck out stubbornly. "You're quite a looker
honey. Sometimes I kind of wish I'd met you first, but we
could still have fun."

Disgust replaced temporarily Amanda's very real alarm
as she stared disbelievingly at the man who stood before
her. Had Herman taken leave of his senses? Wasn't he
aware that Veronica got jealous? Surely, if he loved hi
wife, he wasn't mad enough to jeopardize their whole fu
ture, to say nothing of any future relationship between his
wife and her sister! Veronica, if she ever learned about
this, would never believe Amanda had done nothing to
encourage him. The taut pain of disillusionment caught
Amanda and held her. Men, she decided irrationally
were all the same.

"One step nearer," she said coldly, her blue eyes
flashing, "and I'll tell Veronica about this myself!"

"You must be joking!" There was a sharp little silence
as, momentarily nonplussed, Herman halted. "Oh, come
on, honey, you've had no objections so far." His eyes lin
gered greedily on the smooth curve of Amanda's throat
the vibrant paleness of her skin.

"What on earth do you mean?"

"Well . . . you must know what I mean, honey!" Her
man's lips twisted smugly. "Why, since you got back
you've trailed Veronica and me around. I kinda got the
notion you were fond of me."

"Fond of you!" Amanda choked on a wave of pure indignation. He had a nerve! "Herman," she said clearly,
"you're quite mistaken. I hadn't given it a thought, one
way or another. I only went out with the two of you because you both insisted, and I thought Veronica would be
hurt if I refused. I think I was beginning to like you, but
don't get me wrong."

"Honey," Herman was smirking, "I don't think I have,
in spite of what you say. I'm an attractive man—a little
younger than your sister."

Amanda edged backward, her hands behind her, praying and groping. This scene had all the makings of some cheap charade, and she might need something more solid than her wits. Her fingers contacted and curled around an ornate marble candlestick.

"Honey...." All of a sudden he was too near, breathing all over her. "I think a girl like you needs somebody. Why not me, baby? You're beautiful, baby...."

Simultaneously, as he made a grab for her, Amanda lifted the candlestick, but before she could do anything with it Veronica shrieked from the doorway behind them. Long afterward that cry was to ring in Amanda's ears.

"You little slut!" Veronica screamed. "Just what do you think you're doing? How dare you entice poor Herman!"

Entice poor Herman? Wide-eyed with shock, Amanda stared at her sister. She had certainly done no such thing! She knew it; Veronica knew it, but she hadn't waited to discover the truth. Yet, in that split second of stunned silence, as she stood speechless, Amanda realized it was the only way out. Veronica's first marriage had failed—this one must not! Quite clearly, perhaps because she knew her so well, Amanda read her sister's thoughts. For Veronica to put any other construction on the sordid little scene in front of her would spell doom to her hopes of future happiness; all her well-laid plans. And along with that happiness would go her outraged pride, Veronica's exaggerated sense of dignity, which must be preserved, come what might.

But it wasn't altogether this that caused Amanda to restrain the hot denial that rose impulsively to her lips. In the fraction of time while this went through her head she remembered Veronica's kindness, her generosity in helping her after their father had married again. In the space of seconds, it seemed, she could make or break Veronica's marriage and, whatever happened, she could never

bear the responsibility of that. Of course there could be
just a chance that Veronica might be willing to see reason.
She said, rather desperately, "It wasn't quite as you
think, Veronica. You're jumping to all the wrong conclusions." Meant to be pacifying, the words came out stiffly.
Veronica was far from impressed.

"I suppose," she said icily, "that Herman thought the
bathroom empty and came in by mistake."

"Something like that...."

"Not really." Herman, who had stood looking dumb-
founded by his wife's unexpected appearance, now found
his tongue and added clumsily to the nightmare. "I heard
Amanda shout. It seemed she was in some kind of trouble. I didn't stop to think, darling, I just charged in."

And she had thought him slow-witted! Convulsively
Amanda swallowed a slither of pure hate, choking on a
suddenly dry throat. Any further protest seemed futile. "I
think I'll go and pack a case," she whispered, her face
white. "I guess I won't be going to America after all."

"You certainly won't! Not with us, at any rate." Veronica's furious reply hit Amanda sharply as she pushed past
her out of the room, and Herman was left behind as Veronica followed her down the passage into her bedroom.
In vain Amanda tried to stop her by closing the door.

Veronica burst it open, propelled, it seemed, by an unrestrained temper as she regarded Amanda's scantily clad
figure. It was almost as if she was seeing her for the first
time as a woman—grown and attractive, eclipsing the
schoolgirl image that she had clung to for so long. "I can
see now," she continued coldly when Amanda didn't
speak, "that it was a mistake to ask you to come with us in
the first place."

At that Amanda turned, unable to stop herself retort-
ing, "You only asked me to go because you know no one
in Washington and you were always terrified of being
lonely. You begged me to go! You might recall that I

wasn't too keen to go back again so soon. I only agreed because I didn't want to hurt you by refusing."

Veronica ignored this, going curtly on as though Amanda hadn't spoken. "You've changed! I hadn't realized how much, I should never have let you go with the Randalls. Obviously you've picked up habits you'd be better without."

Amanda's head spun. "The Randalls were your idea, too. You know that! They were your friends to begin with."

Hurt beyond speech, Amanda turned from her sister's coldly accusing face. Suddenly, in a lightning flashback over the brief years of her life, she saw that the most formative periods had been almost wholly directed by Veronica. Boarding school had been Veronica's idea, although she hadn't gone to one herself. Then, after their father had married again, hadn't it been Veronica who had suggested that Amanda should live with her at the flat? And it had been two years later, when Amanda left school, that she had begged her to go to America with the Randalls, people whom she had got to know through her work, who had been rather desperate to find a reliable au pair girl to look after their two children, while the Randalls, both scientists, did research work in Florida.

"It will only be for six months," she remembered Veronica saying. "It will give you a breathing space. Time enough to decide what you really want to do. Bill Randall did me a good turn once, so I do owe him something. Besides, it's not very convenient for me to have you around right now. I may be busy."

So without further protest Amanda had gone with the Randalls, but the six months had stretched into two years, during which they had been loath to part with her. Not until a letter had arrived from Veronica to say she had married again had Amanda suddenly realized she was twenty, and that life was somehow passing her by. With an urgent desire to return home came the knowledge that, very quickly, she must establish herself in some sort of career. That to remain in America, looking after children, wasn't exactly what she wanted. So she had left quickly, refusing to listen to the combined persuasions of the four Randalls, unwilling that they should make her change her mind.

Unfortunately she was to find her arrival in London marred by unforeseen problems. Because of Veronica's marriage she had anticipated staying with her father and stepmother on the small farm that Richard had inherited in Devon, but to her surprise Veronica had objected.

"You ought not to have come home, Amanda," she had said. "If you'd waited, instead of arriving out of the blue, you could have joined Herman and me in Washington. Herman has already promised to find you suitable employment, and you could also have helped me. Now we'll have the added expense of paying your fare back."

Amanda had only shrugged, not finding within herself the heart to argue, yet unable to completely understand Veronica's point of view. She had been married only three months. Didn't she and Herman want to be on their own? Surely Herman could provide all the companionship Veronica needed, as well as alleviate the loneliness she seemed so desperately afraid of? Yet, to her surprise, Herman had added his pleas to Veronica's, and Amanda, against her better judgment, had given in.

It was really the only thing she could do, Veronica had told her firmly. It would have been little use going down to Devon. Eva, their stepmother, definitely wouldn't want her. Nor were the neighbors, with one or two exceptions, very friendly, either. Daddy, of course, was always too busy, and Eva's word was law.

Amanda wasn't altogether gullible, but had decided it didn't really matter so very much. She had only spent two brief weekends on the farm herself, just before she had left school. It had rained heavily during both her visits, and her father had seemed preoccupied, not very interested in his young daughter. She couldn't remember much about Eva at all. She did remember, though, being secretly glad to return to London.

She had been determined, however, despite anything Veronica might say, to see the family before she went off again. But when she had announced her intentions, Veronica had explained that Richard, a well-known biologist, was in central Nepal, somewhere near Sikkim, and that Eva with him. They weren't expected home for another month. That had been almost three weeks ago, so it would be at least another week before they were back, Amanda calculated.

Now it seemed fairly obvious, family or no family, that she and Veronica had reached a parting of the ways, but before she went Amanda felt compelled to make one thing clear. Into the waiting silence she said quickly, "The Randalls are nice! Work was perhaps the only bad habit they indulged in. We never had time for anything else."

"You don't expect me to believe that!" Veronica raged. "To think I trusted you! I arranged to meet Herman this evening, as you know. What do you think I felt like when he didn't turn up?"

Hastily, feeling it futile to argue any further, Amanda snatched up an overnight bag, pushing into it a pair of pajamas, a few other odds and ends before removing her bathrobe and scrambling into some clothes. While she dressed she was aware of Veronica watching with coldly critical eyes. "You can send the rest of my things to Paddington," she said.

"You're not going to daddy!" Veronica's expression grew suddenly wary.

Jealousy again, Amanda decided, this time not really caring. If Veronica was so keen to be rid of her, could it matter where she went? She replied levelly, her voice de-

void of emotion, "As he's in Nepal that doesn't make
sense. Wherever I go, I can collect my luggage more con
veniently from Paddington. I might even go back to the
Randalls," she added rather wildly.

"I doubt they'd have you!"

"Maybe not. . . ." Wearily Amanda thrust bemused
fingers across her forehead glancing toward her large
trunk, already packed and labeled for America. "You'd
better tear those labels off," she said.

"With pleasure!" Clearly unforgiving, Veronica shut
her mouth sharply. "And I shouldn't advise you to go
near the family, not even when they return. Certainly I
shouldn't think they'd have you—not after they hear
what I have to tell them!"

Two days later, as Amanda sat on the train to Devon,
she could still see the wild, tormented anger on Veronica's face. It still seemed incredible that Veronica should
have gone to such lengths about one small incident, that
she had allowed her inborn jealousy to overrule common
sense and lead her to believe the worst. She had still been
throwing insults as Amanda left the flat. Herman had
been nowhere to be seen. Amanda shivered in spite of the
warmth of the train. Perhaps Veronica was not entirely to
blame. The fault must surely lie with Herman, or perhaps
it could be placed more squarely on her own head for allowing herself to be persuaded to go to America with
them in the first place!

Amanda had realized this as she had almost run from
the flat. She had known then there could be no going
back. That nothing anyone might say or do could retrieve
the situation. There was only one sensible thing to
do—absolutely imperative! She must keep out of Veronica's way. Even if Veronica had second thoughts and tried
to contact her. For everyone's sake Amanda knew she
must hide, and remain hidden until Veronica and Herman
sailed.

Amanda stirred unhappily on her second-class seat. For all her well-meant resolutions, she was still fond of her sister, and it didn't help to know that Veronica was trying to get in touch with her, might indeed even now be looking for her. Amanda had learned this when she had rung the elderly cousin who had been their housekeeper until daddy had married again. Quite suddenly Amanda had known an urge to see her. She had also hoped to find a bed for a few nights. Staying in a hotel, she found, was a rather lonely business.

Unfortunately the cousin had a friend staying with her and couldn't accommodate Amanda. She didn't sound as though she even wanted to, and Amanda soon found out why. "Veronica's been around," the old woman shouted down the line. "She's been looking for you everywhere. Said you'd run away. I don't want to be involved in any family quarrel!"

Quickly, with a mumbled word of thanks and farewell, Amanda had replaced the receiver, glancing furtively over her shoulder as she did so, half expecting Veronica to be lurking by her side. From that moment onward she had panicked. If Veronica was looking for her, then there was every chance she would find her, especially if Herman was to give a hand. Working at the embassy he might employ all kinds of tactics. And if Veronica wanted to find her it could only be to express a condescending forgiveness, to ask her to carry on with their plans as arranged. But Amanda knew quite clearly that she didn't want to go back to America, and definitely not now, not after the fiasco with Herman!

Yet, if Veronica were to find her, how could she explain all this? Amanda's brow had knitted in very real perplexity. All her life, or for as long as she could remember, she had allowed herself to be dominated by her sister's stronger personality. Now, although not so willing to be overruled, Amanda was genuinely apprehensive of facing her, having little real doubt that after such a meeting she would find herself agreeing weakly to anything Veronica suggested.

With what seemed to be a brilliant flash of insight Amanda knew there was only one place where she might hope to avoid her. Devonshire! With the family away there was no one in the house. In the circumstances it was the last place where Veronica would think of looking. She could stay there on her own without anyone knowing, and in three or four days' time, with Veronica and Herman gone, she would be safe. And she could scarcely be accused of breaking the law by hiding in her parents' home. Without stopping to consider the wisdom of such a plan, Amanda had, with great haste, packed a rucksack, paid her hotel bill and rushed to buy a ticket to the west country.

In the confined space of the compartment Amanda eased her long, slim legs as best she could and sighed. In retrospect this was all probably quite ridiculous, and it was silly to pretend she had a guilty conscience, especially when for the first time in her life she felt really free. Veronica was happily married and would be much better without her. Once in America she would soon settle down and make new friends. America was a very wonderful experience for anyone, married or single. Veronica would soon become absorbed in her new life and forget all about her young sister and one stupid little incident in a bathroom.

In a way, Amanda mused, lulled by the rhythm of iron wheels on an iron track, to stay at Combe Farm on her own was probably the best idea she had had for some time. It would certainly give her time to decide exactly what she was going to do. The salary that the Randalls had paid hadn't been very generous, although she had been treated as one of the family, but now she had very little left, just enough to see her through until she found another job, which shouldn't take long.

The train ran through Exeter and she left it at Newton Abbot to catch a bus. Unfortunately, after this, she made her first mistake by getting out at the wrong village and had to wait an hour for another bus!

"It's easily done," the driver commented when she ruefully related what had happened. "You're a stranger in these parts, then, miss?"

"Sort of..." she mumbled, aware of the man's curious stare, annoyed at having drawn attention to herself in this manner when it was essential she remained anonymous.

But much the same thing occurred when at last she arrived at Ashburton and went in search of a taxi. Because of the time she had so foolishly lost, the November afternoon was rapidly darkening and, to her dismay, Amanda found she could remember few landmarks in the bleak countryside. A taxi would appear to be essential. Deliberately she had timed her arrival, hoping that in the dusk of late afternoon no one would notice her, but she had forgotten just how dark a country area could be. Such secrecy, she realized, might be silly, yet she knew that in small communities, especially during winter, a stranger was quickly noticed. Should Veronica, pursuing every possibility, ring up a friend in the neighborhood, then she might easily learn of Amanda's presence and come to the right conclusions. Determined to eliminate even the slightest risk, Amanda resolved to take every precaution!

Surely it must be the easiest thing in the world to slip into a taxi without undue comment? Amanda had done it dozens of times. This taxi driver, however, seemed to regard her bedraggled appearance, her lack of luggage with suspicion. So much suspicion, it seemed, that he asked her twice about it, obviously not satisfied with her evasive reply. But how could she explain to the man, if indeed it was any of his business, that she hadn't any luggage because her sister hadn't sent it to Paddington, or anywhere else, so far as she could discover? It seemed clear that Veronica was hanging onto it until the last moment, and it was this fact above all others that convinced Amanda that Veronica was continuing with her search.

"I just want to go a few miles down the road," she muttered as she climbed in beside him, hoping vaguely he wouldn't probe any further. Despite the dampness of her apparel she was startled that the man evidently mistook her for a boy, addressing her as "young fellow," a mistake that Amanda, on second thoughts, decided not to rectify. As a boy she might be safer from suspicion.

"I can't think where you can be off to on a night like this!" the man retorted gruffly, casting a sideways glance over a shivering Amanda. "Do you know what time it is?"

"It's only five o'clock," Amanda protested with some bewilderment, keeping her voice low.

"Five o'clock," the man snorted, "on a November night on Dartmoor. Rain and snow coming down! Just proves how much sense you've got. Beats me why a young fellow like yourself wouldn't choose to stay at home. You look as though a whiff of wind would blow you away."

Amanda shrugged, with more bravado than she actually felt. The man was probably right, although she would have died rather than admit it. The weather was really vile and she felt chilled to the bone, and longed suddenly for a hot bath and a meal, in that order. In her rucksack she had food, enough to last for several days, and, once in the house, she would soon have a fire going. She refused to dwell on the possibility that the place might be barred up too thoroughly for her to get in. She could scarcely ask this man to wait—or to assist her in breaking and entering!

Through the driving wind and snow she thought she saw a sign that said Combe Farm. She couldn't be sure, but when she asked the driver he nodded and she immediately asked to be put down. "I'll walk the few yards back," she told him, pressing the fare into his hand. "I might even go on a bit farther." Her deliberate attempt to mislead him was to be her undoing, only she didn't realize it until afterward.

Once out on the cold, dark road her wavering confidence deserted her as the craziness of her plan suddenly hit her. The taxi waited obligingly until she found her torch, then roared off with a derisive farewell hoot into the night, leaving her standing, a solitary figure, enveloped in a shroud of swirling snow.

Momentarily Amanda remained where she was until her eyes grew accustomed to the gray light. Her father had inherited this small estate shortly after he had remarried and, without hesitation, had sold his London home and moved in. This had been almost five years ago. Now, with a peculiar ache in her heart, Amanda wished things had been different, that she had gone with them. One could scarcely blame Eva for not taking much interest in a stepdaughter who had shown no great desire to know her. Amanda shrugged, as she started off. Might not it all be wishful thinking? Veronica had spent a lot of time here while Amanda had been in America, and she had remarked on several occasions that Eva hadn't put herself out to be kind. Amanda's own two weekends she could barely remember, and she didn't suppose there was much point in thinking about them now as she trudged along.

The brunt of the storm didn't seem to hit her until she turned the first bend. There she caught the full force of sleet and wind, a full concentration of the elements that battered and spun her until she stumbled and fell hard into an overgrown ditch. Feeling decidedly the worse for wear, she pulled herself out, laughing almost hysterically at her plight, aware of soft tears mingling with the rain on her cheeks. Quickly she sobered up, suddenly frightened. If she didn't pull herself together, she might still be lying here come morning. People still perished in storms, and she still had some way to go. With determination she forced her tired legs to continue, running and slithering along the last few yards of lane. Until, with a final spurt she reached the house. Relief, swift and palpitating washed over her, and she moved, a sudden rush, her hair beneath her woolen cap haloed with snow, blue denim jacket plastered about her, wet through, yet staring at the house, a black shape, scarcely discernible, looming through the darkness in front of her.

Coming to a sudden halt, she swept a slightly shaking hand across her face, brushing the snow from her lashes, and with it a long strand of wet hair from her eyes. Her fingers caught the edge of her cap, lifting it slightly, and the rising wind did the rest, whipping it from her head, blowing it away. Oh, well, what did it matter? She was home now. Why bother about the loss of one small hat?

All the same, the rain through her hair was uncomfortable, even though the rest of her was soaked. Taking a few tentative steps forward, she flashed her torch around, surveying the old stone facade of the house. The sooner she was inside the better. She was probably no less susceptible to pneumonia than anyone else.

It was quite obvious that the place was deserted. Although Amanda had known what to expect, she could not suppress a faint shudder of dismay as her glance fell on the unlit windows. A light in just one of them, she thought wistfully, would have been a most welcome sight. It soon became equally obvious that the doors were all locked securely. Stumbling against one, she gave a gigantic push, but it didn't budge an inch. It was then that she recalled vaguely an attic window that had always been open. Just slightly open, but Eva had complained that the rain came in and ran through to the bedroom below, and no one, she had said, would see about getting it repaired!

Daddy had never repaired anything in his life! It had been a family joke, and Amanda prayed—actually prayed—he hadn't changed. There might be a chance, if only slight, that the window would still be the same.

Several minutes later, having negotiated the back of the house and found a ladder, Amanda stared almost happily up at the window, relieved to find it was much as it used to be. In the wavering light from her torch she noted the slight gap between the top of the window and the frame that others might not have noticed if they hadn't known what to look for. "Thank goodness for that," said Amanda aloud.

The window, set in the sloping attic roof, wasn't so high, but without a ladder it would have been impossible to climb up. It had been, she silently acknowledged, a slice of sheer luck to have found one so handy, and rather fervently she hoped her luck would hold. The roof looked slippery, half covered as it was with snow, but if she was careful it should present no insurmountable problem.

The ladder was very like the one that she had used often when working for the Randalls. The twins had been overfond of climbing trees! Gently she eased out the extension, working as quickly as she could with frozen fingers, then propped it against the wall. It appeared secure when she tested it. With only a dim light it was difficult to be sure. She must just try it and see.

Lifting her rucksack firmly onto her back, she crawled up the rungs, her body shivering in its thin covering. Desperately she was beginning to realize she had to get in—her head felt most peculiar. If she couldn't reach the attic window, then she must break in down below. Perhaps she had been foolish not to do so in the first place.

Concentrating completely on the task in front of her, Amanda never heard the footsteps beneath her. Perhaps, on the blanket of freshly fallen snow, the man's light approach had been silent, any sound impossible to hear above the wild howl of the wind. Whatever it was, she was totally unprepared for the threatening shout that rang

thunderously in her ears. A voice, which seemed to hol
more force than the storm itself, demanded to know wha
she was up to.

Afterward, a long time afterward, Amanda was to re
gard the phrasing of that question with some amusemen
but her views, in retrospect, were far divorced from he
terror in that panic-stricken moment. A moment whe
her heart jerked in her breast with a frightening intensity
and her numbed hands lost their grip on the thin woode
slats. In the split second, as she turned, in a blind panic
her glance fell on the man below. Illuminated in the ligh
from the storm lantern he held, he appeared huge, men
acing, a pagan image straight from some heathen corne
of Dartmoor. It was there in his face, curiously etche
against the darkness, brutally at one with the elements.

"Come down off that ladder," he repeated, "or I'll ti
you straight off into the snow!"

That cool, controlled voice had a ludicrous effect. Sh
stiffened into rigidity, her hands slipping as she lost he
balance. Then she was falling, her feet slithering from th
ladder, and her voice, released suddenly from the froze
regions of her throat, came with a wild cry of despair
There was only a fraction of time, just one flash of aware
ness before she fell, enveloped in his answering shout o
impatience. Then her head hit the corner of a jutting
piece of roof and there came merciful oblivion. She knew
nothing of the strong arms that enfolded her as her uncon
scious body tumbled the last few feet to the ground.

SHE CAME TO A LITTLE WHILE LATER, conscious of pain, o
someone forcing brandy between her cold lips. The same
person was holding her firmly, in some enclosed space
sheltered from the storm. This was only a fleeting impression as she lifted weighted eyelids, as she attempted to see
clearly the face floating above her own. It seemed there
might be a thread of relief in the voice that spoke to her.

"When I told you to come down off that ladder, I didn't nean you to take me so literally, young man! We don't ake too kindly to intruders in this part of the world, but ve don't wish them any particular harm. The police will leal with you."

Helplessly Amanda knew she must have dreamt that hread of relief. Indignant anger surged in spite of the awul pain at the side of her head. It registered vaguely that, ike the taxi driver, he thought she was a boy, but not even this seemed to justify his brutal comment. His face still swam hazily, and it could have been the brandy that gave her the strength to retort sharply, "I could have been killed. You choose not to think of that!"

She might have known he would have the diabolical nerve to grin maliciously, "But you weren't were you? Perhaps you deserve to be worse than you are. Young vagabonds who roam the countryside should learn not to complain if fate doesn't always deal with them kindly. You break into property, then expect the owner to take a lenient view. If I had my way, youths like you would all be under lock and key."

Over Amanda was sweeping a peculiar nausea that she strove to control. Her teeth were chattering, the pain in her head unbearable, yet from somewhere she gathered enough courage to reply, "It's men like you who ought to be shut up!" Her remark might be quite unreasonable, she knew, but somehow, if such a thing were possible, it made her feel better.

She didn't allow for the manner in which his arms fell away with a punishing abruptness, and without support she slumped back, unable to save herself. Faintly, above a strange roaring in her ears, she heard his muttered expletive as he grabbed her roughly again. This time he propped her up harshly on the seat of the Land Rover, securing a seat belt tightly around her, pushing her head

CHAPTER TWO

AMANDA'S HEAD ACHED. On second thoughts it didn't actually ache, it pounded, and her whole body seemed to be throbbing with heat. Suddenly frightened, she lay quite still, not knowing where she was, suspended in space like some lost spirit crying out for recognition. Where was she—what was she doing here? She was only aware that she lay on something soft. This much was slowly becoming apparent.

She took a deep breath and it hurt, so carefully she tried to open her eyes. There was a light above her head. It swirled, filling her whole vision, almost blinding her. It was a pitiless, dancing light, creating bizarre images, demigods who rose up and shrieked at her. They were potentially dangerous, so quietly, so they wouldn't notice, she let her heavy lashes fall, concentrating wholly with her mind.

Feeling totally inadequate she tried to marshal her wayward illusions into some semblance of order. With nervous hands, as if she were playing a game, she attempted to explore her immediate vicinity. It might be she was hurt in some way and was lying on a bed. Surely nothing else could be so comfortable, and there were pillows, she thought, beneath her head. Cautiously, like some small child afraid of the unknown, she turned onto her side hoping that the movement, any movement, would jerk some hidden chord of her memory. As if to assist it she forced her reluctant thoughts backward until, with another flash of blinding light, it came, so easily, so devastatingly, like an avalanche, bringing with it shock and total consternation.

With the gasp that escaped her taut lips, Amanda's fingers went swiftly to her temples, attempting to block out the picture of her own folly—to soften the blow.

How could she have been so foolish? For one brief second she prayed this might be a nightmare from which she would wake up. The farm, the house, the window and the ladder all came back to taunt her, parading with the cruel demons who already mocked her. Then as her demons paraded, there came the shape of one who had shouted. The human one, who had caused her to fall and hurt her head. A man with a face as dark as the night about him!

"Oh, no . . . " she moaned aloud, as full realization followed quickly, flooding her memory with every tiny detail. How could he have known she was there? Perhaps she was already in the hands of the police, about to be accused of breaking and entering—something that she'd joked about previously. Or worse still, whoever it was who had waylaid her had probably already contacted the flat. Veronica could be on her way! "Oh, no," Amanda repeated again, despairingly.

With renewed alarm she forced her eyes open, this time to focus clearly on her immediate surroundings. The room was large, obviously a bedroom, and comfortably though plainly furnished. But not Combe Farm, of that she was certain. She couldn't recall any apartment such as this. The bed was king-size, huge and canopied, she herself a small ridge in the middle of it. The carpet seemed deep with a smooth pile, and across the windows the curtains hung in wide folds of fine, soft velvet, effectively muting the sounds of the storm outside.

Nervously Amanda stirred, dragging her eyes away from the window. The central heating must be turned up because she was hot—too hot. Unless it was the thought of Veronica that caused the heat to pour through her aching body. Surely a blow on the head couldn't be sufficient to make her feel like this? Rather desperately she pushed back against her pillows, struggling to sit upright. Where was everybody? Oughtn't there to be someone here? It seemed she had been abandoned, left to die, while whoever it was who had brought her here regaled himself in another part of the house.

Her eyes wide, the pupils dilated like a young gazelle ready for flight, Amanda tensed, waiting, but there was only silence, apart from the fiendish scream of the wind. Then gradually a vibration impinged upon her ears, growing louder and louder. Somewhere in the house a telephone was ringing, the stringent tones echoing shrilly, until suddenly it stopped. Someone had apparently picked up the receiver, although she could hear no sound of a voice.

Swiftly, making up her mind in one impulsive moment, she flung back the sheets that covered her and rolled out of bed, fighting the wave of faintness that caught her as she swung her feet to the ground. Steadying herself, she stared with some bewilderment at the clothes she was wearing. She was dressed in what appeared to be a man's pajama jacket. Smooth, like silk, a beautiful fine material, which clung to her slender figure, reaching almost to her knees. Below it her long, slim legs were bare, the skin flawless, still faintly tanned from her stay in America. Apart from this one thin garment she didn't have another stitch on. Whoever had undressed her had done a thorough job!

Regaining her balance after a few seconds, although still feeling decidedly peculiar, Amanda made her way toward the door. No good could come of contemplating that which could not be helped. Obviously she must have been wet through, and after all, it had been her own silly fault. It was essential now that she find the lady of the house, to thank her as quickly as possible before arranging to be on her way. No doubt the people here would be glad to see the last of her.

After letting herself silently out onto the narrow corridor she stood very still, her well-shaped head on one side, listening. Somewhere down in the lower regions someone was talking. The sound was faint, but she could definitely hear it. Stealthily, on bare feet, Amanda crept along the passage, a little nearer to the top of the stairs. Here the stout oaken balustrade allowed her to look down into the hall below.

As she had suspected, someone was using the telephone. As she craned forward, her forehead pressed against the wooden slats, an almost audible exclamation escaped her. She could see the man who was speaking, not very clearly as he had his back toward her, but she had little doubt, from the extreme darkness of his head, the forcefulness of his voice, that it was the same man who had been the cause of all her misfortunes. The same man who'd tipped her off the ladder, perhaps inadvertently, but he had been responsible all the same. It was he, she felt sure, who had literally dosed her with brandy and held her with such indifferent detachment when she had been sick.

For a moment, too stunned to move, Amanda stared, clutching the rails tightly with agitated fingers. This house, wherever it was, must belong to him. If nothing else his careless demeanor against the telephone proclaimed it. Of course she might have guessed he would bring her here, considering the way he'd almost thrown her into his Land Rover, but her mind was still confused, the events of the last few hours coming back only slowly.

Then suddenly, as she leaned nearer pondering with some bewilderment on a suitable course of action, she heard him saying quite clearly to the person he was talking to, "You have no reason to worry, Veronica. I can assure you that everything is as it should be. I had a card from Richard only this morning. He doesn't expect to be home for another week, so it would be pointless to come down, especially when you're so busy arranging to get away. If it's any consolation there's a storm raging and I should think we might be cut off for several days. You know what storms can be like on Dartmoor."

Veronica? In the slight pause that followed, as he listened while his caller answered, Amanda remained tense with apprehension. It must be her sister! The bit about Richard, who was their father, confirmed it. It would be a remarkable coincidence if this was not so. Intently she concentrated, every nerve tight. The man was speaking again, his voice even from this distance seemingly lighter.

"I quite agree, Veronica, you can't let Herman down. You must go to America. Herman certainly won't want to go alone. And if you sail in four days' time Richard wouldn't expect you to make a special trip in weather like this just to see that the farm's okay, although I'll tell him you rang."

Another pause, then his voice again, softly ironical yet with undertones of laughter. "A bride of three months ought not to say such things, my dear. If circumstances had been different, who knows." His wide shoulders lifted, indicating a faintly rueful smile at the corners of his mouth. "As it is," he continued, "I'll look forward to seeing you when you come back."

How dared he! Blind anger did nothing to disperse Amanda's general feeling of delirium. The whole situation seemed even more incongruous than it had a few minutes ago. How dared he make love to Veronica, because that, as clear as daylight, was what he'd been up to! Amanda might reluctantly confess to being without a deal of experience, but she was no fool. The tender, anticipatory note in his voice spoke for itself. Every syllable had held a caress—were all men tarred with the same brush! First Herman—now him! Furiously from her lofty perch, Amanda flung down total condemnation, in that instance completely disillusioned with every man she could think of.

Not until a long time afterward did she stop to consider Veronica's part in that little intrigue. As the murmur of the man's deep voice continued, Amanda's only concern after her first wrath was that Veronica should not discover she was here. For four days, until Veronica and Herman sailed, she must contrive to preserve some anonymity whatever the cost. Perhaps in a way it had been decreed by a protective God that she should overhear this telephone conversation. Otherwise she might never have known of the friendship between Veronica and the man below, and to be forewarned was to be forearmed, or so it was said!

Swiftly, feeling fractionally better, Amanda turned, intent on preserving what secrecy she could. Then suddenly, to her utter chagrin, she sneezed—not a delicate, orientated kind of sneeze that might have passed unnoticed, but a loudly undignified paroxysm of sound, guaranteed to attract attention. The gods, it would seem, had deserted her!

To Amanda, crouching palpitating among the shadows, the dropping of the telephone receiver was an explosion in her ears. The relegating sound of plastic hitting plastic as the man swung abruptly, his eyes, across the dividing space, pinning hers, his glance the calculating glance of a stranger. Unable to stir, her heartbeats magnified by her heightening awareness, she was struck immobile by the weight of a peculiar tension. Even from here she could see that his was a hard, handsome face, the face of a man totally self-reliant, with the ability to hit always harder than his opponent. Tall, dark, broad-shouldered, lean hipped, virile . . . Amanda thought she might go on forever. He was also, she told herself severely, for fear some part of her got the wrong impression, a philanderer. Not a trait to be admired under any circumstances!

Only this much had she time to digest as, without removing his eyes from her face, he was up the stairs in a

trice, one hand beneath her elbow, sweeping her ruthlessly to her feet, steadying her grimly when she lost her
balance. She flushed and foolishly resented getting caught
again.

"If you're not back to bed within seconds," he said,
"you'll wish to goodness that I'd left you to perish in the
snow!" He took no notice of her flushed cheeks, her
faintly indignant air, as he thrust her before him sharply
down the passage like a bundle of rags he could dispose of
at any minute should he so wish.

Once in the large bedroom, Amanda tried to shake off
his hand. The whole of her body was throbbing with heat
and a sickly kind of excitement. It seemed a ridiculous
moment to tell herself she'd never cared for a man with
green eyes. Beautiful eyes, clear and luminous though his
might be, they held all the coolness of a rock pool and
were just about as intimidating. She turned a vivid face to
him, determined he shouldn't guess how ill she was feeling.

"I don't want to go back to bed, and you can't make
me! I must be on my way. If I might have my clothes, then
perhaps I can thank your wife for her assistance. I'd be
very much obliged if you would also ring for a taxi."

"I don't have any wife." He watched her narrowly, his
tone mild enough, even slightly bored. He ignored her request for clothing and a taxi. He didn't even ask if she felt
strong enough to travel. Obviously her state of health was
a matter of sheer indifference to him.

Heavily Amanda floundered, her thoughts going
around in circles. "No wife?" she repeated stupidly, with
an almost vague bewilderment. Somehow she had known
a man like this would be married. He must be well into his
thirties and the type that would appeal to most women,
and his was surely a face of some experience, of diabolical
self-assurance. It seemed she had jumped to the wrong
conclusions. She remembered his conversation with Ve-

ronica. Apparently he indulged in affairs with other men
wives, thus relegating the necessity of having one of h
own. Tentatively she tried again. "Your mother, then, c
whoever it is who runs the house for you?"

"No mother, either. I live on my own." The green eye
seemed to dance ironically, or it might have been a tric
of the light. "I'm sure such a circumstance shouldn'
worry an independent young lady like you."

Stunned, Amanda sank down onto the bed agains
which she had been defiantly standing. She closed he
eyes, attempting to shut out his derisive face as shoc
raced through her. She was creamy pale, her forehea
faintly beaded with perspiration. If there was no woma
in the house, then who had undressed her? She certainl
hadn't been wearing a pajama top when she'd arrived a
Combe Farm! Surely this man couldn't have—wouldn'
have . . . ? Why, she didn't even know his name. Nor di
she particularly want to. She couldn't even bear to thin
that he had touched her. She had been uncon
scious—there lay the only grain of comfort. Making a su
perhuman effort, she opened her eyes wide and looke
straight at him. Quite clearly, from the expression in his
he had read her thoughts. "You appear to find it amusing
Mr., er, whoever you are!" She thought her tone of voic
devastating.

He gave a short laugh, the glint in his eye deepening
"If you'd chosen to mention that you were a girl it woul
have made little difference. You were wet through
scarcely the time for false modesty. Even now I shoul
think you're running quite a high temperature, and ye
you talk of being on your way! Why, you haven't even go
a penny in your pocket!"

Alarm jerked Amanda up to her feet again as a tremo
shot through her—a surge of dismay, quickly to be re
placed by sheer fright. In her handbag she had had quite a
sum of money, more probably, than it had been wise to

carry, and certainly enough to meet any contingency. More than enough to take her to the nearest hotel, where she should have had the sense to go in the first place! Yet this man said he hadn't found a penny. "My bag?" she gasped, her eyes dilated pools of blank dismay.

"If you mean your rucksack," he muttered dryly, "which was all you had with you, I went through that very thoroughly. I presumed to find some form of identity—a telephone number, perhaps. Somewhere where I might have contacted anxious parents. But all you appeared to possess was a meager supply of basic rations. Like most of your kind you obviously choose to travel light."

His mouth compressed as his eyes traveled over her, filled with censure, yet with a hint of something else. Amanda, however, didn't notice, nor for a second did she speak; his unflattering remarks went over her head. Desperately anxious about her handbag, she couldn't think where it might have gone. Only vaguely did she seem to recall leaving the taxi. The lane to the farm was only a snow-filled memory, too hazy to reconstruct. No matter how she applied herself she couldn't remember losing her handbag, and to have lost it she must! Instinctively she knew that this man, who had chosen not to give his name when she had almost pointedly asked, was not a thief. He might have taken her pride when he had removed her clothing, but anything he chose to steal would have no relative value. She must take into account, of course, that he was totally ruthless—it was there in the set of his head, the brilliance of his gaze, the taut line of his well-shaped, sensuous mouth. Whatever happened, she vowed as she had vowed before, he mustn't discover her identity. The loss of her bag would be minimal compared with the disastrous repercussions of this! To be hauled back to town by Veronica, who could be strangely persuasive when it came to getting her own way, was more than Amanda dared think about. Anything—almost anything—was preferable to that.

Hopefully, controlling an inner agitation, she glanced at her inquisitor, intent on evasion while retaining a modicum of truth. "I have no anxious parents," she murmured carefully. "I did have a very little money, but it seems I must have dropped it somewhere. Perhaps I could borrow a few pounds? Just enough to see me through. I should only be a nuisance if I stayed here."

His brilliant glance met hers, staying on her transparent young face. "You're already that," he mocked bluntly. "You and your kind are a nuisance to the community. I shouldn't wish to be personally responsible for inflicting you upon them. Country people have enough to do in weather like this without adding to their burdens. Besides, if I were to lend you money, what chance would I have of ever seeing it again?"

"You can't keep me here against my will!" Stung by his detestable attack, Amanda retaliated wildly, aroused beyond the limits of discretion, wanting to hurt him as he hurt her, even while realizing the futility of such an endeavor. He might have been kinder; he could have shown one twinge of compassion; it might have occurred to him that there could be extenuating circumstances. But no, his glance was wholly derisive, the glance of a man who had no time, or patience, with human frailty. Perhaps, Amanda admitted, he was justified in some of his opinions, but he hadn't given her the benefit of one single doubt. She might have been anyone lost or in distress, she didn't necessarily have to be a rootless delinquent, a vagabond roaming the face of the earth. Well, let him think what he liked! No longer did she feel in any way indebted to him. His unsparing condemnation had at least absolved her from that. "I'm sorry I asked you for anything," she added stiffly, resenting his watching cynicism. "Neither should I wish to worry your neighbors. If I could just have my clothes?"

"You're too ill." It was a statement, not to be questioned. His voice was smooth, on an even keel, containing, surprisingly, a thread of patience, almost as if something about the situation intrigued him in spite of himself. Almost as if he was prepared to humor her fractionally.

Yet she persisted. "If you think I'm ill, why don't you ring your local doctor? I'm sure you exaggerate, but he could set your mind at rest." She didn't add that a doctor might also provide a means of escape. If she appealed to him he might be persuaded to take her back to town.

"I was coming to that," his mouth shaped laconically. "I've been trying to get hold of a doctor all evening—for advice only, I might say—but all the roads are blocked with snow, he could never get here in person. Maybe you don't know about Dartmoor in a blizzard, but we locals have learned to treat such weather with respect."

With a sinking heart Amanda stared at him, not doubting the authenticity of what he said. Mutely she shook her head. There would seem to be no escape. Yet he couldn't expect her to give in gracefully, although did she have any other alternative? Not wishing to consider the complications of this point, she confessed fretfully, "I don't know anything about Dartmoor, in a storm or otherwise."

"Then when were you here?" he shot at her, his derisive tone having little regard for the precarious state of her health.

"Here—oh...." She glanced at him blankly a full minute before she understood. Quickly she looked away from him, something—surely not her wits, saving her. "I think it was during the summer, years ago."

"Years ago?" His voice was sharp with a kind of wary impatience. "You've certainly been to Combe Farm before, otherwise you wouldn't have known about that window. You couldn't have spotted it otherwise as it was almost covered with snow, and the chap with the taxi told me himself that it was already dark when he left you."

So that was how he had found out! He had some sort of liaison with that crabby old taxi driver! Bitterly she reflected he would never miss a thing. A mastermind for detail! The odd thing was he hadn't asked her name. A girl's only defense against a man like this would be to play it cool. He couldn't very well shake the information out of her. Dumbly she said, "All large houses have attic windows, usually with some defect. I was only guessing, and I happened to be lucky—or so I thought until you came along."

"You could have been luckier," he agreed blandly, his darkening expression indicating that he did not for one moment believe her sorry little tale. "You could have managed to creep inside, only to find a cold tomb of a house in which you might easily have perished."

"I could have switched on the electricity. I should soon have warmed up." Her widening eyes flew to his face, unconscious of how illogical her argument was.

"Wrong again, Miss Persistence." His green eyes were as malicious as a cat's. "The current is off, and the cupboard containing the switches padlocked. Next time, before you break into a building, you should check."

And he enjoyed even the mental spectacle of her freezing to death! He had the nerve to suggest she should be grateful, yet even his care hadn't prevented her from catching a terrible cold. Quickly she turned her head as she sneezed violently again. At that moment she could imagine no nicer fate than to be allowed to lie down quietly and die. "Next time," she murmured bitterly, "I'll do just that." She wasn't exactly sure to what she was alluding.

"That's better." A look of deliberation seemed to harden his face. "Who knows what other surprises you might have in store for you."

"You could be right!" How could she tell him she wanted no more surprises? Since she had arrived home from America life had been full of them, and none of them pleasant. For the life of her Amanda couldn't think how one thing could evolve so easily, yet mistakenly, from another. But the fact remained, she had been caught up in a series of silly events from which her own stupidity had in no way extricated her. Confused, she blinked into the dark, enigmatic face so near her own. "Nothing," she tacked on vaguely, "ever seems to turn out as one expects."

"Not when you're leading this sort of life!"

"Why, you sound just like my father!" Suddenly, unaccountably she giggled, unaware of his sharpening glance. Softly, as her slightly hysterical laughter subsided, the urge to argue further deserted her, and she stared at him again with some of her former bewilderment, all eyes, very large and expressive, as tormented as a turbulent summer sea. Familiar tremors were once more evading her limbs, and everything receded in the most peculiar fashion. Again the room started playing tricks, the ceiling wavering ridiculously, the floor coming up to meet her, and not to be outdone, the storm outside roaring with a most frightening loudness in her ears. It seemed all too much, combined with the impregnable strength of the man before her. She felt as weak as a kitten, and just as helpless under his dissecting green eyes. With the faintest of frowns etching her smooth brow, Amanda subsided back onto her bed and promptly passed out.

WHEN SHE WOKE IT WAS MORNING; she knew it was morning because of the change of light. It slanted from a different angle; not directly above her head anymore, and the quality was different, a cold, transparent gray, not interesting enough to invite further contemplation, so she prepared to go back to sleep. When someone spoke she knew a small, unreasonable surge of resentment.

"You're making too great a habit of this, young lady. I

warn you, if you pass out on me again I won't be responsible for my reactions."

The voice plummeted, discordant on her ears; smooth, of even timbre, nothing in the tone to disturb the superb aura of drowsy comfort that cocooned her like cotton wool. It was only the precise context of the words that she found irritating.

Slowly, from a vague feeling that it was expected of her, she opened her eyes, her wavering glance at first refusing to focus. Dark patches trembled until, through the mistiness, a man's face shaped from the shadows. That man! Shock caused her to blink, clearing miraculously last remnants of fog. This time the confusion disappeared completely, along with the cotton wool!

"Who are you?" she whispered, staring up at him, her pale fingers suddenly clutching his arm as if trying to convey that the question was important to her. Beneath the thin material of his shirt she could feel the hard muscles flexing, and a tremor shot through her. She couldn't remember whether he was friend or foe. He didn't appear to be either.

His green eyes regarded her with a great detachment, but he obliged, if a little ironically. "Jason Meade, at your service, ma'am. And yours?"

She couldn't mistake his meaning, but her own name curiously evaded her. A closed door refused to open in her mind. With a soft bewilderment she brushed taut fingers across her forehead. "I can't remember," she told him.

At once he withdrew, tilting backward in his chair so that her hand slid from his arm. Yet there lurked in his face a hint of impatient concern. "If I could believe that—" he frowned, his eyes intent on her face. "You gave yourself an almighty thump on your head. Can't you really recall a thing?"

"Of course . . . . " Amanda felt the nerves of her stomach tightening. She could remember so much! "It's just my name!"

"You could mean you don't want to tell me? For your information, I've nursed you through a day and a couple of nights. You could perhaps owe me that little bit of advice!"

Her widening eyes stayed on his face, the color intensifying as, startled, she attempted to concentrate. A day and two nights. If nothing else it meant Veronica hadn't yet sailed! Slowly, as she digested this, something else clicked into place. She was Amanda Trent, who must remain in hiding until her sister left for America. Indelibly on her subconsciousness must be impressed the need for continued silence—nothing else could have stopped her from giving herself away! This man employed devious methods. He had probed for information, knowing she was in no fit state to withhold it. Only her guardian angel could have saved her. He also supplied a fictitious name!

"I'm sorry," she whispered, hastily squashing an uncomfortable twinge of guilt that plagued her in spite of her neat calculations. "You're quite right, I do owe you something, and it's all coming back. I'm Miranda Smith." In London, once, they had had a char lady called Miranda Smith. There must be thousands of Miranda Smiths! This one had been particularly obliging, and Amanda was sure she wouldn't object to anyone borrowing her name. Wrapped in a warm blanket of smugness, Amanda smiled sweetly up at Jason Meade. "You can call me Miss Smith," she said ingenuously.

His mouth firmed, still with a trace of irony. "If you don't mind I'll try Miranda. After the informality of the last two days anything else might strain the credibility. A name isn't all that important, but it's convenient."

"I suppose so." Her voice was husky, the necessity to break away from that unwavering scrutiny uppermost in her mind. Obviously he didn't quite believe her, but was prepared to let it slide. In spite of a peculiar lethargy she felt her cheeks stain rose red as the other side of his remark hit her forcibly. She guessed, from the way he said it, that, since he had brought her here, there had been no one else around. They had been alone together! In country districts, she supposed, this would be commonly known as flouting the conventions. Not many would take into account that she had been ill for most of the time. And she must surely have been ill, otherwise she couldn't possibly feel so weak. She braced herself, pushed back her hair and drew a deep breath.

"You said," she began carefully, "that I've been here quite a while. Have I been very ill?"

"You could say that . . . ." His chin lifted, dropping again slightly. "At a guess I should say you've just missed pneumonia. Risking another guess, I should say you're in fairly good condition, otherwise you couldn't have fought it off."

If he were a farmer he could be talking of some of his own livestock! For a fleeting moment her eyes slipped to his chin. His chin was decided, even aggressive. His mouth mobile and sensuous, as she had thought before. His shoulders were dauntingly broad. Not a man to be argued with or taken lightly—or to be deceived in any way. Something inside her filled with odd little tremblings and she said quickly, "I can't remember being really ill. I believe I did catch all the usual childish things, measles and such like, but nothing since."

"Possibly because of the outdoor life you lead," he noted disparagingly. "It's a mistake, however, to think you're permanently immune. Things usually catch up on one sooner or later—even the most hardened criminals will tell you that."

"I thought we were talking about illness," she retorted sharply, not liking the way his continued allusions to her questionable status were beginning to hurt. Color swept into her face, then just as suddenly left it again as she slumped back against her pillows, strangely and utterly spent. Fencing with him, coping with even the simplest twisting of words, was proving an intolerable strain.

She didn't notice that his glance went over her keenly, assessing the paleness of her cheeks, the dark shadows hollowed beneath her eyes, her general air of exhaustion. But she did notice when he rose to his feet and walked toward the door. Dismay surged through her heart in a confusing fashion as she watched him leaving, a frightening feeling of desolation she couldn't account for. Was he still annoyed with her? Perhaps she had spoken too impulsively. "Where are you going?" she asked nervously.

"I'm going to make you a drink," he announced coolly. "It will give you a chance to settle down, otherwise you'll be talking yourself into a relapse. I ought to have thought of it sooner. You're too diverting, Miranda, with your sharp little tongue."

Ignoring the last bit of his discourse, she protested feebly, "I'm not particularly thirsty. You might only be wasting your time."

"Not my time, Miranda." He turned to grin over his shoulder dryly as he disappeared through the door. "There happens to be a lady who's giving me a hand. She's been singularly obliging so I don't want her upset. I should advise you to swallow whatever she chooses to bring without protest. She's known to be a bit of a tyrant—so be warned!"

Amanda stared in his direction long after he'd gone. So there had been someone else in the house after all! Indignation blended strangely with a touch of relief. He might have told her! Not, she assured herself hastily, that she had been worrying, but at least it was nice to know that the proprieties had been observed. It might make things slightly easier in the problem-strewn future that she didn't want to think about.

Jason Meade.... Slowly she whispered his name aloud, feeling ridiculously daring. What sort of a man was he, she wondered. He was certainly an attractive one with his dark good looks. The sort of man for which any woman might spare a second glance. It was his expression that Amanda didn't like. His face, even in repose, was too hard and brooding. Almost as if he had sampled all life had to offer, and was disillusioned. Yet, just before he had left, she had been beginning to imagine him more approachable. Perhaps she was wrong? Perhaps there was nothing in that dark countenance to encourage anyone, let alone a mere girl!

Impatient with herself and the trend of her wandering thoughts, she turned her head toward the window, against which the snow still clung. As she watched she became certain that snow was, in fact, still falling, although, through the feathered and frosted glass, it was difficult to be sure. Curiosity overcoming her general feeling of weariness, Amanda crept out of bed toward the window. No one had arrived yet with the promised refreshment. Whatever this woman's virtues, swiftness was apparently not one of them.

Once across the room, Amanda rubbed her small nose against the pane, as she had often done as a child, and looked out. She had been right. It was snowing, but the wind had died down and the flakes were falling gently, softly beautiful, making whiter the already white world outside. Glancing at the sky, she noted the heavy, overcast gray that seemed to promise ignominiously that there was more bad weather to come. Helplessly Amanda shuddered in spite of having always loved storms such as this. It was nice, she supposed, on picture postcards, or when one was a child, but right now she would have been happier with rain. Down below her window there had obviously been a track of sorts dug out to the drive entrance, but otherwise she could see no sign of any road being properly cleared. Beyond the drive, over the silent white distances, she could discern no movement of any kind. Nothing to indicate there was another soul in the world besides herself. Not anything, even in the immediate vicinity of the house, to be seen!

With one last despairing shudder Amanda turned from the wintry scene and, vaguely uneasy, went back to bed. She was a prisoner—this much was clearly apparent. A prisoner of circumstances and her own folly, and there seemed nothing she could do about it. Weakly she lay back, pulling the warm blankets up over her cold body, pushing back her heavy silken hair from her forehead, still feeling extraordinarily tired. When the woman did arrive with her tea she would ask her not to disturb her for the remainder of the day. All she wanted to do, she would tell her, was to sleep and sleep.

CHAPTER THREE

TWO DAYS LATER Amanda was up feeling much better. She knew it as soon as she woke that morning. Frost and snow still sparkled on her window, but the sun was shining, and in place of her former weariness was a surprising feeling of well-being.

Her jeans and shirt, she saw, had been freshly laundered and placed neatly on top of a small chest of drawers. Relieved that they hadn't been relegated to the dustbin, or left forgotten at the bottom of some laundry basket, Amanda scrambled quickly out of bed and put them on. Carefully she folded the man-size pajamas she had been wearing with a mixture of despair and relief. She did have one pair of her own in her rucksack, and wondered where on earth they could be. She must remember to ask Mrs. Drew.

Usually so quick in her movements as she was, it took Amanda quite a time to tidy her room and make her bed. She was puzzled and not a little dismayed to find her legs still shaky, and that the slightest exertion brought the dampness of perspiration to her face. In the end she confessed herself unequal to the task, and, vaguely unsatisfied with her endeavors, decided to venture downstairs. There didn't appear to be anyone about, but she could see.

She was a stranger in a strange house. A house, it seemed, of some size, with many confusing turnings. Eventually it was the smell of bacon frying that took her unerringly to the kitchen and Mrs. Drew.

Mrs. Drew was busy at the sink and threw Amanda a

rather startled glance over her shoulder as the girl stood uncertainly in the doorway. "Are you sure you should be up?" she asked bluntly, but with some concern. "I did think yesterday that you looked better, but I'm not sure that Mr. Jason will approve."

"I'm much better, thank you, Mrs. Drew," Amanda smiled, ignoring what the woman said about Jason as she gazed about her curiously. For a lone man Jason Meade did himself well! No old-fashioned country kitchen this, but a modern fitted apartment, light, bright and spacious. A connoisseur's kitchen, all elegant chrome and gleaming tiles. A positive housewife's dream. And overall such glorious warmth, in direct contrast to the bitter cold outside. It must cost quite a packet to centrally heat a house this size. If nothing else, Amanda concluded with a wry grimace, Mr. Meade must be a man of some means!

"You'll have to be careful, of course," Mrs. Drew was advising. "A proper nasty dose you had an' no mistake!"

"But I'm young and strong and I'll soon get over it," Amanda rejoined haphazardly, her mind still on Jason Meade's kitchen. The kitchen in the flat had amounted to little more than a box, and the one in the house that the Randalls had rented in America had scarcely been much better. How exciting to work in one such as this! Amanda didn't think she was very domesticated, but her fingers itched suddenly to try out the superb-looking electric cooker. "You don't have to worry about me, Mrs. Drew," she added, as the woman seemed to be waiting expectantly for something more. "I can look after myself."

"That's as may be, but you'll have to take care."

"Of course . . ." Amanda smiled again quickly. She had no wish to upset the admirable Mrs. Drew who had been so very kind to her. Her smooth brow wrinkled thoughtfully. Somewhere, in the confusion of the last few days, she seemed to remember Jason stating that Mrs. Drew

was a bit of a tyrant. She couldn't think how he had come
by the notion. Of course she might have been mistaken.
She had been confused a lot as she had lain in bed. There
had been times when she had wanted to get up—when
she had actually tried to get up, only to find the room
whirling strangely around her. Then strong hands had
held her down, gripping the soft flesh of her arms, hurting
almost, until she stopped struggling and went back to
sleep again. Surely Mrs. Drew's hands didn't have that
exact firmness, nor her voice the same deep, soothing
tones?

As if to confirm her fears, Mrs. Drew seemed disposed
to talk. "Mr. Jason's looked after you like a mother while
you've been ill. I may be speaking out of turn, but I do
hope you'll remember to thank him. There were times
when you were quite delirious and it took all his strength
to hold you down. And him supposed to be on holiday,
an' all."

"On holiday?" Amanda blinked, startled. Why should
he be on holiday? Wasn't he a farmer? And surely farmers didn't take holidays in weather like this? He could, of
course, be a businessman having a winter break. Why
hadn't she thought of it? But when she asked Mrs. Drew,
the good lady shook her head.

"You'd better ask Mr. Jason yourself, dear. I only live
here with my husband who looks after Mr. Jason's stable.
I only come in here occasionally when Mr. Jason is at
home, which isn't very often in the summer."

"Oh, I see. . . . " Amanda didn't but wasn't sure if it
would be circumspect to say so. She wasn't sure if it
would be wise to admit she knew little about Jason
Meade, or his movements. It might not do to tell Mrs.
Drew that, until she had arrived in the storm, she hadn't
even known such a person existed. Nor did she have any
idea how much Jason had told Mrs. Drew. It was all too
confusing! Perhaps it might have been better if she had
waited before coming to the kitchen.

Now she stood frowning uncomfortably, and was unable to suppress a start of relief when Jason Meade spoke coolly behind her.

"Miss Smith will have breakfast with me this morning, Mrs. Drew. I have things to discuss with her."

Amanda turned, somewhat startled. She hadn't heard his approach and her eyes swung curiously to his feet, to the thick gray socks he wore beneath tough cord trousers. His Wellingtons he must have discarded, not bothering to replace them with anything else. Never before had she had breakfast with a man in stockinged feet!

Slightly amused, his eyes rested on her uncertain face and she guessed he had read her thoughts. "You've been out?" she asked hastily, and rather inanely, as with a swift smile at Mrs. Drew she followed him from the room.

"Clever girl," he murmured companionably, taking her arm and guiding her easily, his fingers firm beneath her elbow. "It's not often one discovers a girl with such powers of deduction, especially on one's own doorstep."

"You didn't find me on your doorstep," she retorted, stung by his sarcasm but unable to ignore it, while her senses screamed for her to do just that. "You hauled me here unconscious."

"But Mrs. Drew doesn't know that."

"You mean . . . ." Halfway into the dining room Amanda stopped, almost wrenching her arm from his detaining fingers. She stared at him, catching the deeply green gaze and holding it. "You mean," she continued, "that Mrs. Drew actually imagines I was caught in the storm and came here looking for shelter?"

"Right first time! The girl really has brains." There was a carelessly jeering note in his voice that Amanda hated. He did seem in a mood this morning! The devilish glint was back in his eyes again, his darkness accentuated by the heavy line of his brows.

Color swept into her face. "Would she believe you?"

"Why not? People do get lost in these parts, only they're usually men, and at other times of the year."

"Then it's not exactly unusual?" Amanda stepped farther into the elegantly furnished room and perched herself uncomfortably on the edge of the chair he drew out for her with a studious politeness.

"Dartmoor," he replied as he seated himself opposite "is a lady of many moods, and none of them particularly trustworthy. It has three hundred square miles or so of desolate moorland, beautiful at times beyond words, but strangely capricious. Glorious, many would tell you, on a summer's day, but a devil incarnate in weather like this It's scarcely the most popular form of amusement, rescuing fair maidens in distress, and it does add to the hazards of winter."

"You're joking!" Amanda's clear, attractive voice was sullen as she stared mutinously down at her plate.

"Maybe I am—" his glance was enigmatical "—but I can be as serious as you like. I can't tell how concerned you are about your reputation. You might be a ship passing in the night, but the past has a funny way of catching up. Mrs. Drew doesn't know you arrived the evening before she did. I told her, for my sins, that I'd found you in an outbuilding at daybreak—a slight deviation from the truth, but it may suffice."

Amanda flushed as he leaned across to fill her cup, the cloudy aroma of the coffee hovering sardonically between them. There was a funny, pulsating little silence that she found impossible to break. One hand crept to her throat in a surge of bewildered embarrassment even while she told herself to be sensible and forget the whole thing. The fact that it was this man who had removed her wet clothing was surely nothing to get in such a state about! He might easily have been a doctor, and it had been the only sensible thing to do. Yet the thought of his hands on her body suffused the whole of it with heat. A flame that she had never known before coursed through her, leaving her curiously weak and shaken.

Her eyes jerked to his as she heard the patient note of irony in his voice. "Stop worrying about yourself, Miranda. The female form when half-frozen and wet through doesn't interest me at all. For what it's worth you could try looking at it this way. It was imperative that your clothes be removed and you were in no fit state to do it yourself. I'm not sure now that I wouldn't have left them on if I'd guessed you were such a little prude."

Not prepared all of a sudden to be reasonable, or to forgive that remark, she said sharply, "You've done nothing but dig at the state of my morals ever since I came here. Why didn't you send right away for Mrs. Drew? It might have saved you an awful lot of bother."

"It might indeed," he grinned mockingly, "had I but known Mrs. Drew was available. She was supposed to be visiting her sister, nor was it actually her fault that she wasn't. Her husband, whom you've not met, was to have driven her to the station, but unfortunately one of my horses went sick and he wouldn't leave the beast. I could have taken her myself, had I known, but I was away that afternoon and knew nothing of this until the next morning, when, I might add, I was delighted when Tom told me Mrs. Drew was still here."

Not wholly convinced, Amanda countered a little wildly, "There's still the taxi driver! You seem to have forgotten about him. He knew exactly what time I arrived."

Abruptly he cut her off with one of his imperious gestures. "I was coming to that. I distinctly recall several times when he referred to you as a young lad, so there's absolutely no reason why he should connect his passenger with my Miranda Smith. In the first place he only rang because he knows I'm keeping an eye on Combe Farm while the owner and his wife are away. You're not the first intruder I've been informed about, nor likely to be the last.

If this man should be in touch with me again, I will simply tell him I failed to find any trace of you, but such an incident is so commonplace, I doubt if he will."

"You're doing an awful lot to safeguard my reputation!" Confused, Amanda concentrated on the green-and-gold dining room, striving for breath. That he called her his Miranda was probably only a figure of speech, yet such a lot of what he said made her feel helplessly uncomfortable; sent cold shivers racing down her neck. If he ever discovered her true identity, then heaven help her, one day!

He laughed ironically, his white teeth glinting. "Why should I bother about your reputation, Miss Miranda? Maybe it's my own I'm worried about."

This was too much! She released a long-pent-up breath. He couldn't be serious! And yet . . . . She frowned doubtfully as Mrs. Drew came in carrying bacon and eggs. There could be some woman somewhere who might be upset to know what had actually happened. Women, she suspected, so far as Jason Meade was concerned, had their uses, but there might be one whom he regarded in a different light from any other. One woman whose respect and admiration he craved. Not anyone like herself or Veronica, whom he might enjoy teasing. Considering this as Mrs. Drew fussed around the breakfast table, a strange depression settled that she couldn't account for.

When Mrs. Drew departed, having satisfied herself they had everything they required, Amanda thrust such unreasonable thoughts from her mind and stated with a touch of sheer bravado, "I'm feeling much better this morning, Mr. Meade. Quite well enough to leave, in fact, so all your well-meant evasions are a waste of time. I'll get away directly after breakfast."

"How?" His green eyes were coolly skeptical between thick, dark, almost feminine lashes.

"Well . . . ." Her eyes met his briefly, faintly hostile, yet unable to contain that momentary hard contact. "By road, I suppose. I won't even bother you for a lift."

"Such brave independence!" He leaned toward her, coffee cup in hand, sharp, sardonic humor about his wryly tilted mouth. "As the roads are still full of snow you wouldn't get far, I'm afraid. And as I haven't time to rescue you again I suggest you content yourself at Merington until our climate improves."

"Merington?" Amanda's glance lifted quickly. "This is the name of your house?"

"My house and small estate, which comprises briefly this house and one farm. The farm I rent out. I have a very good tenant."

Amanda's spine pricked and tautened defensively. His tone stated clearly that he hoped he had relieved her curiosity, but she had only asked the name of his house! She had no wish to be informed of his business, always supposing one rented farm was all it amounted to, which she doubted! Coolly she brushed back a tangle of hair and reverted to their former conversation. "Don't plows, or whatever is used now to clear snow, still operate in this district?"

His dark face registered only a mild dryness. "My dear girl," he murmured smoothly, "to begin with, my drive is private and almost a mile in length. On top of this, owing, I believe, to the present state of the economy, byroads are not being cleared unless absolutely necessary. Unfortunately, as the telephone wires have also succumbed to the elements, I was unable to explain to anyone about your sore head or my sick horse, but as you've both apparently recovered, it seems I no longer have a case."

"What I'm trying to say—" Amanda began stiffly.

"Just forget it," he clamped down impatiently, his dark, level glance perfectly hard and steady. "No amount of argument will make any difference at the moment. Besides—" his eyes ran over her so directly that inexplicably her whole body tingled "—what strength do you have right now? Just out of bed after a bad dose of flu, how far do you imagine you'd get? As a matter of fact I doubt your good sense in getting up this morning, and I definitely forbid you to even think of leaving the house!"

"You couldn't stop me!"

"Don't repeat yourself, Miranda. Just try it and see."

Staring sullenly at her toast, which was all she could manage, she turned her head swiftly to look at him, feeling hot and discomfited, at a definite disadvantage. His voice held hard menace, and his dark head added to the picture, too devastating to challenge. "All right!" she very nearly hissed at him, her wide blue eyes brightly antagonistic. "But you might regret not letting me go!"

"Before I let you go, Miranda, you'll see a doctor and have an X ray, just to make sure everything is all right. Does it still hurt?" he inquired suavely. "Your head, I mean?"

"No, not really." Surprise threaded her voice as she touched the tender spot with her fingers, vowing silently that wild horses wouldn't drag her to any hospital with Jason Meade. "I'm sure you're worrying unnecessarily," she said. "I certainly haven't fractured my skull, if that's what you think?"

"I'm not qualified to think anything, Miranda, and neither are you, but I do have my share of common sense. Besides, it could be argued that it was my fault you fell from that ladder."

"And you do take your responsibilities seriously, Mr. Meade." Her eyes widened innocently, sweeping his face. "But then a man like you would."

"I'm overcome." The look he slanted her was vividly mocking. "One of these days, Miranda, you'll land in trouble with your wild little tongue. Another man might not be so tolerant."

She was breathless all of a sudden, nervous enough to

glance away. That could mean other things! There was an odd inflection in his voice that she couldn't begin to dissect. Belatedly she tried to salvage a little poise. "What I said was on the level, Mr. Meade. You don't have to look for hidden meanings."

"I take it, then, that you mean to flatter me?" He smiled in a leisurely way. "Perhaps we might both learn to understand each other better, Miranda, given time."

Carefully Amanda lowered her lashes, a pulse in her throat jerking painfully for no reason she could think of. How could she hope to cope with sarcasm so blatant? As soon as the weather cleared she would be gone. They had no time, and he knew it.

Seeking desperately for a safer topic, she asked impulsively, "If I'm not to go out this morning, what would you suggest I do?"

"You never stop trying, do you?" His gaze slid consideringly to her mutinous mouth. "You can amuse yourself in the library. There's a TV and enough books to see you through several winters. Unless, of course, you don't read. Today young people seldom do."

Amanda's blue eyes darkened coldly. "You talk as though I'm just out of the schoolroom!"

"Not long out, I should say. How old are you, Miranda?"

"Old enough . . . " she replied reluctantly, her brow knitted with delicate uncertainty.

"I asked you a question, Miranda! That's no sort of an answer!" There was about him a barely suppressed male impatience.

"Rescuing me doesn't give you automatic rights! You don't have to know everything about me!" Amanda's eyes flashed with indignation and a certain wariness, remembering too late what he had said about her tongue. But even in simple questions there could be danger. This man was too astute by far!

If he was aware of the wariness, the stubborn set of sof lips, he took no notice. "Miranda?" he prompted gently.

"Oh, twenty, if you really must know!" Without nota ble grace, she jumped to her feet, leaving untouched he second cup of coffee. "If you'll excuse me," she added tossing her head like an obstinate child, "I think I'll take your advice and read some books. At least they can't lec ture and probe!"

But having the last word, Amanda found, wasn't a very satisfactory business. For the remainder of that day and most of the next she saw very little of Jason Meade. In the library she played records and watched the snow-clad moors outside. Preoccupied with her thoughts, she found she couldn't settle to a book, although the deep armchair by the fire were inviting.

The loss of her shoulder bag still worried her greatly but the contents she considered so lethal she dared no mention it again. Sitting by the fire, piecing together as best she could the curious happenings of that momentous night, she came at last to the conclusion that she must have dropped it in the lane at Combe Farm. Vaguely now, she seemed to recall falling into some kind of ditch. If she was unable to search for it herself, there was at least some comfort to be derived from the fact that as long as the snow lay, her bag would be covered and her secret safe. Safer than herself, perhaps, beneath the predatory male gaze of Jason Meade! The thought came entirely out of the blue, completely unfounded, and for a moment Amanda had the grace to feel ashamed. Yet such thoughts came unbidden, bringing a tremulous excite ment, a depth of response, quite foreign to anything she had known before. Jason Meade was quite a man, she had to admit it! Apart from his hard good looks, he was full of domineering authority and polished sophistication. Never in a hundred years would she find enough experience to cope with a man like that, yet for an instant, on a wave of inexplicable longing, she wished she had!

A log on the fire flared, bursting into a shower of sparks before burning itself out in the grate. Unconsciously Amanda shuddered. Such thoughts as she had been thinking were crazy. She must be mad! Perhaps she should have her head examined, as Jason had suggested. The blow she had sustained when she fell must have affected her reasoning and her senses as well. Jason Meade was not for her, nor did she really want him. If some vagrant part of her was clamoring for amorous amusement, then she must look elsewhere!

In the meantime, such ridiculous notions aside, to stay here was probably as convenient as anywhere else—until the family came home. With Mrs. Drew and her husband she was adequately chaperoned. Then surely she could quite easily escape and return to Combe Farm. Jason Meade need never know what had become of her, and, because of his doubtful opinion of her, she didn't think he would try to find out.

If he did visit Combe Farm she must endeavor to keep out of his way. He would probably never connect Richard Trent's retiring young daughter with Miranda Smith, and besides, in no time at all she would be gone. It would be sensible to return to London, to stay in some cheap digs and take a training of some sort. It shouldn't be too difficult with a little patience.

Come teatime on the following afternoon, Amanda discovered that patience was a commodity she seemed short of. Used as she had been during the last two years to leading an outdoor life, to be confined to the house she found extremely tedious. The ache in her limbs appeared to have gone completely, and apart from a slight lassitude she was beginning to feel quite fit again—so much so that she began to resent being ignored by Jason, whom she hadn't seen all day!

Neglect, she decided, was what it amounted to, and as she sat at the kitchen table sharing a pot of tea with Mrs.

Drew she was unable to resist asking her where he could be. "Surely, in this winter," she said, "he can't find a lot to do outside. I hope he's not staying out because of me?"

It was indiscreet, she knew, to air her feelings so indiscriminately, and she wasn't surprised to find Mrs. Drew frowning disapprovingly and shaking her head. "There's an awful lot to do in weather like this, Miranda! Why, they've hardly stopped for more than a sandwich and a glass of beer since dawn. Snow makes a lot of extra work anywhere, but in no place more so than a stable. My husband, Tom, could never have managed on his own. Mr. Jason knows everything there is to know about horses, and he doesn't believe in wasting time."

Amanda, who knew nothing about horses, apart from the little she had picked up in Florida when the twins had developed a sudden urge to ride, felt unable to argue with Mrs. Drew's apparently logical statements. "I'm afraid I'm not a country girl," she smiled, "but I'm going to borrow a pair of gumboots and go and see for myself. Otherwise I'm going to die of boredom more easily than the flu."

Mrs. Drew heaved a huge, skeptical sigh that Amanda pretended not to hear as she turned and ran upstairs to fetch her jacket. Her feet skipped the wide staircase, the animation that lifted her spirits at the thought of being out touching her face, bringing fresh color to her pale cheeks. Mrs. Drew might not approve, nor might Jason, but fresh air, Amanda felt sure, couldn't do her any harm. It was probably what she needed after being cooped up for so long.

Outside it was colder than she had expected and she thought longingly of the thick coat packed with the rest of her clothes at the flat. The thin jerkin she wore provided little protection against the frost and snow, and she felt annoyed with herself again for not bringing something warmer. Even if she had managed to break into Combe

Farm, she might have known what to expect on Dartmoor!

Away from the immediate vicinity of the house, Amanda turned her attention to the drive. There was no one about, no one to stop her escaping, but she saw at once that there would be no need. As Jason had pointed out, the road was full of snow, and there seemed no sign yet of a thaw setting in. After a few minutes of plowing through the frozen waste she gave up, leaning against a small, upright piece of fencing until she regained her breath, staring out across the countryside. In the late afternoon sunshine the snow and frost sparkled and glistened, turning the moors and fells into a miniature Antarctic, desolate and grim, yet fairylike in its gleaming whiteness—a remote, treeless wilderness, somewhere Amanda had read, and, looking over Dartmoor now, she was inclined to believe it. A wild waste of granite and bog, guarded by grim tors, that bowed to neither man nor beast! With a mild shudder Amanda turned away. She was getting too fanciful; it must be the atmosphere of the place! She must go and find Jason Meade. The human elements might be easier to deal with.

Merington, she noticed as she struggled back, was a rambling old house, as cozy-looking outside as it was in—cozy by contrast with the moor, at any rate. The low, deep-set windows and square, squat chimneys looked as if they had withstood the storms of centuries, and the thick belt of Scots pines behind it provided a protective barrier between the house and the barren lands beyond. What sort of a man was Jason Meade to live here by choice, Amanda wondered as she plowed around the corner of the copse. At times, during winters like this, the loneliness must be almost too great to be endured. Again curiosity beset her as to his real profession. He wasn't just a country landlord, of that she was certain.

The afternoon was wearing on before Amanda reached

the stables. She found them by following a roughly hewn track through a collection of old, apparently unused buildings and through another thick belt of trees into a field. Here, to her surprise, she saw that the snow had been cleared from paths and yards, to make an area where horses would be able to exercise comparatively easily. The stables seemed quite extensive, well kept by any standards, this much was clearly obvious in spite of the snow, but of Jason Meade there was no sign. She must just look and see.

She turned, the sun, settling almost to the horizon, slanting into her eyes and nearly blinding her. When she did manage to focus, she found herself staring straight at him as he emerged from a doorway on her right.

"What the devil are you doing here?" he exclaimed, his voice flat and hard, not in the least welcoming.

She spun her head a little from side to side, dazed by his unexpected appearance, even though she had known he must be around. Why, when she saw him, did her legs turn curiously weak, and her pulses jerk in such a crazy fashion? There was even a familiar faintness creeping over her that she could never account for!

Then he was towering in front of her, brilliant impatient eyes traveling over her with intense irritation, noting the tumbled bare head, the peculiar intensity of her face with its marked pallor. "You little fool!" His hard, lean fingers gripped her arms, shaking her none too gently. "Didn't I tell you to stay inside? I've enough on here without you adding to my worries!"

The faintness passed—it was probably the impact of brutal fingers and hard-hitting words that sobered her immediately. "I don't intend adding to your troubles," she choked. "I came to see if I could help!" Which wasn't exactly the truth, but the truth would never suffice. What tolerance would he have with a girl who had only been looking for air?

"Help!" His hands tightened compulsively as his jaw clamped. "Help with what, might I ask? You're swaying around like a leaf in the wind, not yet recovered from a bad dose of flu."

A tremor ran through her, but she beat it down. "You accused me only yesterday of repeating myself, Mr. Meade!"

"I don't want any backchat from you, Miranda!" His dark face was sardonic, and the color mounted beneath her skin. "I'm going to send you back to the house."

"Please, Jason...."

"Jason...." His voice mocked her, yet changed slightly, subtly. "I was wondering when you'd get around to it."

"I'm sorry—I didn't mean..." she trailed off helplessly. Why should she be apologizing for using his name when he had been using hers freely?

"Don't apologize, Miranda, I like it. It puts our relationship on an entirely different footing."

Amanda blinked, her blue eyes darkening, staring up into his. There was some kind of laughter beating in his voice that she didn't begin to understand. The impatience had gone, at least momentarily; even the grip of his fingers slackened, became gentle. Yet none of this did she find reassuring, and her thick lashes flickered and came down. "I don't really think it makes much difference," she replied carefully.

"Don't you, Miranda?" His hands slid away, and his laughter was hard and brief and his eyes rested on the full curve of her mouth. "All the difference in the world, I should think, but we'll see, my little waif." One arm came up and curved around her shoulders as he turned her. "Come and see my horses if you must, but don't be too keen to offer assistance. In weather like this I'm hard put to it to resist a helping hand—or anything else, for that matter."

There was an odd, disturbing look on his face that flicked tiny tremors down her spine, sent sharp warning signals along her nerves that she was rash enough to ignore. He enjoyed taunting and teasing, but it would mean little. Possibly the sudden spell of bad weather had stirred a devil in him. Many men looked for scapegoats when overworked. If she could in any way relieve his feelings, then it might repay in some measure that which she owed him.

That evening Jason took her on a personally conducted tour of his stables, and all the next day Amanda worked by his side, her renewed offer of assistance accepted. In a few short hours his horses became a delight, a nameless terror; the pleasure of hands sliding down warm skin; the wonderful release of an all-enveloping hug when Jason was looking the other way. He didn't altogether approve, and she found herself resentful when he said she was too impulsive, when he warned her of the perils and none of the pleasures. The huge chestnut gelding she steered clear of, fastidious and thoroughbred though he might be. A big dapple gray she eyed warily, also, but there were others, many others. One especially, a little chestnut filly, perfect in every detail, she liked very much, and would have given much to possess.

"You could hunt that one well." Jason, catching her in the throes of ecstatic contemplation, passed the remark dryly.

Startled out of her reverie, Amanda glanced around at him. She was supposed to be spreading fresh straw, a lighter job that was all he would allow. She hadn't heard his approach. Now, flushing slightly, she considered what he said. "I shouldn't want to hunt. I've never liked the sound of it."

"Well, we certainly don't need to agree on that controversial subject." His eyes glinted derisively, warning her subtly that, while tolerant, he would be in no way receptive to her views.

Stung, Amanda tossed her dark head. "I don't even ride."

"I could always teach you." That and more, his eyes promised.

Again she experienced a tremor in her stomach—the feeling that she was falling through space. She said breathlessly, without thinking, "I tried once and fell off. I don't have the aptitude."

"You could be surprised." His smile glinted whitely. "I believe otherwise. You certainly have the right approach, which my horses appear to appreciate. Anyone else would have been trampled underfoot long ago. Have you ever worked in a stable, Miranda?"

"If I had I should have learned to ride."

"You wouldn't fancy it? Tom isn't as young as he used to be, and he could do with some help. You might do worse," he added with gentle emphasis.

She moved her head fretfully, evading that brilliant green glance. "Is that an invitation, Mr. Meade?"

"Jason," he corrected softly. "It might be a more rewarding existence than wandering footloose."

"A sort of rehabilitation center?"

"You said that, Miranda, not I. I'm not interested in the young, generally, or the saving of their tender skins."

"You can be quite brutal when you choose, Mr. Meade!" Resentfully she dug her hands into the pockets of the fur-lined coat he had loaned her. It was huge, far too big, but it was warm and the fur collar caressed her smooth cheeks snugly.

His eyes swept her face, the creamy skin. "Now what's that supposed to mean?"

"Oh, never mind, but I'm afraid I can't accept your offer." She moved back tensely. "It would never work out."

She retreated, but he was quicker, and she shivered uncontrollably as his hand grasped her shoulder, closing painfully over the bone. "You don't believe in giving yourself a chance, do you, Miranda? What I'm offering might not be the ultimate, but you would never need to go hungry or penniless again."

"What you're offering, Mr. Meade, could be just as questionable. I should hate to merely change one form of bondage for another."

His tingling grip tightened with disturbing intimacy. "There are lots of things, Miranda, I might be fully justified in pointing out, only politeness and something else, which I can't quite clearly define, holds me back. But before you so rashly discard my offer you'd be well advised to think it over. Such an opportunity might not come again."

The hard edge of his voice bothered her and she looked away, her fingers clenching. "Some things," she said swiftly, "are better not considered. Instinctively one knows."

"Because instinctively one suspects the worst," he mocked, his expression dark, his eyes immobile on her set face. "Don't you realize how like you're getting to a small wild animal, afraid to trust anything or anyone anymore?"

Her hand moved up convulsively to push past him. "Your horses are nice, Mr. Meade, but not for me. That's all there is to it. You exaggerate the rest. Now, if you don't mind, I'm going to help Mrs. Drew with dinner. I promised, in case you're thinking I'm running away!"

"Now why ever should I think that, young lady?" An enigmatic smile played about his mouth. "You couldn't run far in this weather anyway. Go and assist Mrs. Drew by all means. I'll be in for dinner this evening and shall expect you to join me. I have another proposition that you might find more interesting than my stables."

Amanda walked away from him, along the snow-cleared path back to the house. He was used to being obeyed, but the thought of having dinner with him filled her with a tremulous apprehension. He seemed very keen that she should stay where he could keep an eye on her. How much longer, she wondered, could she hold out against him?

CHAPTER FOUR

WHILE MRS. DREW APPRECIATED AMANDA'S HELP in the kitchen, she noticed the girl looked tired, and when the casserole was simmering gently in the oven she advised her to go to her room and rest.

"Lie on your bed and close your eyes for an hour, my dear, otherwise Mr. Jason will be after me for working you too hard. He won't want to look at a pale face throughout dinner."

Reluctantly, if not altogether unwillingly, Amanda agreed, although about dining with Jason she was full of reservations. "I really think I should have mine in here with you, Mrs. Drew. I'm not very suitably dressed for the dining room. I have only these trousers which I've worn continually."

"Mr. Jason usually changes." Doubtfully Mrs. Drew nodded, glancing at Amanda's denim-clad legs, her slight frown indicating that she agreed in some measure with what Amanda had said. "It would have been better if you'd had a nice dress," she added thoughtfully. "There are some dresses belonging to Mr. Jason's sister, who's abroad at the moment with her husband. Miss Alison has far more dresses than she knows what to do with, and I'm sure she wouldn't mind your borrowing one for the evening, especially as you're both much the same size, but I'm afraid it's not for me to suggest it, and, being a man, it probably wouldn't occur to Mr. Jason."

"Oh, no, please don't say anything!" Amanda smiled, yet grew hot when she thought of what Jason might think. He might imagine she was dressing up for his benefit, and she certainly didn't want him to think that! "It was nice of you to worry about me," she went on quickly, "but the storm will soon be over and I'll be gone. My pants will just have to hold out a little longer, that's all."

Mrs. Drew sighed. "Tom was just saying that the wind is changing. The snow could all be away, come morning."

"By morning?" Abruptly, on her way to the door, Amanda jerked to a halt. "As quickly as that, Mrs. Drew?"

"Quite easily, with the wind in the right direction."

Mrs. Drew obviously spoke from experience, yet doubtfully Amanda remained frowning. "It doesn't seem possible. Doesn't it cause flooding, Mrs. Drew?"

"Sometimes—sometimes not," Mrs. Drew shrugged. "There's nothing so strange as weather. I've seen snow disappear, almost without a trace, you might say. Dartmoor is full of rivers and streams, but fortunately we aren't on a river here. Now take Combe Farm for instance, what Mr. Jason is keeping an eye on while his friends are away. They sit nearly on top of a river and sometimes, in a flood, the water comes almost up to the door."

"Combe Farm?" Amanda heard herself repeating stupidly.

"Yes. That and the river about four miles away, so we're quite safe here."

"I see. . . . " Nervously Amanda probed, unaware that she was giving the wrong impression. "Is that as the crow flies—the four miles, I mean?"

"Well, yes, I suppose so. You turn right at the end of the drive and the road runs straight. But you don't need to worry, dear," the housekeeper smiled reassuringly. "We're too high up at Merington to be in danger."

"Of course not," said Amanda, escaping.

As she ran up to her room she took Mrs. Drew's advice, throwing herself on to her bed without being fully aware of what she was doing. If the snow was to go through the night, then so must she! It wouldn't do to be caught unprepared, but the idea of sneaking out like a fugitive in the early hours was curiously daunting. She even knew a peculiar reluctance to leave Merington at all. In the few short days that she had been here she had formed a surprising attachment for the place, foolish perhaps when she had known she must leave. Strange fancies crowded through her head. Why not make a clean breast of everything and beg Jason to let her stay and help with his horses? It would be a job, and one that immediately appealed to her. Perhaps she might live with the Drews, in their cottage, or even cycle over each day from Combe Farm.

Such a notion, however, she squashed almost before it was born. By setting up a fabrication of fictitious stories she had burned her boats too badly ever to hope to get away with such an idea. Jason, if he was ever to discover the truth, would never forgive her. No man, however indifferent, enjoyed being made a fool of. And as for the family at Combe Farm, Richard and Eva almost certainly wouldn't approve!

With a sigh Amanda turned, burying her hot face against her pillows, admitting that she was drawn to Jason Meade in some incomprehensible way, and instinctively sensing that he was not indifferent to her. Why, she could not even begin to guess. As quickly as she had flopped down onto her bed, she rolled off it to scramble across the floor to consider herself in the dressing-table mirror. She saw that since her illness she looked as thin as a cat, but with huge blue eyes instead of green, gleaming with the desperation of the homeless. Yet her thinness, and perhaps the shirt that appeared to have shrunk since Mrs. Drew dried it, did nothing to hide the taut curves of her body, lending a certain provocative mystery to her fine-boned face, adding sensuous shadows about her high cheekbones and mouth, physical features that she noted without being fully able to assimilate. What, she wondered, seeing only a complete lack of glamour, would any man see in her? True, she had known few very well. There had been Herman—not that she considered Jason in any way like him. Jason, she felt sure, would never attempt to assault her! He might acknowledge that he wanted her, but would apply more finesse. With him there would be no clumsy fumblings in a bathroom, but might he not get what he wanted in the end? Possibly, of the two, Jason would be the more dangerous, and she mustn't allow a different approach to blind her to the fact.

She could find nothing in the mirror to convince her she was irresistible, but men were surely creatures of some promiscuity. Many, she admitted, striving honestly, would consider a wandering girl like herself as fair game. If Jason Meade thought of her in this way, then it would be up to her to correct such an impression, but she doubted if he ever thought of her at all, apart from the odd moment when she happened to cross his path.

Impatiently she turned away from her reflection in the glass. There were other things more important than her appearance. A means of escape, for instance! Amanda walked to the window and spent a long time contemplating the night.

She had washed her face and was almost ready to go down when Mrs. Drew knocked on the door and looked in. "Mr. Jason says you're to go along to Miss Alison's room and help yourself to anything you like."

"Oh, Mrs. Drew, I told you not to mention it!" Annoyed, Amanda felt swift color staining her cheeks. This was just the sort of thing she had hoped to avoid.

"I didn't, dear!" Crossly Mrs. Drew pursed prim lips. "When Mr. Jason came in he mentioned it himself! I'm too old to bother about such things, or for running upstairs for that matter," she added breathlessly.

Suitably chastised, Amanda flushed deeper. "I'm sorry, Mrs. Drew, but you shouldn't have bothered to come up. I really don't need a dress or anything else, as I told you before."

"Well, when the master makes inquiries, don't forget to tell him I told you!" Mumbling to herself, the woman departed, leaving Amanda staring after her, indignation etched on her face.

"You didn't find anything suitable, I see?" Jason queried as she ran downstairs.

He was standing in the hall, near the spot where he had been when she had first looked over the balustrade and seen him properly for the first time. On this occasion, it seemed he might almost have been waiting for her. Her eyes went swiftly over him as he stood, immaculate in his dark suit, the light from above him gleaming on black hair, very thick and curling crisply, following the well-shaped line of his head. For all her convincing argument with herself in the bedroom, excitement began to flow through her, lighting her eyes so that they glimmered, reflecting a thousand sapphire stars. Hastily, as she drew nearer, she flickered long lashes, hiding the sudden whirl of her senses, the traitorous pulsing of her heart. Where this man was concerned she must keep a firm grip on herself, his attractiveness would defeat any wavering resolutions.

On reaching the bottom step of the stairs she carefully inclined her small head. "Thank you," she answered tonelessly, averting her gaze, "but I didn't want anything—or need it. What I'm wearing will do quite nicely."

"You feel comfortable in something you've worn all day?" His voice held only a mild curiosity, yet his eyes, as they went over her, held anything but mildness and stirred her blood, precipitating a need to defend herself.

"I feel more at ease in my own things," she uttered,

feeling at that moment quite the reverse but reluctant to say so.

"Which isn't quite the same thing," he said shortly, his gaze lingering with a hint of disapproval on her rather creased attire. Once a tramp always a tramp—Amanda decided she read his thoughts quite clearly, and found herself stiffening with resentment. Otherwise, now that he had mentioned his sister's clothes himself, she might have given in gracefully. For a brief second she had been tempted.

Instead she murmured, avoiding his eyes, "I should be quite happy to have my dinner in the kitchen with the Drews."

"Happier than having it with me, perhaps. But I don't feel like my own company this evening, Miranda, so you must endure. And as I told you before, I have something to discuss with you. It matters little what you choose to wear."

There was obviously nothing more to be said. Amanda drew a quick fortifying breath as she followed him across the hall, studying unobserved the back of his handsome dark head, the unrelenting set of his broad shoulders. As she passed the telephone, she asked without meaning to, "Has the line been repaired yet? I haven't heard it ringing since I arrived."

His head inclined slightly so that she saw his hard profile, the ironic tilt of one dark eyebrow. "As I've been unable to report it out of order, it's scarcely likely."

"But someone," she protested, "could have reported it from outside."

"Quite possibly, Miranda. Services, in weather like this, can be erratic, and I don't intend to complain. I only know I can't use it."

"You were using it on the night I arrived!" She had said it once already, yet something inside her forced her to repeat it, a crazy thing to do, because he had been talking to

Veronica, and her persistence would almost certainly start
him thinking. He was astute enough not to miss a move.
Momentarily, however, Amanda was unable to resist it.
His relationship with Veronica was beginning to hurt in-
sidiously. Only, Amanda assured herself, because after all
the trouble she'd gone to it would be completely illogical
if Veronica's marriage was to fail due to another source
altogether!

"Someone happened to ring me. . . ." As she had
feared, his eyes were suddenly sharper as he stood aside
to let her pass before him through the dining-room door.
"Afterward the line went dead. Did you, by any chance,
overhear that conversation, Miranda?"

He knew she had, the knowledge was there in the dark,
mocking depth of his eyes, and his expression told her to
mind her own business! He expected to conduct any number of affairs without implied criticism, while already he
had judged and condemned one lone girl without one
scrap of concrete evidence!

If she had been lovelier, more experienced, Amanda
vowed she would have done her uttermost to attract him,
to have made him fall in love with her. It might not have
been too difficult if she had been a little more sophisticated, a little more knowledgeable as to what made a man
tick. Then she could have snapped her fingers at him, sent
him away with a broken heart, or a degree less assurance.
If nothing else it might have served to demonstrate the
pain of philandering with the affections of others.

"A penny for them, Miranda? At times you have an infuriating habit of retreating into a world of your own. I
asked you a question."

"I'm sorry. . . ." Amanda sat down as he pushed her
chair beneath her with a punishing little jerk. "Many
things on that particular evening are hazy, Mr. Meade. I
was only trying to remember."

"Well, don't strain yourself, my dear," he replied dry-

y. Not seating himself immediately, he went to the sideboard, absently contemplating a selection of bottles. "Would you rather drink Muscadet or a German Riesling perhaps with your smoked salmon? Mrs. Drew appears to have excelled herself this evening—or was it you?"

Amanda shook her head, disclaiming any credit. "Thank you," she murmured as he waited coolly, his eyes on her face. "I'll have the Muscadet, but only a little. After being ill too much might go to my head."

"You didn't guess, did you, Miranda?" Jason carried the bottle to the table, asking the question suavely as he filled her glass. He smiled as he pushed it toward her, and the humorous look came back to his eyes.

Plagued by apprehension, she glanced up sharply. "What is that supposed to mean? Another black mark, I suppose?"

"Don't be foolish!" He lifted his own drink in a silent toast, faintly mocking. "You appear to have a one-track mind, but I'm not sure if I follow you."

"Sorry," she muttered, without notable grace, unable to return his gesture. "It doesn't really matter." Confused, she looked down at her hands, with an effort holding them still on the table. From off them she had washed all signs of her stint in the stables, and her long, slender fingers were smooth if still faintly tanned from her stay in America.

Her hands diverted him, although he sounded vaguely irritated as he reached over and picked one up, his lean fingers closing over hers, turning the palm up and examining it carefully. "You've rather beautiful hands, Miranda. This tan, which you appear to have all over—where did you come by it? On the Continent?"

"No. . . ." She seemed to choke on her breath as, startled, she glanced at him—quickly before averting her eyes. Her allover tan, he said! Her pulses jerked and the hand he held clenched convulsively. It would have been

so easy to tell him—in Florida, playing with the twins!
But she couldn't possibly give him even that small detail
of information without arousing the suspicions she was so
scared of. Which was crazy, really, because Veronica
must have sailed yesterday, and if she had any sense she
would say so, lightly, making a joke of it. No need to
mention Herman. All she need say was that she hadn't
wanted to go, and was scared Veronica would make a
fuss. But it was far from the simple task she had anticipated. Too much deception lay between herself and this man
who held her hand with so light yet so tenuous a grip.
Never in a thousand years dared she risk the torrent of furious contempt that would surely pour on her head before
her first words were out! Besides, there was always a slim
chance that Veronica might not have gone as arranged.
Confusion surged, rippling nervously through her slight
body. No—she must just wait and disappear. It would be
so much easier.

"Just, no?" Startled from her anxious reverie, she became aware of his brilliant gaze whipping across her, and
when she flushed unhappily and nodded, he prompted
cynically, "Sometimes, Miranda, I'm convinced you don't
know truth from fiction. In my line of business, my dear,
I've learned to recognize a tan that isn't British."

"Your line of business," she repeated, the color coming
under her skin as she almost snatched away her hand.
Then, in spite of her flash of truculence, she leaned forward, her blue eyes vividly alight. "You mean, your business apart from the farm?"

"I don't farm, Miranda. I've never pretended to."

"So you said, but I—"

"Never mind," he interrupted briefly, his smile softly
derisive. "Eat up your dinner—Mrs. Drew has left it all
on the hot plate. If you like you can serve the casserole,
and, afterward, I'll tell you all about it."

Mrs. Drew's casserole was delicious. They went into

the lounge for coffee. "I use the library mostly, but this makes a change." Jason poured coffee that was already percolating on a low table before the fire. He didn't attempt to supplement the one side light that Mrs. Drew had apparently switched on, and the room appeared cozy beneath its gentle glow.

Amanda took her coffee with a murmured word of thanks, gazing at the marble fireplace, the exquisite painting above the mantel of a Victorian lady surrounded by her children and dogs. Her eyes left the painting to take in the elegance of the room, the gleaming paneling of the walls, the crystal wall lights, the superb, silky-looking carpet, the pictures hung against soft green wallpaper. The button-back chair she sat in was covered in soft blue and gold, picking up the colors of the carpet, and opposite stood a fine Regency sofa. Another, in gold brocade, was placed on her right, and after pouring his own coffee, Jason lowered onto it his not insubstantial weight.

"Do you like it?" he asked softly, aware of her close surveillance. "You haven't been in here before?"

She drew a cool, expressive little breath. "I don't roam uninvited in a house where I'm not even a guest! I like your library, Mr. Meade. I've enjoyed playing your records, but I'm afraid I couldn't settle to reading any of your books."

He grinned for a moment as if her studied little speech amused him, his eyes steady on her flushed young face. "You find it difficult to settle to anything, perhaps?"

"I would like to train for something," she retorted swiftly and impulsively. "If you're referring to a job? I will have to earn my living."

"One might have thought there were easier ways," he said lightly, and she bit her full bottom lip painfully, not entirely fooled by the ironic glint in his eyes. When she made no reply he added smoothly, "Does hotel work appeal to you at all, Miranda?"

"Hotel work?" She moved her tongue quickly over her sore lip, her blue eyes bewildered. "I'm afraid I've never even thought about it. When I have considered a career it was never to do with people. Animals maybe, or children, but nothing so competitive as working in a hotel."

"Such work, my dear, is no more competitive than anything else. Besides, you turned down my offer of a job in my stables."

Amanda sighed, for a moment confused, and put down her coffee cup with a tiny clatter. "Mr. Meade," she said emphatically, "you don't have to worry about finding me employment. I'm not your responsibility. All in good time I'll find something myself."

He ignored this completely. "I happen to own a string of hotels, many of which suffer to some extent from a shortage of staff. Yes, even in times like these," he stated, seeing her raised eyebrows, her dubious expression. "A lot of hotel staff like to move around, and as much of our work is seasonal, perhaps this is just as well. But I do have places that are open all the year round and it would be quite easy to find you something."

"Such as?" Why didn't she turn his offer down flat? She felt not one spark of interest, so she assured herself. Why, she would much rather stay and help with his horses—if she had been bound to make a choice, which she wasn't. No, she might as well be honest, if only with herself. The question so glibly on her lips had been prompted more by curiosity than anything else—the fact that she had discovered Jason Meade's occupation, if owning a string of hotels could be described as such!

She heard his relaxed drawl. "I'm not sure exactly where you'd fit in. I should have to know a little more about you."

"Then, after I agreed to be interviewed, you'd come to the regretable conclusion that my qualifications are in no way suitable."

He intercepted her line of thought with trained perception. "I don't need to know everything about you, Miranda. You have no faith in people."

Her color came and ebbed with confusion and she glanced at him sideways, catching his ambiguous gaze. "A man like you would only need to know so much. You would have no difficulty in putting two and two together."

"Supplying the deficiencies, you mean?" his voice mocked.

"Whichever way you care to put it."

He considered her for a long moment from under slanting black brows, his eyes narrowed on her slightly averted face. "Are your parents still alive, Miranda? I distinctly remember you mentioning your father, as if he at any rate was very much so."

Amanda's fingers clenched nervously. Did he never miss a thing? "My parents can be of no interest to you, Mr. Meade." Wildly she answered, not prepared to listen to the small voice of reason that warned her of future recriminations.

"So you refuse to tell me anything? Where you're going, where you've been?"

"The latter could be easier."

"Not if you'd allow me to help."

That way could only be dangerous, she knew, but did not say so aloud. Instead she silently shook her silky head. "You only want to help me because you feel responsible for my tumble off the ladder—you said so yourself. After the snow has gone, and me with it, I doubt if your conscience will continue to trouble you."

"So we've come to the end of the road, you and I? Or is it, I wonder, just the beginning?"

She moved uneasily in her soft chair, aware that his eyes hadn't moved from her face. "You don't have to trouble."

An exasperated sigh escaped his tight lips. "To be quite

frank, Miranda, I'm asking myself, right now, why I bother. My common sense tells me to let you go. And yet . . . ? Have you ever been intrigued by anyone, Miranda?"

"You, in a way." Amanda smiled with courageous frankness. "You say you have hotels, yet you apparently choose to live here by yourself. Why?"

"And she asks, with a rare economy in words!" An amused quirk broke the set contours of his mouth, lightening the brooding glint in his eye. "It would seem that curiosity can be motivated by entirely different emotions. But do you expect, I wonder, the same sort of answers as you give me?"

Amanda flushed, but before she could speak he went on. "Don't worry," he mocked, "mine is the more generous nature. During summer, Miranda, I have little time to spend here. It's in the winter that I indulge myself by stealing a few weeks at Merington with my horses. In summer I have to ration myself to weekends."

Amanda's thick lashes flickered. "But you don't keep any staff? Mrs. Drew mentioned that you did most of the work yourself. Wouldn't a smaller place, under the circumstances, have been better?"

"It might, my dear, but Mrs. Drew obviously didn't tell you I was left this house, and happen to like it. And to be able to look after myself for a change I consider a very real privilege. As a matter of fact Mrs. Drew does come in and tidy me up occasionally, but one lone bachelor doesn't create much work."

"Your sister . . . ?"

"Yes, Alison." One dark eyebrow rose fractionally. "She and her husband do spend a little time with me."

And he had accused her of being economical with words!

"It's really a family home," she mused, unthinking, and went pink with confusion when he added smoothly,

"A house for children." A slight pause, silence, apart

from a rising wind against the window. "First, Miranda, I should have to find myself a wife. As I've told you before, people around here observe the conventions."

"I'm surprised you haven't done so before now." To hide a very real disconcertion the words tripped impulsively off her tongue.

"Perhaps I haven't met the right girl," he grinned, not obviously put out by Amanda's pertinent question. "I can assure you that when I do she won't be long in knowing about it."

A faint shudder traversed the length of Amanda's spine, quivering into definite awareness. In spite of his tolerance something in his voice seemed to hold a soft threat, a hint that she could go so far but no further without some definite retaliation. The cool glitter in his eyes spoke to her, giving emphasis to what he said. If Jason loved a girl what chance would she have of ever escaping?

The faint underlying threat in his voice pinned her to her chair. "I shouldn't believe in wasting any time, Miranda."

Curiously at a loss for words, conscious of tension in mind and body, she shook her head, her hair, a silken cloud beginning to grow long again, falling across her warm cheeks. Retreating with the wavering instincts of a coward, she said, "I think I'll go to bed, if you don't mind. The snow seems to have made me tired."

"Your too recent attack of flu, you mean, although being out in the snow could be a contributing factor."

He spoke brusquely, there was nothing to warn her as she jumped to her feet he would catch hold of her wrist to pull her swiftly against him. "Poor Miranda," he murmured as she jerked against his side, "did you imagine I would let you escape so easily?"

For one moment, when she might have been free, Amanda was startled, too taken by surprise to move, too shocked to find within herself even the smallest gesture of protest. Tension mounted in her, fine and taut, a prickle of sensitive awareness, while she sought to convince herself that nothing he had said had in any way prepared her for a development like this. His hands slid into the small of her back as he pulled her completely into his arms, his eyes faintly enigmatical. "Poor Miranda," he said again, very softly. "Aren't you even going to struggle?"

For a man whose business was hotels his muscles were surprisingly hard and tough, and there was some violence in the way he drew her to his side. Through her thin shirt she could feel the thump of his heart against her bare skin, and her head spun a little as she quivered from the first shock of reaction. She didn't struggle—she didn't, all of a sudden, want to struggle, a strange sensation of finality subduing any reactionary feelings sweeping over her like a cloud. She couldn't begin to guess why he had pulled her into his arms. Maybe there didn't have to be a reason? Perhaps like Herman he just plainly wanted her, and like Herman he was endeavoring to take what he desired? Yet the thought of this man didn't shock her as Herman had shocked her. Jason was someone entirely different. If he wanted her he might be content at first with kisses, to woo her gently until he was sure she cared enough to give herself completely. With Jason a girl wouldn't need to be scared.

Lost in the extravagance of her thoughts, she gave no indication of having even heard what he said. With a soft sigh she relaxed against him, one hand, seemingly of its own accord, finding its way under his jacket, hugging him to her, finding an exquisite delight in just being near him, allowing totally alien emotions to wash over her, sweeping her up. It was unbelievable, yet utterly magical that anything could be like this!

"Miranda—" his voice was low as his hand slid under her hair, forcing her face up "—are you telling me the truth about yourself? Girls who wander as you do are not usually without some experience, but how could I ever be sure? You're young and seemingly innocent, yet how could I tell?"

"I don't know. . . ." In her drugged state Amanda was scarcely aware of what he was saying, the reply she gave barely more audible than the pulse that beat unevenly at the base of her throat. When he deliberately bent his dark head and put his mouth to it the gasp that escaped her parted lips came more clearly to his ears.

"Miranda." His voice deepened, thickening slightly as he spoke against her soft skin. "You're small, so slender, I could crush you. Yet you're all woman, or will be before I'm done with you. You aren't scared of me, are you?"

His arms tightened and a surge of something like flame closed over her, blocking out everything else. What did she care whether he thought her innocent or not? In his arms she had certainly no wish to remain so; the impulse to surrender smoldered in every vein. She drew a soft, shuddery breath and lifted her lips to his, one hand going urgently to his face. When his head came down and he found her mouth, her muffled cry seemed to strike right into him.

To run right through him, as did the way in which she responded to that first touch of his lips, surrendering to his will with compulsive desire, not attempting to hide in any way the complete submission of her body beneath the dominant strength of his. Beneath his mouth her trembling lips parted, quivered in what might have been a soft moan, but he continued to kiss her, pressing her head back into the hard curve of the settee, his hands holding her, arousing in her an ever increasing response.

"Miranda!" He spoke her name again, then released her lips momentarily while he still held her close, his eyes studying her, oddly hesitant, yet clearly determined, not willing to relinquish an inch what was so nearly within his grasp. "Miranda," he said softly, "you won't have any regrets."

She stirred, aware that he waited, taking a long time to open her eyes. Never had she known this consuming, intolerable weakness, such burning excitement, such complete indifference to the consequences of her behavior. Why must he ask questions, expect answers that her feverish mind refused to give, while she only wanted to drift and drift, to allow herself to be consumed by the tumult of her senses.

"Please, Jason," she whispered, her haze going no farther than his mouth, her heavy lashes falling again as his eyes glittered formidably and he began once more to kiss her, the pressure of his lips on her hot skin bringing a burning delight, an aching desire to belong to him completely. No longer was she Amanda, prudent young daughter of Professor Trent, rather proud of her virtue but someone entirely different. In Jason Meade's arms her whole preconceived conception of herself was shattered. She was just another woman, seemingly more wanton than most!

Jason kissed her. He heard and understood the wild sweet longing in her voice and left her in no doubt that he was more than able to furnish all she desired. The pressure of his mouth softened and deepened until reality wasn't there anymore, just a high, wild singing in her ears, a thunderous clamoring of emotions.

Then suddenly, as the pressure of his mouth began to change subtly and his arms hurt, a penetrating knocking somewhere in the hall broke through a moment charged with tension. The man lifted his head with a soft exclamation, and Amanda was released, to fall back against the disordered cushions, jerked back rudely to full realization. Horror replaced the sensuous clouds in her eyes as she stared up at Jason. A knock on a door had saved her! This was the only message to register on her numbed brain. Unrealistically Victorian, she could think of nothing else as Jason, after one decisive glance, turned quickly and left the room.

Not wanting to give herself time to think or even to tidy her tumbled hair, Amanda struggled to her feet and rushed after him, the excitement in her veins changing to shame and a sad little fury.

Tom Drew was standing in the hall beside the library door. She heard him explaining to Jason, "I'm sorry, Mr. Meade, I thought you was in here. No wonder I couldn't get you to hear!"

She heard Jason say, "Well?" tersely.

"It's the little filly, sir," Tom replied. "I think she's going to have her foal and I think there could be complications. I'd like you to come and have a look, and I certainly think we'll need the vet."

Tom's hurried explanation stopped Amanda in her tracks, her startled glance swinging to Jason, her quick compassion for all four-legged animals showing in the anxious concern that widened her shadowed blue eyes. Had Jason forgotten no phone was working? There could be no help in that direction. "Tom," she said quickly, unconsciously following the line of her thoughts, "what are you going to do about that?"

Tom, about to turn away, stopped and stared at her, his keen country eye apparently noting for the first time her slightly disheveled appearance. "I don't rightly follow you, miss," he replied slowly.

"I think she means the telephone, Tom." Jason glanced toward her briefly before adding. "Just go back to the stables, old man, I'll be with you in a minute."

"Go to bed, Miranda," he ordered, almost before the man had time to turn around. "There's nothing more you can do tonight."

Nothing more you can do tonight! Like a parrot Amanda repeated the words silently in her mind. "Couldn't I come and help?" she offered. "I'm used to emergencies."

"Not this sort, my dear." His eyes mocked intentionally, and suddenly she hated him.

She had been stupid in the drawing room, and sillier still to imagine that such an interlude with Jason might put their relationship on a friendlier footing. An interlude such as they had shared had been no foundation for anything so comforting as friendship!

"Go to bed, Miranda," Jason repeated, reaching for his coat, his eyes glinting off her face, reading her thoughts with ironic agreement. "There's always tomorrow." The sardonic inflection in his voice made her want to cry.

Growing hot and cold by degrees, Amanda watched him go. In his refusal to accept her help it seemed he had totally rejected her. Could any girl's humiliation be so complete? How could she ever have imagined she might have loved a man like that! She ought to have known that in a few short days such a thing was impossible. Men! On a wave of bitterness she hated the lot of them. Herman, who had made her aware if only indirectly of her body, and now Jason, who must from experience have been only too conscious of her half-awakened state, and only too ready to supply further tuition.

Rushing upstairs, she flung herself onto her bed for the second time that evening, burying her face in her pillow, feeling the skin burning against the cool linen. She longed desperately for morning, another day, when she would leave Merington for good. Sometime during the next evening she would escape, and once at Combe Farm she would be safe forever. Jason Meade she need never see again!

CHAPTER FIVE

By LATE THE FOLLOWING AFTERNOON most of the snow had disappeared and Amanda knew it was time for her to go. And when she did go it couldn't have been easier, although her actual journey to Combe Farm was an experience she wouldn't choose to repeat.

She had scarcely seen Jason all day. She had planned to be up early, but exhausted by a surfeit of emotion she had overslept, and it was past breakfast time when she woke to find Mrs. Drew standing beside her bed with a tray.

"What time is it?" She'd stared up at Mrs. Drew, her eyes wide with dismay.

"Just gone ten, dear. Mr. Jason said to let you sleep. They've been out all night with that little horse and she hasn't had her foal yet." Her eyes wandered curiously to Miranda's pink cheeks, her expression faintly disapproving. "Mr. Jason said you would be tired, but I must say you look all right to me."

"Of course," Amanda murmured tersely. "You shouldn't have bothered bringing me breakfast, anyway."

"Mr. Jason insisted. I've never known him to be like this before."

Amanda had ignored this, not sure what lay behind Mrs. Drew's remark, but annoyed with herself for sleeping in, especially today when she had so much to plan. Perhaps even now the thaw had set in and Jason was waiting to take her into town, to reassure himself about her head? She certainly needed her head examined, but in a different way from what he had in mind!

"Has the vet arrived?" she asked quickly, as Mrs. Drew, still frowning suspiciously, turned to go.

"He's been here half the night and he's coming back again this morning." Inadvertently she told Amanda all she had needed to know.

As soon as the door had closed behind Mrs. Drew she had put aside her breakfast tray and scrambled out of bed, rushing to the window to stare out across the garden to the moors beyond. As she had thought, the vet had got here because the snow had all gone. It didn't seem possible, Amanda had blinked, scarcely able to believe her eyes. Just odd patches remained, giving a curious patchwork effect to an otherwise drab landscape. In front of the house the gravel was clear, apart from long pieces of broken gray ice imprinted with tire marks. It was only on the drive, where the drifting snow had packed hard and deep, that a quantity still lay, but even this had been traversed by the vet's car, as was obvious from the swiveling tracks.

Quickly, after a hasty wash, Amanda dressed and ran downstairs, depositing her tray in the kitchen before running outside. It seemed important to discover if her eyes had been deceiving her from her bedroom window. To her satisfaction it was a morning filled with the promise of a fine day, the wind from the south soft and surprisingly warm after the icy temperatures of late. She went only as far as the garden wall where she turned as if for a final look at the old house, her eyes wandering over the old gray stone, her gaze clinging unconsciously to the deep-set drawing-room window where the evening before Jason had almost forced her to respond to him. Useless to recall her own part in that little fiasco. It was only by condemning him completely that she would be able to banish him from her heart.

She hadn't searched for him that morning, much as she had been tempted to. Much as she had longed to go down to the stables she had thought it wiser to stay indoors and help Mrs. Drew. In this fashion she hoped to allay any suspicions. She might even convince Jason she hadn't actually noticed the change in the weather, or if she had that she had deliberately decided to ignore it so that she might remain at Merington a little longer.

When Mrs. Drew took a basket of sandwiches and tea to the men at four o'clock Amanda stayed behind, grasping the opportunity, after drinking a mug of tea herself, to search for her rucksack in the old brick laundry behind the kitchen. There would be nothing much to put in it, but Jason might think it odd if she left it behind. She had found it almost immediately, and had just been about to pick it up when, to her utter surprise, Jason himself spoke behind her.

He had spoken softly, but her hand that had gone out to pick up the bag had drawn back as if stung. "I was wondering where you'd got to, Miranda Smith," he had said.

She had swung around then, totally defensive, praying his sharp eyes hadn't spotted her intentions, saying with some confusion the first thing to enter her head. "I didn't come down to the stables because I thought you didn't want me anymore."

He had stared at her without answering, and the only sound had been the faint hum from the big deep-freeze behind them, the whisper of the wind beneath the door. It was as if all the taut emotions of the night before had built up to this. A tension between them, almost physical in its reality, too explosive to touch. "Jason!" she whispered unconsciously.

He had moved in on her then, his glance wholly mocking. "You do make the silliest remarks." He had taken a handful of her hair, his hand at her throat, thrusting her back hard against the cold stone wall, his body so near her own she was unable to move. He had bent his head and kissed her full on the mouth. "Miranda," he had said, "I want to apologize for last night. I was in too much of a hurry. This evening will be different, you'll see."

"No!" said Amanda.

"Yes!" he had replied with meaningful persistence.

Mrs. Drew had returned and Amanda had wrenched herself free with a shudder that went through every inch of her body. There had been no mistaking his intentions. After his horse recovered, he would return to the house and there would be no resisting him! It was imperative that she get away in good time. She overheard him telling Mrs. Drew he should be in before midnight. He might even come to her room. Long before then she must be gone, gone without a trace and on her way to Combe Farm.

It was easier than she had thought possible. Immediately after dinner Mrs. Drew said she was going to bed. She had had a headache all day and felt tired.

"I'll wash up," Amanda said, hurrying her on her way. "You pop upstairs and when I'm finished I'll bring you a nice cup of tea. Mr. Meade and Tom have all they need down at the stables, so you don't need to worry on that score. I think they have enough food to last a week!"

Mrs. Drew nodded, needing no persuading, and Amanda swiftly performed the promised tasks, feeling it was the least she could do before she went. Boiling the kettle, she made up a flask and carried it up to Mrs. Drew. "This should last you all night, should you need it," she smiled.

After that there was nothing left to do but write a short note to Jason, which she left in her room. In it she thanked him for allowing her to stay at Merington and explained that she had borrowed three pounds from the petty cash box in the kitchen that she would return as soon as possible. She signed herself simply, Miranda.

The three pounds she actually did take, stuffing them regretfully into her trouser pocket. If the family wasn't back and she couldn't get in or find her shoulder bag, then she might need some money to see her through until she could get to a bank in the morning. Besides, she thought with a rather miserable shrug as she let herself out, it would seem more in keeping with the beatnik character she had adopted to take something that did not belong to her. Jason, no doubt, would not be surprised.

A half-moon shone intermittently through the clouds as she left the house. It bathed the wild moors in a surprisingly clear light, but cast long shadows to which Amanda clung, afraid that someone might see her leaving. The drive was still rough with patches of unmelted snow and she tended to stumble, but a peculiar ache in her heart worried her more than her slithering feet, and almost before she reached the end of the drive she was crazily tempted to turn back before anyone discovered her absence.

Thrusting such thoughts to one side, Amanda carried on, walking easily once she was out onto the public road that, to her relief, was clearly signposted. During daylight hours Dartmoor hadn't appeared particularly desolate, but at night a vast opaque gloom seemed to envelop hill and combe alike, at times almost blotting out visibility, giving a rather frightening sense of unreality. As she walked the wind dropped, and the heavy, damp mist that often follows a thaw seemed to creep up around her feet, creating odd distortions, making ordinarily inconspicuous hummocks look like mountains, and the tors to tower in grotesque formations, giving an atmosphere of cruelty and mystery Amanda couldn't shake off. She knew a distinct feeling of mild terror, a feeling that the spirit of the moor was not friendly toward strangers, but rather resentful of those who came from other parts and invaded her fastness. Her blood ran cold as she glanced across the treeless, trackless waste and thought of the pagan rites that might have been enacted here centuries ago, might still be today if the atmosphere of the place was anything to go by.

Jason Meade, she pondered, thinking with a faint shudder of his grim darkness, would surely have ancestors who had practiced such black magic. Maybe he still employed a little of that dark propensity himself? Just enough to enable him to capture with surprising ease the emotions of one foolishly impressionable female, should he so desire! If she hurried, she might consider herself fortunate at having escaped so lightly. Wild longings and bitter regrets could be merely a trick, born of the atmosphere of these wild empty spaces. Witchcraft, transient through space, urging her to return, to surrender herself completely to Jason's arms, was to be ignored as utterly ridiculous! Like a mirage to which she could be heading only to find it didn't exist at all, except in her imagination.

A bird flew out of its hiding place where it had settled for the night, startling her, and then she laughed at her own nervous fancies as she came at last to the rambling group of buildings that she took to be Combe Farm. As she turned off the road there was a brief prayer in her heart that she would find Richard and Eva at home. Otherwise she would be sunk! There would be nothing for it but to walk to the nearest village, miles away, and try to find a bed for the night. It would be a long walk, and she would rather not think of the suspicious glances she would be sure to meet at the end of it. Rather than face them, she would as soon sleep here in a barn—only Jason might find her. This time, she thought bitterly, he could add stealing to his former charges of breaking and entering!

It was only when she was actually in the lane leading to the farm that she remembered her bag. To her utter surprise and delight she found it, caught high, yet concealed in a bush that grew out of the side of the gutter. No one would ever have guessed it was there unless they had known where to look, and Amanda's relief in finding it was only surpassed by the fact that the contents appeared to be safely inside, and almost bone-dry. It seemed her luck had changed decidedly for the better, and hugging her bag to her she was further cheered by the light that she saw suddenly shining from one of the farmhouse windows. Someone, it seemed, had just switched it on, as it hadn't been there a minute ago. It could surely only be the family?

Heart in her mouth, Amanda ran down the rest of the lane, feeling decidedly foolish, urgently hopeful. No one would ever believe a story such as she had to tell, but then no one must know it! It might be dreadful having to tell a deliberate lie, but better to do that than cause her father and Eva agonies of embarrassment. Besides, the sordid little tale of the last few days might be better not related.

As things turned out she had no need to worry. Richard Trent himself answered the door, and with a faintly surprised grunt bent and kissed her cheek. "Almost," he said, "I didn't recognize you. We only got back ourselves this morning."

Almost as if she had only been gone since yesterday. Amanda wondered, with a wry grin, if her father, always the most absentminded, recalled exactly how long she had been away.

Eva's greeting was warmer. To Amanda's surprise she found herself folded in a startled but delighted embrace. "Amanda, my dear, we thought you were on your way back to America!"

"I changed my mind," Amanda explained.

No one disagreed. They seemed to accept this as quite logical. "But you've been in London?" Richard asked.

"Yes. My luggage is still at Paddington," she added quickly, hoping to gloss over this part of the business. With luck no one would ask about times or dates.

"You didn't want to bring it in case we weren't back. It might have been wiser to have rung, but it doesn't matter now that you're here." Eva smiled cheerfully, inclining her graying head. "Well, your luggage is no problem, we can send for it right away, but first we'd better go and make up your bed. The heating has been off, but the house is beginning to warm up."

"Of course," Richard beamed, still absently, "it's wonderful to have you."

"Wonderful," Eva echoed, and, suddenly with a swift feeling of gratitude Amanda felt like weeping. She hadn't dreamed of a homecoming quite like this. She hadn't anticipated being turned away, but she hadn't thought it possible that two people whom she had seen so little of for years could be so welcoming, especially Eva. Stepmothers, after all, were supposedly unfriendly, but this was surely a fabrication. It was just that she and Eva had never had a chance to know each other properly. Wistfully Amanda thought of time lost, of opportunities that might not come again. Yet it seemed that she and Eva could still be friends, and it never did to dwell too much on that which was past. With an infinitely lighter heart she followed her stepmother upstairs. It was only later, when she was in bed, that she realized no one had so much as mentioned Veronica!

Next morning Eva came to her room and talked. Like Mrs. Drew she carried a breakfast tray, and Amanda felt delightfully spoiled. She sighed with sheer pleasure. It was nice, if only this once, to be fussed over as if she was someone who really mattered. "At this rate you'll never get rid of me," she smiled as Eva placed the tray before her on the bed.

Eva said she was far too thin and looked as if she could stand a little spoiling. And, as she had only just come, who wanted to get rid of her anyway? "I think we've left you to your own devices long enough," she said firmly.

Eva, Amanda decided, was much nicer than she remembered. She looked nice, too, with her softly curling hair and gray eyes, her rather matronly figure. She felt oddly surprised that Veronica didn't care for her very much.

"It's good to be here, if only for a little while," she murmured as Eva, obviously inclined to talk, pulled up a chair and sat down.

"Try to eat everything up, dear," Eva said mildly as Amanda drank her coffee but scarcely touched her bacon and eggs. "You need a bit of flesh on your bones, as I've just told you."

"I'm sorry, Eva." Amanda toyed ruefully with her plate of bacon and eggs. "I don't feel very hungry, and I know good food costs the earth these days."

Eva shrugged. "That wasn't the point, darling. Your father's just home from a very successful expedition, so we don't have to consider expense. Not yet...."

There was something in the way Eva said it. Amanda glanced at her quickly. "You mean...?"

A light sigh escaped Eva's lips as she rose and walked to the window. "I suppose I mean he hasn't changed. Your father is an exceedingly clever biologist, dear, and in the last few weeks has collected enough material to fill several books. He could quite easily make a very good living by doing just that. But no! He'll do his usual tour of lectures, write a few short articles for leading magazines, and I believe there's a TV program in the offing. Then, after living comfortably for several months, we'll spend whatever's left over on gathering another lot of material in some equally remote corner of the universe."

Amanda frowned lightly over the rim of her cup. "Some women would say it was the ideal life. You didn't like Nepal?"

"Of course I liked it, dear. Who wouldn't?" Eva's face lighted up momentarily. "We've been before, as you know, to central Nepal, but this time we went to Dolpo, one of the drier zones in the west. We had to wait until the monsoons were over in September, then we flew in by light plane, after which we had quite a long trek, but it was wonderful. I suppose I'm still young enough to enjoy that sort of thing, despite the hardships."

"But old enough to worry about the future, you mean? Richard isn't as young as he used to be."

A half-ashamed smile touched Eva's lips as she noted Amanda's anxious expression. "I suppose that just about puts it in a nutshell, and it's rather lovely to have one of the family to mention it to, although I'd hate you to imagine it was a major issue."

"I don't suppose daddy will ever change." For as long as Amanda could remember her father had roamed the world. It seemed hardly likely he would stop now. "Hasn't he anything put away for his old age?" She smiled at Eva ruefully. "I know he'll never retire, but the day must come when physically he'll be unable to travel."

"Not a sausage," Eva replied. "He doesn't believe in any of the conventional safeguards."

Amanda grinned, appreciating her stepmother's frankness.

"What about the farm?" she ventured. "Doesn't this present any security?"

"Not really. . . ." Eva made a little moue. "It has possibilities. Richard might be more explicit, but there's only about a hundred acres of rather poor land, not worth a great deal. We rent it out to a farmer at a nominal sum. Of course, there's the river, but we've not had much luck with that, so far."

"The river?" Curiously Amanda waited, but Eva, all of a sudden, appeared to think she had said enough.

"Poor Amanda!" she cried. "Scarcely over the doorstep, and here I am loading you with all my troubles."

"But I don't mind in the least," Amanda protested. "I've always thought this is what real families are for—sharing each other's troubles."

"Poor child. . . ." Suddenly compassionate, Eva frowned. "You don't seem to have had much in the way of family life up till now. After I married your father I must have seemed only too willing to let Veronica take over."

"That wasn't exactly your fault," Amanda assured her quickly. "Veronica thought it would be better for me to live with her. Besides, I was old enough to choose."

"At sixteen, a very young sixteen, at that, and still at boarding school! You naturally chose to stay with your sister because she was familiar. I should have tried to arrange things differently instead of taking the easy way out."

"Never mind," Amanda smiled, unexpectedly warmed by Eva's honesty. "I'm here with you now, although I'm not sure how long I can stay. I shall have to get work, or some sort of training. Perhaps you can help me sort something out?"

"Of course," Eva agreed, while narrowly studying Amanda's too pale face. "But why not wait a few weeks, spend some time with your father and me? Surely there's no hurry."

"I seem to have wasted so much time already." Evasively Amanda searched for an excuse. She couldn't stay here and risk running into Jason Meade. Even to avoid him for a short time might be difficult. Yet she could scarcely explain this to Eva.

Eva was frowning again. "Didn't you enjoy being in America?"

"The twins were darlings," Amanda replied quickly, "and the Randalls were nice. But I wasn't exactly getting anywhere."

"Young people have so much ambition nowadays—" There was the noise of a car engine thrusting into the yard below, cutting off whatever else Eva was going to say. Stopped in mid-sentence, she turned to the window to look out.

"Who is it?" Unconsciously Amanda found herself whispering, fearful that she might well know the answer.

"Someone calling, I expect. I'm just wondering if Richard is around. He went out for a breath of fresh air and I

haven't heard him return." Eva pushed aside the net curtain and glanced downward. "Why, it's Jason Meade!"
She spoke after only a slight hesitation of which Amanda
was scarcely aware. "He's our neighbor, in a manner of
speaking, although he lives some distance away. He's
been keeping an eye on Combe Farm for us, but Richard
rang him only this morning to say we were back. We did
try last night, before you arrived, but the lines were down
or something because we couldn't get through. I'd better
pop down and see what he wants. He's not the most patient of men at the best of times."

Irrationally Amanda was almost glad to see her go,
fearful that Eva should notice the blood spinning into her
face. Her body felt suddenly alive with conflicting emotions, and she sank back against her pillows in an agony of
dismay. If she had expected to encounter Jason again, it
certainly hadn't been as quickly as this! Her heart
pounded and a pulse beat painfully at her temple as she
imagined him openly denouncing her to her parents before marching upstairs to drag her out of bed to take his
revenge where it really hurt. Eyes glazed with shock,
Amanda brushed a trickle of perspiration from her forehead, attempting to steady her shattered nerves. She must
try to pull herself together. Jason Meade was a sophisticated man—he wouldn't go to such ridiculous lengths. If
he thought of revenge at all it would be in a crueler, more
refined fashion, something definitely more subtle than a
few well-placed wallops with his hand.

With difficulty Amanda controlled a near sob. This
morning she had woken feeling visibly relaxed, well able
to cope with any vagaries of her emotions, quite determined to ignore the insidious longings that assailed her
heart each time she thought of Jason. Her imagination
she had blamed almost exclusively, an equal mixture of
weakness and romanticism, precipitated undoubtedly by
her recent attack of influenza. In a few ruthless seconds

she had been able to dispatch him from her thoughts completely. Yet he had only to appear like this—she didn't actually have to even see him, to make her realize the absolute futility of such resolutions. Jason Meade attracted her in an almost hypnotic fashion, this much she was now forced to admit. She could only pray she wasn't falling in love with him!

Eva's footsteps quickened as she ran downstairs, and there came the sound of a door opening, distant voices. In spite of Amanda's abject fears curiosity prevailed. Impulsively she slid out of bed and silently crept from her room, moving cautiously to the head of the stairs. She seemed to be making a habit of this kind of thing! Combe Farm was much smaller than Merington, having just four up and four down with a straight wide stair up the middle. Without being seen herself, Amanda was unable to see down below, but she could hear what Eva was saying.

"Do come in, Jason," she said. "How nice it is to see you. It's good of you to call so soon."

"Not at all, Eva. . . ." Jason's deep voice carried. "But I'm afraid this isn't exactly a social call."

Then, to Amanda's utter chagrin, Eva said quickly, almost as if she suspected someone listening and was afraid that Jason's missive might be confidential, "Won't you join me for coffee, Jason? I have it ready in the kitchen."

Jason must have nodded his assent as Amanda didn't hear any more, just the sound of their footsteps receding, the murmur of Eva's low voice as the kitchen door closed. On a tremulously drawn breath Amanda went back to her room, her eyes dark with a hint of strain.

Not long afterward she heard Jason go. From behind the concealing lace curtains her view was unimpaired. Down there, standing beside his car, he wasn't so many yards away, and she stared bleakly at the top of his dark head as he bent to hear something Eva was saying. When he looked up she could almost see the tired lines on his

face, the grim set of his firmly shaped mouth, and sh
wondered, inadvertently, if the little mare had safely ha
her foal. She would hate to think anything had gone seri
ously wrong, yet what else could account for Jason's for
bidding expression? Certainly not her own disappearance
Most likely he had forgotten all about her, in spite of he
brief fears to the contrary.

"Richard hasn't turned up yet, but Jason wouldn't wait
Scarcely stopped long enough to have his coffee," Eva
said, when Amanda came downstairs a little later. "He
just called to see if we'd noticed anyone around. It seem
there've been a few suspicious strangers lately."

"Really!"

"Umm. . . ." Eva had already forgotten. "I told him
there was no one here but the three of us. He knows
Richard has a young daughter, and I told him you'd come
from town with us. It saved going into details. Besides, he
was in a hurry."

A little later, when the washing-up was completed, she
glanced at Amanda rather quickly and said, "I think I'd
better mention, darling, before your father returns, that
we've had a letter from Veronica. It was with the rest of
our mail yesterday when we collected it from the post
office."

Amanda's heart beat apprehensively. Veronica had
threatened, but she hadn't taken her very seriously. Yet
whatever she had written couldn't have been so very in
criminating. Eva didn't look particularly put out.

"She said," Eva went on, "that you'd had some silly
misunderstanding, and you had disappeared. She had
hoped to find you, but you seemed to have vanished without a trace. Your old nanny had heard from you, so she
was sure you must be all right, but she and Herman had
searched in vain."

Amanda's face went white. "Was this all she said?"

"Not exactly, dear." Eva frowned doubtfully. "There

were, I must admit, a few disparaging remarks about your morals, that you'd tried to lead poor Herman astray. Richard doesn't care for Herman, I'm afraid, so he just laughed at that one. He promptly put the letter in the fire and merely said you'd probably only learned the gentle art of self-defense. We all know Veronica could never tolerate opposition of any kind."

Clearly there wasn't much sympathy between Eva and Veronica, but Richard and Veronica had always been good friends. Amanda murmured unhappily, glancing away from Eva's slightly curious face, "I hope my quarrel with Veronica didn't upset daddy too badly?"

Eva made a wry grimace. "Veronica and your father weren't very amicably disposed last time they saw each other," she confessed, "but that had nothing to do with you."

"No?"

"No—" Eva hesitated "—it had to do with the river."

"The river?"

"In a way. . . ." Again there was a slight hesitation. "You see, dear, we have almost a mile of rather valuable salmon fishing on the river. Some of the best fishing in Devon, I believe, and it runs through the middle of our land. Well, Jason Meade, who was here this morning, whom you have yet to meet, would like it. He would like it because he has a hotel that adjoins our land, and it would be an invaluable addition to his business."

There was an odd little silence. Jason Meade, Amanda thought desperately—was she never to escape him completely? That he was involved with the family here at Combe Farm was becoming obvious. His involvement with Veronica she already knew about, if in a roundabout way, but that it could be because of a river seemed highly improbable. It was a surprise, too, to learn he had a hotel so near! Alarming as well as surprising, making Amanda realize how difficult it might be to avoid him. She said, "I don't see what the river has to do with Veronica."

Eva smiled ruefully, unaware of Amanda's unhappiness. "Well, if Richard were to get a good price for the land, including the river, we could put it aside as a sort of nest egg. Remember we talked of it earlier? We aren't in any great hurry, but this is why Richard is holding out for a good price, and he thought Jason might give him one. Veronica, you see, had almost promised he would."

"How could she do that?" Cold suspicion clutched Amanda's heart, even before Eva enlightened her.

"We were sure that Jason was in love with Veronica and intended marriage. At weekends, when Veronica came down from London and Jason was at Merington, they saw a lot of each other. Jason Meade is a wealthy man, my dear, as well as a very attractive one. Can you wonder he's so popular with the opposite sex? But there's no reason to suppose he won't settle down one day and marry. We had hoped it would be with Veronica, but it seems we were mistaken."

Later, while she explored down by the river, Amanda grimly considered what Eva had told her. Not until now, when she was on her own, had she even dared to think about it. Had Veronica really been in love with Jason, or he with her? She hardly supposed it likely that Jason Meade would stop at nothing to get his hands on a mile of fishing, but undoubtedly it would be an asset, and he might have been encouraging Veronica with this in mind. On the other hand, he might have been genuinely in love with her and turned bitter when she rejected him for another man.

If Richard had hoped to procure a more than agreeable price from Jason, a price that would provide the security Eva craved, and also leave a roof over their heads as Jason would have little use for the house at Combe Farm, then he, too, might be feeling bitter. But was Richard being absolutely fair in blaming Veronica? Veronica might have her faults, but it seemed to Amanda that she had been dangled like a bait on the end of a hook. First by Richard in order to get more money for his land, and then by Jason in a despicable attempt to purchase what he wanted cheaply. Only one thing puzzled Amanda greatly. How had her sister, after knowing a man like Jason Meade, escaped wholehearted enough to marry someone else?

Over lunch Eva said to Richard, "Jason called. He seemed a bit unsettled about something—I can't remember exactly. I believe he did ask if we'd seen any suspicious characters around. Anyway, he wants us to go over for a drink one evening. Amanda, too. I said we'd better wait a few days until we were settled in, and he promised to ring nearer the weekend."

Amanda's heart sank as she heard Richard agree. If she had thought vaguely that any social contact between Combe Farm and Merington might have ended with Veronica's marriage then she had been mistaken. On the surface at least there was still apparently some pretense of friendship. Perhaps both Richard and Jason still hoped to achieve their goal, if in other ways.

One thing Amanda was sure about: she wouldn't herself be attending any cocktail party at Merington. She would have to think of some excuse. This time it might not be so difficult, but if there were to be continuous comings and goings then the whole situation would be impossible. She would either have to return to London, or, failing this, to see Jason personally and confess. It should be relatively easy to explain, to make light of the whole matter. Surely the latter would be the more sensible thing to do? Yet, as before, she shrank from his anger, and the possibility that he might choose to inflict some form of revenge that she would rather not contemplate. How could she when she remembered the force of her feelings for him, the quivering awareness she had felt in his arms? A shiver went through her, an agony of sensitive nerves, leaving her as completely indecisive as before.

The end of the week came and went with Richard and Eva spending an enjoyable Saturday evening at Merington. Amanda stayed unhappily at home. It had been, Eva told her, quite a party!

"One could scarcely believe it," she laughed, buttering Sunday morning toast. "They've had quite a storm. After all the fine weather this week it doesn't seem possible, but Jason was telling us he's been snowed up for days!"

"Does he live there by himself?" Amanda heard herself asking, not because she didn't know the answer, but rather because of a sudden urgent desire to go on talking about him. If she couldn't see him it was, in some small measure, a solace to her aching heart to hear what he was doing.

"All by himself," Eva confirmed brightly. "He does have a Mrs. Drew who lives with her husband in a cottage, and comes in when Jason is entertaining. But otherwise he appears to enjoy being on his own. I suppose it does make a change from his usual routine as during summer he's among people all the time."

"He might get married?" Why couldn't she leave it alone?

Eva smiled. "I don't know if I'd enjoy being married to a man like that. He would want all his own way."

It wasn't until the following week that Amanda received her first big fright. Eva asked if she would drive Richard into Newton Abbot where he had some rather urgent business to see to. Eva was too busy to go herself.

"I know he drives, darling," she retorted when Amanda pointed this out, "but his eyesight isn't as good as it used to be—or he's just getting more absentminded, I'm not sure which. Anyway, I would feel happier if you would go with him. I have this talk about Nepalese women to give to the local W.I. this evening, and I don't seem to have it even half prepared."

Amanda's luggage had arrived and had all been unpacked and put away in the huge old oak wardrobe in her room, but mistakenly she had decided to wear her old denim slacks, thinking they would be more comfortable to drive in than a skirt. Her mood brighter, she drove her father without mishap to Newton Abbot. She hadn't realized how good it was to be out and about again. For almost two weeks she had hardly dared to leave the immediate vicinity of the farm for fear of meeting Jason. Now she felt like a fly released from a web of its own making, lighthearted enough to laugh a little at her own foolish fancies. Time, she supposed, had a way of blunting the edge of even the worst fears.

On the way the moors swept before her, drab in November, but with rivers and tors, wide distances to explore. And she had wasted time hiding from a man who had probably never given her another thought.

And if these conclusions brought only a negative comfort, at least they released some of Amanda's frozen vitality, which enabled her to park the car and say goodbye to Richard on a new wave of optimism. She arranged to meet him later, after he had completed his business.

Afterward she wandered, touring the shops, exploring a little, Devon Square and the town's Italian-style Courtenay Park, but it grew too cold and dull to see very much. It was then, in the gathering dusk as she went in search of a news-agent to buy Eva a magazine, that she saw him. He came driving down the street as she waited to cross. He was driving a beautiful blue Mercedes coupe that drew her eyes automatically. And, just as she stared at it, he turned his head, meeting her eyes in a blinding flash of recognition!

Just for one split second, as she stood unable to move, as the blood pounded untrammeled through her body, did she stare at him. Then the big car moved with the heavy flow of evening traffic and he was gone.

CHAPTER SIX

AS THEY DROVE FROM THE MULTI-STORY CAR PARK Richard Trent glanced reflectively at his daughter's white face, and there was unusual concern in his voice as he said, "I wish you'd let me get you a drink before we left. I can't think what Eva will say."

Trying to keep her own voice on an even keel, Amanda replied, "Stop worrying, daddy. I had some tea in a small café about three, and as you've had something yourself there doesn't seem to be much point in drowning ourselves in more."

Richard sighed, frowning at his briefcase before he turned to thrust it suddenly onto the back seat. "I have two daughters," he mused heavily, "and I'm not sure that I understand either of them."

"Well, there's still time!" Unable, in spite of herself, to restrain a slight smile, Amanda replied lightly. The slightly exaggerated pathos in her father's tones had not escaped her. She could have pointed out that owing to his penchant for foreign parts he had rarely given himself a chance to understand anything. His family had usually been relegated to second place, and any responsibility he might have felt had usually been thrust onto other people. Was it surprising if he was beginning to realize this for himself?

He pondered, still frowning. "It would seem I've been guilty of neglect, although it didn't occur to me at the time. Perhaps your American trip was a mistake—Veronica appears to think so."

"It was Veronica's idea to begin with."

"Yes, and while I didn't know Bill Randall personally, I knew of his reputation. He and his wife are a brilliant team. I thought you could do worse. And when I spoke to him on the telephone, he did promise to keep an eye on you."

"Which he did," Amanda retorted flatly, her eyes stoically on the road ahead. "You mustn't take what Veronica told you regarding that too seriously. The Randalls scarcely let me out of their sight, which occasionally grew irksome."

"You were with them almost two years...."

Doubt edged her father's tones and Amanda's lips tightened impatiently. "If you remember, most of the time we lived in the Everglades—a luxurious cabin, I'll admit, but in a very isolated position. Apart from the rest of the research outfit, who were mostly married couples, I often saw no one else for weeks on end. And it was Veronica's idea that I stayed on."

Richard stirred uncomfortably, as if his conscience suddenly troubled him. "I'm afraid I've always let Veronica have too much of her own way, especially where you've been concerned, and she repays me by marrying the wrong man!"

Amanda's smile flickered again, this time with genuine amusement. She need not have worried that Richard would concentrate long on her troubles when he obviously imagined he had plenty of his own. The slightly self-centered set of his face pronounced it. Veronica's marriage had clearly disappointed him, but probably only because it had interfered with his immediate plans. There was only an unexplainable relief in her own heart that Veronica hadn't married Jason Meade. "Veronica appears to be in love with Herman," she pointed out after a small pause.

"Yes, yes...." Richard's mood changed testily. "Herman's all right, I suppose. But that doesn't alter the fact that she married him without a thought for her parents. She could have managed things better, I'm convinced."

Much of this Amanda couldn't fathom out. "Because of the river, I suppose?"

Richard sniffed self-righteously. "I perceive you and Eva have been talking?"

Amanda sighed. She had promised Eva she wouldn't say anything about knowing, but it had just slipped out. "Eva only said you hoped to sell the fishing. I don't think she intended betraying any secrets. It was probably only because Mr. Meade called that she mentioned it at all."

Richard said, "The point is they were friendly, and I think she could have exerted some influence. She knew it was important. She could at least have waited until we had a favorable decision."

Amanda changed gear on a steep hill, driving on silently, her thoughts preoccupied. For as long as she could remember Richard had always been childishly indignant when people chose not to think his way, but if he was disappointed in Veronica what would he say if he was to learn of her own unfortunate adventures with Jason Meade? He would consider—and rightly—that so far as the river was concerned, his younger daughter had probably finished off his chances of selling it completely. Viewed from his angle it seemed more imperative than ever that Jason shouldn't discover her true identity. And absolutely essential that she return to London as soon as possible.

Feeling Richard's impatient eyes on her face, she suggested soothingly and with more composure than she felt, "If the river would prove a marvelous asset to Mr. Meade I shouldn't have thought he'd let anyone or anything stand in his way. If, as you say, he was annoyed when Veronica married someone else, well, this is understandable, but I'm sure he's not a man to mix business with pleasure."

"You haven't by any chance met him?" All of a sudden Richard looked suspicious, noting the faint flush of color on Amanda's cheeks.

"No, of course not," she gulped, her voice shaking, praying he wouldn't notice. Sometimes he could be surprisingly astute. It was dreadful having to hide the truth, but worse still to be forced to tell deliberate lies. A wave of remorse hit her, almost physical in its impact, making her feel slightly sick. Why was it that everything appeared much worse than it had this morning? Seeing Jason in Newton Abbot seemed the culmination of two weeks of misery, affecting her more than she dared to admit. Rather desperately she tried to shut out the image of his dark face, to concentrate on the more practical aspects. There was relief in the knowledge she had posted the three pounds that she had owed him. Even if he hadn't seen her he would have known she was still in Devon from the postmark on the envelope, so it was little use pretending to be alarmed on that account. Her unhappiness stemmed from the vivid reactions that she had felt flood through her as she had watched him drive past. The vivid flash of anger, flicking her momentarily from eyes diamond-hard beneath dark brows, was with her yet, and it was with some effort that she dragged her thoughts away and began talking with her father of other things.

Driving home that evening she had planned to return to London within the next few days, but try as she might, she could not bring herself to suggest it. Although they didn't actually put it into words, there emanated from Richard and Eva the distinct impression that she was needed, and, rather than hurt them, she hid her own uncertainty and stayed on. Time, at Combe Farm, she found, swirled by like the Sea of Tranquillity, the short, dark days making the evenings cozy, rendering a certain languor to the spirit, a drugged dullness to overcome any instinctive urge to escape. Valuable time was lost when even the thought of a career was something to be put to one side until tomorrow. Eva, furiously preparing Christmas cakes and puddings, refused almost point-blank to allow Amanda to do anything constructive.

"I refuse to be done out of a real family Christmas," she declared. "Something will turn up in the New Year, you'll see."

Amanda nodded, faintly troubled but not unwilling to be persuaded as she whisked eggs and creamed butter, following carefully Eva's instructions. The farmhouse kitchen, though not as big as Jason's, was warm and comfortable, more homely with a kettle singing on the old coal range and a cat with two kittens purring beside it. There was also Sam, Eva's small Jack Russell terrier, who had been boarded out while they'd been away. Now, king of the castle once more, he sat nodding approvingly like a little old man, yapping at every small noise he heard but adding immeasurably to the domestic scene. While Eva was abroad he had been left with one of her friends who lived a few miles away. This same friend, she said, was giving a small dance and barbecue during the following week, in aid of charity, and she had bought three tickets.

"She gives it every year," she explained, not noticing Amanda's despairing face, "and usually there are a lot of young people. It would be nice for you to meet someone of your own age. You might even find someone special. You're a very attractive girl, darling, suppose I do say it myself."

"There seems little point in knowing people if eventually I'm to work in London," Amanda replied evasively.

"Nonsense," Eva retorted briskly, picking up a cup of coffee for Richard. "Even if you did, there are always weekends. I don't intend losing sight of you again."

Not even a little comforted, Amanda worked hard throughout the remainder of the day. It was only by working like a Trojan and keeping herself occupied that she was able to keep her unhappy thoughts at bay. Later that evening when Veronica rang from Washington her mood was such that she didn't really care what her sister might say.

Eva, as usual, answered the call. Richard had no great respect for telephones and liked to pretend they weren't there. "That was Veronica," she told them a few minutes later. "I'm afraid she's still worrying about you, Amanda, but I was able to put her mind at rest."

"You told her I was here?" Amanda glanced quickly toward her father, who, apart from an indifferent nod, had subsided behind his newspaper again.

Eva said of course she had told Veronica she was here, and enjoying herself enormously. And quite the belle of the neighborhood! "Well, you could be, my dear," she added brightly, "if you would bother to circulate a bit."

"What had Veronica to say about that?" Amanda asked on a surge of dismay. What on earth had possessed Eva to say such a thing? She must know Veronica got jealous! And, even from America, Veronica's jealousy could have repercussions.

"Ha," said Eva, quite unrepentant, and oblivious, too, of Amanda's consternation. "I'm afraid she didn't seem to like it one bit!"

Afterward Amanda tried to convince herself she was letting a ridiculous imagination have too much of its own way. There was absolutely nothing Veronica could do. In her own mind Amanda had previously gone over all the possibilities and found them negative. It was possible that Veronica might try again to blacken her character, especially now she knew she was here, but she had little to go on, and Amanda doubted if either Richard or Eva would so much as listen. That her renewed doubts were in any way wrapped up with Jason Meade she refused to consider. She didn't intend seeing him again, so it mattered not one jot whether he knew about Herman and the bathroom or not. Such a tale was unlikely to interest him in any case, even if he should ever come to realize who she was. And Amanda was determined he should not!

All three Trents had been invited to the party the next week, and as Eva kept the tickets displayed on the mantelpiece in the sitting room, it was impossible to forget. This time Amanda couldn't bring herself to produce her usual excuse, and in the end she said frankly, if rather shamefacedly, that she would rather not go. Richard, as usual not greatly interested, only shrugged, but Eva was cross. "You'll never make friends at this rate," she protested. "You should try to be sociable. Besides, what are people to think?"

Remorse pricked Amanda severely as she watched them depart, and impulsively she almost changed her mind about staying at home. But it was a temptation that couldn't be contemplated, much as she felt like a change of scene. An evening spent entirely alone with her own turbulent thoughts might be anything but inviting, yet what other choice did she really have? To run the risk of meeting Jason Meade was sheer foolishness, especially now that Richard's river supplied a further complication. Richard had said only that morning that he had seen Jason, and Jason was still thinking of buying. Her own personal problems might not matter so much once that was settled. The thing she hated most was having to hurt Eva without being able to explain the reason why.

After they had gone she had a bath, then drying herself quickly, she put on her jeans again, not bothering to change into a dress. There didn't seem much point when she was on her own and, when the moon was brighter, she might take the dog along the lane for his evening walk.

In the sitting room she turned down the lights and switched on the TV. There wasn't anything she really wanted to watch, but it might prove a distraction if nothing else. She didn't feel hungry enough to eat any supper and it was too early to go out with Sam. In fact the program she chose proved diverting—a period play set in Cornwall, in the last century, and the male lead was played by a man in his late thirties, a man who looked very much like Jason Meade. Dark, he was, with the same hint of ruthlessness about his mouth, the same impression of latent strength, of temper held finely in check, controlling but not entirely subduing a smoldering suggestion of passion.

Amanda shuddered as he swept the girl he desired into his arms, kissing her rebellious lips with deliberate intent, his arms restraining her struggling body with practiced ease. So absorbed was she that she failed to hear the car draw up outside. Nor was she aware of a door slamming, and someone walking toward the house, until Sam started barking. Even then, with her senses pleasantly relaxed, she found nothing alarming in the knock that sounded through the house as the heavy old door knocker rose and fell, as the silence that followed announced clearly someone waited for an answer.

It didn't occur to Amanda to ponder deeply on who might be there. Though sensitive to a degree, she wasn't by nature particularly nervous or frightened at being left on her own. Old houses, for her, held no terror, she had always found them comforting. With a quiet word to Sam she switched off the TV. It was possibly a neighbor with a message, or calling casually to borrow something, not an entirely unheard-of occurrence even at this time of night. Firmly she drew back the old-fashioned bolt that Eva always told her to use if she was in alone, and opened the door with an inquiring smile—a smile that froze on her lips when she saw who it was who stood there on the step. None other than Jason Meade!

Almost daily Amanda had expected something like this to happen, but until now fate had been kind, protecting her, it had seemed, from such a disaster. Now it appeared her luck had run out, as, nerves stretched to breaking point, she stared at him with wide, frightened eyes, wondering if she was seeing aright. In that instant the hall seemed suddenly to be swirling around her, blurring and dissolving as she was swept away in the ice-cold displeasure of his eyes, greeny gray eyes, cold like wintry seas that threatened to drown her, and defensively she flung a hand across her face, hoping that when she looked again he would be gone.

But unfortunately he proved no figment of her imagination. Another glance convinced her, but as she gazed into the dark face of the man who so strangely haunted her dreams, a sense of unreality overtook her. How had she ever hoped to escape him? Shock, eclipsing anything she had known before, paralyzed her tongue, washing the hot color from her cheeks and leaving her creamy pale, visibly shaken. She drew a quick shuddery breath, audible in the charged atmosphere.

Jason spoke first, after that steady, calculating appraisal, and, even knowing he was angry, she was in no way prepared for the harsh coldness of his voice. "Why the hell didn't you tell me?" The question hit her, full of a leashed violence, giving her no quarter.

Taut with a saving indignation, Amanda suddenly found her own voice and answered back, "You never gave me a chance."

"A chance? Good God!" His white teeth snapped together as his hands went out, clamping like steel on her shoulders. "How else would you describe almost a week spent in my company? You had each day, hours, when only a few minutes would have sufficed—and you say you had no chance!"

"I still say it. . . ." Her voice choked, caught in the pulse beating heavily at the base of her throat, burned in the flame that spread where his hands curved the fine bone against her neck. Never had she seen him like this, eyes dark and flashing, furrows of emphasis and tension between his dark brows.

He caught and held her eyes with the hard, cynical look in his. "Let's go inside," he said tersely, almost thrusting her back as he slammed the door. "If nothing else you owe me some sort of explanation."

Almost as if he owned the house he propelled her in front of him into the sitting room, his hands leaving her shoulders to fasten with continuing relentlessness on the soft flesh of her upper arms, eliminating any possibility of escape. In front of the fire he stopped and released her abruptly, as if the touch of her tried even his inexhaustible control. "Now you can begin to talk," he said smoothly. "And we'll have the truth for a change."

Amanda couldn't think straight. Her mind still whirled in dazed little circles. "How did you know I was here?" she gasped. "Or did you just call to see daddy and Eva?"

His narrowed eyes moved over her lovely flushed face, and he laughed sarcastically. "A woman's curiosity must always be satisfied! But it might be a pleasure to tell you so much—just enough to illustrate that deception doesn't really pay."

"I didn't deliberately set out to deceive anyone," she protested.

"Just shut up for a minute, won't you!" He advanced again and she retreated, stumbling back into a chair, from where she continued to stare at him. He towered above her, a hard mocking light flaring in his eyes at her physical helplessness. "Right at this moment," he said, "I'd like to break you in two, but that might not serve any useful purpose. You want to know how I discovered your whereabouts? This evening when your parents arrived at Newton Hall without you, it suddenly struck me that there was something very peculiar about a girl who always stayed at home. You might call it intuition, but I suddenly realized that Richard's mysterious young daughter was none other than you."

"Intuition?" Amanda repeated, shivering in spite of herself. This man was surely half devil, as she had suspected when she had left his house on the moors.

"Don't look at me like that," he rasped, eyes glittering. "I've always found it extremely useful."

"Not regarding me, surely!" she challenged.

"But yes," he replied with soft irony that was wholly deceptive. "I talked, I'll admit deliberately, to Eva. She was hurt and rather puzzled at not being able to persuade you to come out. And while she talked I thought of other occasions. The time when I called at Combe Farm the morning after you'd disappeared. The evening I asked you all around for drinks and only Richard and Eva turned up. Then, a few minutes after seeing you in Newton Abbot, I happened also to spot Richard. Suddenly this evening at Newton everything seemed to fall into place. I was, shall we say, convinced that I knew exactly where to find Miranda Smith. And as you see I wasn't mistaken."

His eyes held hers, moving across her face coolly, but his voice bit into her like a whiplash. Amanda made a desperate bid to emulate that coolness. "So," she said, "you left the party and barged straight in here. You didn't wonder if you'd be welcome!"

"You misjudge me, my dear." His voice was silky. "I'm not totally a barbarian. I had to return for a short while to Merington, and merely suggested to Eva that I call here on my way back, that I might, by using a little gentle persuasion, induce you to change your mind and return with me to the ball."

"That was despicable! Of course I shan't come."

"But I think you will, Miranda. . . ." His tones held a suave threat, his continuing use of her fictitious name indicating that he was not yet prepared to overlook that which was past. "The night is still young," he went on. "Time enough for you to change your mind. But first you're going to tell me why you didn't tell me who you were in the first place, and why you walked out on me without a word of thanks?"

"I left a note!" Already she had decided not to go with him one yard, and a fine defiance flared in her eyes as she stared up at him from the comparative safety of her chair. In an evening jacket with a white, ruffled shirt, he looked incredibly handsome, but also devastatingly hard. Not a man to be distracted from a chosen course, or turned by feminine wiles into something less than he was. The few words she murmured could hardly have made less impression.

He repeated now, with enticing sharpness, "You left a note—and Mrs. Drew found it."

"I left it on my dressing table."

"And how did you expect me to find it on your dressing table?"

Color flooded Amanda's face vividly as she became aware of the trap he had set so deviously. Jason knew what she had thought he had in mind that evening and was punishing her accordingly. When she didn't reply, but sat in sullen silence, he reached down, jerking her to her feet with a ruthless gesture, his fingers hurting again on her arm.

"You thought I intended coming to your room," he said.

"No. . . ." Her flush deepened, both mentally and physically. His hands hurt, yet filled her with a riotous fire, and she squirmed. "That is—I don't know," she gasped, illogically breathless. "You thought I was just wandering around, looking for amusement. A man doesn't always respect a girl like that."

"Miranda," he rapped, his eyes traveling over her narrowly, "it could quite easily have happened, but I assure you I had no intention of going to your room that night. However, such an incident might serve to illustrate the absolute folly of your actions. Another man might not have resisted such a temptation. Why in heaven's name didn't you tell me who you were to start with? You could have saved yourself much embarrassment. Didn't you realize you were playing a dangerous game?"

Amanda's breath hurt sharply, and her thick lashes flickered. There was some look on his dark face, some indefinite change in him that supplied the missing text to what he said. He wasn't, she thought, a man given to platitudes. Why hadn't he told her outright exactly what he had in mind? He didn't even have to spell it out—she understood only too well! When he had kissed her, held her in his arms, he had only been amusing himself. He had accepted her at face value, and was now making it quite clear that otherwise he wouldn't have touched her. His involvement had been purely of the senses. No serious interpretation must be put on what had been only a little lighthearted dalliance. How strange that such an impression hurt!

Rather desperately her. mind spun back to the beginning, as the green flame behind his smoldering glance warned her his patience stretched thinly. "If you'd waited before tipping me off that ladder," she countered, "you might have been saved a lot of embarrassment yourself."

"Don't be damned silly!" The dark, devastating voice stung and his lean fingers tightened. "You did come around. At any rate, in the house you could have confessed; the effort wouldn't have strained you. What were you doing, anyway, creeping in here like an escaped convict from the prison?"

"I wasn't—" Amanda's small white teeth clamped tight.

"Oh, yes, you were! Don't contradict me, Miss Miranda-Amanda! There was some particular reason, and on top of this, another reason why you didn't tell me. I haven't got it quite worked out, but don't worry, it will come!"

He was hateful, completely despicable, and his guess was too near for comfort. She retorted quickly, "I was ill, if you remember! Was it surprising I couldn't think straight?"

"You'd better think again, Amanda," he said dryly.

"Perhaps I liked your house, Mr. Meade. Combe Farm, with the electricity cut off, didn't sound inviting." Head flung back, she stared at him defiantly.

He wasn't impressed. "But you aren't that sort of a girl—or so you tell me. Obviously your parents don't know you spent a few offbeat days with me. One wonders what they would think should I tell them?"

"You wouldn't dare!"

"Never dare a fool, Miss Smith!"

Amanda gulped, her face hot, breath coming too quickly. "I don't know what you're getting at," she said nervously. "You could be teasing me?"

"Not a hope," he drawled, his eyes on her flushed cheeks. "So what do we do with Miranda Smith? Bury her decently, or would you rather have a public announcement?"

"No, not that!" She turned away from him, jerking her shoulder from his hands as a thrill of fear went through. How she wished she might shatter his enormous self-esteem by laughing in his face, but she dared not. One day, perhaps, if she had patience! She swallowed hard. "I would be grateful if you didn't mention anything to anyone. Not for my own sake," she assured him, "but because of Richard and Eva."

"Naturally," he nodded, the quirk at the side of his mouth sarcastic. "One must consider them."

Amanda ignored this as another thought descended terrifyingly. "What about the Drews?" she gasped. "Have you forgotten?"

"You can safely leave the Drews to me," he replied. "They've been with me for years and have every comfort, something they're not liable to jeopardize in a hurry. Besides, I think they liked you."

"Thank you," Amanda whispered tonelessly.

He laughed, without mirth. "Don't be in too much of a hurry to thank me, Amanda. I'm not in the habit of doing something for nothing."

Incensed at that, she flung around at him furiously.

"You intend using blackmail!"

He grinned at that, but entirely wickedly. "Nothing so dramatic, Amanda, although if you care to put it that way, yes. I was merely about to suggest you made a little more effort to be pleasant."

"Which might be difficult," she retorted rashly, "where you're concerned. You haven't exactly put yourself out to be nice to me."

"Haven't I, Amanda?" His eyes glinted. "Your memory isn't nearly as good as my own. However—" as color vividly tinted her skin "—a fresh start might be good for both of us."

Refusing to admit even this much, Amanda asked sullenly, and with a hint of apprehension, "What do you actually want me to do?"

The glint in his eyes deepened with punishing intentness. "That, Amanda, would take too long to explain. To begin with you can go and put on something more suitable for the party—to which I will escort you."

Amanda felt struck, somewhere where it hurt most. Events were moving too rapidly, she needed a breathing space in which to marshal her chaotic thoughts, not to be hauled out immediately like some erring adolescent refusing to go to school. Why should she agree to the demands of this man who stood before her? Would not she be only sinking deeper into a mire of deception by agreeing to do as he wished? Yet, in her heart, she knew for the moment she had no defense. Any defensive tactics she chose to employ must be considered later, when she was in a different frame of mind. Not now, when because of Jason's dominating presence she wasn't able to even think clearly. At the moment it was all beyond her comprehension. He didn't even like her, yet he insisted she went with him to Newton Hall!

Uncertainly she stared up at him. "Surely, if I turn up with you this evening, daddy and Eva will wonder?"

"Nonsense." His tones brooked no further argument. "Didn't I tell them I would collect you?"

Just like that, Amanda thought angrily as she ran upstairs and began searching through her wardrobe for something suitable! Perhaps she ought to have asked what he had in mind? He was the sort of man, she suspected, who liked a woman to look smart. His awareness of beauty was something she felt in her bones. Whatever else a girl might have, she would be of little use to him unless she had also a certain attractiveness. Amanda quivered, an uncontrollable reaction as she flung herself into the task of choosing a dress, attempting, with a dismal lack of success, to banish him from her thoughts.

Why should he want more of her company anyway? Hadn't he been brutally frank with her at Merington? She had attracted him in a certain way, but one way only! So why was he bothering now? Perhaps, in spite of his threats, he would soon lose interest. Perhaps after this one evening? As it was he obviously considered she had made a fool of him by not telling him who she was, and was not prepared to overlook it immediately.

Amanda frowned as she removed a dress from its hanger. She supposed it was, in a way, her own fault that she found herself in her present position. She should have told him, and if she hadn't overheard him talking to Veronica on the telephone she might have done. Yet then she might never have known those days at Merington—that evening in his arms! Swiftly she clamped down on such thoughts and made a determined effort this time, forcing herself to remove the protective wrapper from a white chiffon dress, to shake out the cloudy folds of it. There was another— For a hesitant moment her eyes lingered on a silky blue nylon jersey that she had bought in London and never yet worn. Reluctantly she left it where it was. It was special, not for this evening, she decided firmly, closing the wardrobe door.

As she had already bathed it was a simple matter to discard her slacks and slip into her dress. It was the small things she lingered over. Suddenly it seemed important that she looked nice. The white chiffon was conventional with its low round neckline and long full sleeves, but the skirt swirled about her ankles in a very feminine way when she walked. And a little carefully applied makeup, she decided, would make all the difference. A few minutes later, well satisfied, she brushed out her hair, liking the way if fluffed out onto her shoulders. It was growing quickly, framing her face gently from its center parting, and full of gleaming lights. Her reflection in the mirror told her she looked attractive, and because of this she felt a little confidence returning, so that she was able to glance at Jason with a cool little nod as she ran downstairs again.

"I'm ready;" she stated, lifting her chin and swinging her short creamy fur wrap.

He nodded and came slowly toward her, his eyes appreciative on her slender, curved figure. He said with a slight smile, his glance lingering. "Do you realize this is the first time I've seen you in a dress?"

Determined he shouldn't suspect the uneven beating of her heart, she dropped in a slightly exaggerated curtsy. "I hope you approve of what you see, Mr. Meade," she replied coldly.

"Jason," he instructed, "from now on. You'd do well to remember."

On the way to Newton Hall there were things she intended to ask him, but she suddenly found she could not.

He wasn't, she was discovering, a man easily approachable, and although she had decided to ask him frankly about his relationship with Veronica, the query stayed on the tip of her tongue and got no further. Nor did she dare mention her flight from Merington, in spite of an urgent desire to know exactly when he had discovered her missing, and she silently berated herself for not thinking of it sooner. She ought to have asked earlier, when he had first arrived that evening. She ought to have kept her own wits about her instead of being thrown into such a state of confusion that all the important issues had flown from her head. As she sat beside him every nerve in her body cried out to know how he had felt after she had gone. Yet despairingly she knew he would never tell her, not now. The impulsiveness of the moment when he might have done had gone.

For a long time, it seemed, she sat beside him not speaking, attempting to ignore him, fighting her own personal involvement but incurably defeated by her uncontrollable emotions. There was, she supposed, a certain humor in the situation, but it didn't quite reach her. She had sought to deceive him, and he had turned the tables neatly, obviously enjoying his revenge. He had satisfied her curiosity only so far. He had told her of his fury at her headlong flight from his house, but he would never admit to any heartache. That would be entirely out of character, as well as being untrue. The sort of confession she longed to hear would never pass his lips, and she was only deluding herself ever to think it would.

At last, with a hint of desperation, she asked, "Did the foal arrive safely?"

"Eventually...."

She glanced at his clear-cut profile quickly, some faint inflection in his voice warning her not to pursue the subject, yet she found she couldn't leave it alone. "I wondered," she said.

For one heart-stopping moment Jason turned his head and looked at her, a quick blaze behind his eyes visible even through the darkness. "Wondered, but not worried," he taunted. "I thought you might be waiting that evening to congratulate me."

"But I'd gone...."

"Yes, Amanda, you'd gone."

And devil take you, his tone seemed to say, telling her all she needed to know. He was not a man to be ignored, to be rejected without explanation. By doing so she had committed an unforgivable crime. He might demand— and receive, his pound of flesh, but afterward would come her own inexorable rejection. His eyes told her clearly, he might have spoken the message aloud! Suddenly miserable, Amanda huddled back in her soft leather seat, feeling near to tears.

At Newton Hall Richard and Eva waited. "Why, Jason," Eva exclaimed as she caught sight of Amanda, "you've worked a miracle!" Her eyes lighted up with excited animation. She obviously didn't notice the paleness of Amanda's face.

The corners of Jason's mouth quirked as he replied. "It only needed a little gentle persuasion, or perhaps when I asked she was too polite to refuse."

Eva fussed as if Amanda was two years old. "It's the first step that counts. She'll be all right now."

"You have my word for it." Smoothly enigmatical, Jason removed Amanda's wrap and passed it to Eva. "For my trouble she had promised me the first dance."

His ill humor apparently forgotten, he whirled her away, or perhaps it was still there in the faint pressure of his hands. Amanda resisted their insistence fretfully. "You don't have to talk as if I wasn't around—and I don't remember promising you anything."

"Not in so many words, but you did allow that you owed me something."

She winced. He twisted words and people with a devious cunning. Small wonder he was reputed to be clever! "I don't follow," she protested breathlessly.

He murmured easily, "I'll give you time, Amanda. Myself, I'm always in too much of a hurry." His tingling grip tightened with disturbing intimacy, and she gasped as she thought she understood. There had been another occasion when he had used almost those exact words.

"Please," she choked, pulling away from him, refusing to let herself even think about it. "I'm hungry. Could we try to find some supper?"

Amanda moved prettily. With her head back, her dark hair and blue eyes shining, she was eye-catching in a subtle, tantalizing way. She had a fragile beauty, an untouched air about her combined with an unconsciously sensuous movement of body that drew many masculine eyes. If she wasn't aware of it, Jason Meade was. For a while after supper he left her alone, observing her social success from a distance before taking her home.

Richard and Eva had left early, but insisted that Amanda stayed on. "Jason will look after you," Richard said.

An hour later Jason dropped her off at Combe Farm, depositing her neatly on the doorstep. "You didn't find that such an ordeal," he suggested.

"I enjoyed myself," she admitted reluctantly, "very much. Thank you, er, Jason, for bringing me home."

"Thank you, Amanda," he said softly, and departed.

Just like that! Amanda, having let herself in, stood for a long moment with her back against the door, a cool shudder running down her spine. He really was the most unpredictable man!

CHAPTER SEVEN

A FINER SPELL OF WEATHER tempted Amanda to explore. This, and an unusual restlessness that had been with her since she had gone to the dance with Jason Meade. He hadn't been near her since, and that was almost a week ago, but when she mentioned this to Eva, Eva merely said that he was a busy man and would no doubt be giving them a ring before long. Amanda hadn't noticed the quick glance that had accompanied these apparently indifferent words.

She put on a jacket over her jeans and went down to the river. Previously, because of Jason, she had only dared peep at it from over the rough stone boundary wall, but now that the need for secrecy in that direction could be dispensed with, she walked boldly across the uneven ground toward it.

Away from the house all was quiet. There was no sound to be heard but a raven's croak and the river. She could hear the sound of running water long before she topped the rise and scrambled down through the dark ranks of conifers that clothed its banks. The setting was decorative, the river running down a narrow gorge but sweeping in wide curves, the water swirling into deep pools from rocky shallows. Amanda could see at once it would be an asset to any hotel, especially a sporting one. Long stretches of gravel edged the river, and here and there flat slabs of rock would provide a seat from where an angler's wife might watch her husband's performance. Shelter, too, would be provided from the variety of trees. Well hidden from the road, it afforded complete privacy. It was tailor-made for the job!

Amanda sat for a while on one of the flat rocks herself, contemplating the water. It ran dark, as though the recent snow and rain had brought floodwater from other parts of the moor. Richard said floodwater came down in torrents during a rainy spell. Some of the pools looked dangerously deep, deep enough to swim in, in summer. For many hotel guests this stretch of river would provide a great attraction, and she wondered why Jason hadn't already purchased it, regardless of price.

The day, though fine, didn't pretend to be anything else but late autumn. It was too cold to sit pondering. Amanda scrambled to her feet, walking quickly, trying to warm up. She had sat too long. She followed the rough track as it wound through the valley, liking the remoteness, the feeling of solitude. Above her the sky suggested rain, but she took no notice until huge drops began to fall, pattering noisily onto the tinder-dry leaves around her feet, warning her that she could get wet if she didn't soon find shelter. Knowing she must be near Jason's hotel, Amanda ran on. In her pocket she had a few coppers, enough to purchase some coffee, to provide her with an excuse to wait until the downpour was over.

To her relief she had only a few hundred yards to go. Rounding a corner, she came upon it, a huge castlelike building standing in tree-lined grounds. The size and graceful proportions of it caused her to stop for a moment and gasp. Trust Jason Meade to have only that which was pleasing to the eye! The trees looked exotic, as if some of them had been transplanted from foreign lands, the lawns, even at this time of the year, a beautiful emerald green. And, at the end of the pink-graveled drive, stood a galaxy of smart cars in a variety of sizes. A place that undoubtedly spelled *luxury* in large capital letters. Not a place for a girl in a pair of tattered jeans and an even shabbier jacket. Smiling half ruefully to herself, Amanda ran lightly up the wide front steps into the foyer. Were all Jason's hotels, she wondered, like this one?

She ordered some coffee and sat down in the well-upholstered lounge, disregarding the slightly supercilious stare of the man who served her. She sympathized with his feelings—she did look a bit disreputable—but she hadn't expected to come so far. The weather had been wholly responsible, and she could do nothing about that. Lazily she relaxed, sipping her coffee, staring fitfully out at the rain that had developed into a steady stream, looking as if it was in for the day.

Then a voice hailed her as she gazed through the window. Surprised, she glanced around. It was one of the young men whom she had danced with at Newton Hall. She couldn't even remember his name, but he had a better memory.

"Miss Trent—Amanda!" he exclaimed. "I was just going to give you a ring. Since the dance I've been away I've only just returned."

"You're...?"

"Jeff Ronson," he supplied, laughing as she hesitated. "Can I join you for coffee?" Taking her assent for granted he rang the bell and sat down. "I live not far from here," he explained, "but got caught in the rain. I detest getting wet."

"So do I," Amanda smiled—and he smiled back. At least, she thought wryly, they had something in common.

Jeff was pleasant. He was undemanding and easy to talk to and in his company Amanda relaxed. There was none of the tension she felt with Jason. Jeff was a light-hearted boy, not much older than herself, and very like some of the boys she had met in America. There was nothing complicated here, unless he was to take her too seriously, and she must ensure he did not. He had a nice face and good manners and asked her a few questions, but mostly chatted about himself.

She was laughing with him, at a joke he'd told well, when Jason walked in. He came with another man, his manager by the look of him. A porter hovered behind. Jason was stylishly dressed in a high-necked black sweater and a matching black leather jacket. His clothes were perfectly cut and he was impeccably groomed. He looked virile and handsome and drew many women's eyes. He saw Amanda and stopped, walking straight toward her.

"Good morning, Amanda," he said, his eyes flicking to her companion. "To what do we owe the honor of your visit?"

Amanda flushed, hating her inability to match his coolness, and Jason's mood was cool—she sensed it. Nor did he approve of Jeff; she felt this, too, but thought it none of his business. So she murmured a polite good morning, and nothing more.

He appeared to know the young man by her side, and his next words confirmed it. "Haven't you anything better to do with your time, Jeff?" he asked. "I saw your father yesterday. He seems far from well."

It was Jeff's turn to flush, but sullenly. "I'm only having a quick coffee with Amanda, Mr. Meade. I do happen to be about my father's business."

"Then you'd be wise to continue, I think," Jason retorted crisply. "I'll see to it that Amanda has everything she needs."

To Amanda's astonishment Jeff rose, staring at her rather sheepishly. She couldn't understand his attitude—unless, of course, he worked for Jason. He said, "I'd better run along, Amanda, but don't forget, you did promise to have dinner with me one evening. I'll give you a ring."

Eyes wide, Amanda watched him go. What right did Jason have to interfere? She tried to whip up some indignation at his effrontery in daring to accost her like this, to say nothing of the way in which he'd practically ordered Jeff from the hotel! Words, however, died in her throat. She found herself unable to utter them. She had longed to see Jason and now he was here. She couldn't bear to send him away, just like that.

Scowling, he looked after Jeff's retreating figure, then he turned to his manager and introduced him briefly.

The man bowed deferentially, but there was a gleam of curiosity in his eyes as he looked at Amanda. Jason said curtly, "You can send some fresh coffee. I'll see you later."

Nervously Amanda blinked as he settled himself down beside her. Now that the others had gone she wasn't at all sure she wanted to be alone with him. Jeff had been a welcome change, so cheerful with his inconsequential chatter, and although she couldn't remember agreeing to have dinner with him, it might be good fun to do so. It might take her mind off other things she didn't want to think about.

Jason pulled a chair nearer to her own, pouring the fresh coffee when it arrived, but remaining silent until she turned her head to look at him. "Ah, that's better," he smiled as their eyes met.

Quickly Amanda glanced away again. When Jason smiled like that he was hard to resist, although at times she suspected it was a calculated art, and had nothing to do with his real feelings. He loosened the belt of his jacket, undoing the top buttons. The clothes he wore suited him. There was a distinction about him that made her instantly aware of her own casual dress. Did any man really appreciate a girl in trousers? She became acutely conscious of her unruly appearance: her hair straggling damply around her face; her skin devoid of makeup, apart from a smear of lipstick that the rain had probably washed from her lips. Tentatively she ran the tip of her tongue over them in a rather futile attempt to find out.

"Amanda!" The firm note in his voice brought her attention back sharply. "You might stop daydreaming and tell me how you come to be here. I'm assuming you didn't arrive with Jeff Ronson, if he was sharing your coffee?"

Amanda winced, trying hard to retain a studied indifference. Her chin lifted as she glanced at him distantly. "That surely isn't any of your business, Jason. Nor was it, I think, your prerogative to send Jeff away like a criminal!"

"Must we discuss Jeff Ronson? On closer acquaintance, my dear, he doesn't improve. You'd only be disappointed."

"Well—he's a man, is he not?" She hadn't meant to put it like that.

"If that's all you want...."

She flushed. "That wasn't quite what I intended. You confuse me! I don't mean that way."

He laughed, his eyes derisive on her hot face. "I think you do need a man, Amanda, but all in good time. And not one like Jeff. I'm sure fate will be kinder."

"You seem to know him well!" Her voice rang with light sarcasm. It was futile to persist, but why should Jason have it all his own way? She wasn't a member of his staff, to be ordered at will, to be told what she could or could not do!

Jason's dark brows drew together and he ran an impatient hand around the back of his neck. "His father is an old friend, afflicted with bad health. Young Jeff doesn't pull his weight. His father runs a good business, and he's supposed to help more than he does."

"I see—" Amanda said, but didn't. What Jason told her might be true, but it still seemed no reason why Jeff should obey him immediately. But she wasn't all that interested in Jeff. It was this man sitting so near her who seemed able to set her pulses racing, to cause her heart to start beating in the most unpredictable manner.

Jason leaned forward. "And if it's an evening out you fancy, how about having dinner with me? I'll take you to Torquay. I have another hotel down there that I'd like to show you. You can be ready about six."

"Thank you, but no," Amanda gasped, wholly defen-

sive, not stopping to think. "You don't have to take m
anywhere."

"If it's necessary then I must," he replied, his gree
eyes meeting hers enigmatically. "If I didn't do things i
the proper manner, later on you might feel cheated. A
girl like you, Amanda, tempts a man to use every shortcu
he knows."

"I don't need to be reminded!" she gasped at his ef
frontery.

"You shouldn't have to be reminded of anything," h
agreed coolly. "You should remember enough to think i
wiser to do as I ask without a lot of wearisome argument
You'll be ready tomorrow at six, which should give yo
time to cancel any arrangements you might already have
made."

With a further denial on the tip of her tongue she hesi
tated. His eyes were hard; he was making it quite clea
that he didn't intend to waive his hold over her. Why h
should continue to bother with her at all she couldn'
think. She had imagined that after the ball at Newton Ha
his interest would die. He was older than she was and
much more sophisticated. Beside him she felt naive, un
able to understand the attraction between them, or how
to cope with it. Perhaps like Veronica, he was using her a
a means of access to the river, yet her mind shied away
from such a suggestion, reluctant to believe it. At leas
she knew enough to keep her head, and if he was deter
mined to entertain her, she could take whatever he of
fered with a clear conscience, without feeling in any way
compelled to give him anything in return.

So she checked herself and, after a long moment, sai
primly, "You haven't given me much time, but I'll do my
best."

"I hope so, Amanda," he said dryly, apparently taking
her acquiescence for granted.

"Whatever do you mean?"

He looked pointedly at her tight shirt. "You don't try to enhance yourself. If you've nothing better to wear than the dress you wore at Newton, then you'd better go out and get yourself something."

Scarlet, she flushed. "You really have a nerve," she flashed tautly. "I'll wear what I like!"

"Then I had better like it, too," he rejoined with the uttermost coolness, "or I won't answer for the consequences."

She raised her brows. "Indeed?"

"Indeed," he snapped, leaving her in no doubt as to who was the master. "Wear that old white chiffon and I'll rip it off in two minutes—maybe less if you try me too far. And I'm quite capable of it, you know."

Understandably Amanda never properly remembered her journey from the hotel back to Combe Farm. Jason sent her home in style, refusing to let her walk. After his last outrageous remark about her dress, she had jumped up and left him, almost bumping into his manager as she had turned to go. While the man had whispered to Jason that an urgent call awaited him in the office, she had made her escape, only to find herself followed by one of the porters, complete with instructions from Mr. Meade to drive her home. Unable to find a suitable excuse, especially in the face of the driving rain, she could do nothing else but accept.

Still seething with rage, in spite of a peculiar excitement, she was determined to ignore what Jason said. It had been unpardonable of him to make such an attack on her person. He had no right—or rights; she was not sure which. She probably meant both. Muddled thoughts hurtling through her brain, she ran upstairs, surprised, minutes later, to find herself rummaging despairingly through her wardrobe, considering the row of drab-looking dresses hanging there. She possessed nothing, she was sure, that Jason would approve of.

Minutes later, Eva found her. "Are you looking for anything special, darling?" she asked.

Amanda let her frown stay where it was. "I'm going out for dinner," she confessed without meaning to, "and my escort has requested I wear something decent!" Which wasn't quite how Jason had put it, but just about summed it up.

"Oh, dear. . . ." Eva blinked, mildly startled. "Well, that's certainly an original approach. I must admit, myself, I didn't think much of that rather jaded white chiffon. But who is the man, darling? I would like to know."

Abruptly Amanda told her, not caring for the amused curiosity in Eva's voice. "And I've a good mind to wear my white chiffon again," she added sulkily. "Veronica gave it to me when I left school. I haven't worn it more than twice."

"Once too often, then," Eva said tartly. "I certainly wouldn't advise you to wear it again. Not for Jason. It wouldn't do. Where have you seen him, by the way?" she queried in a rush.

Amanda sighed patiently. She had expected Eva to ask. "It rained while I was out this morning, and I took shelter in the hotel. He came in."

"Just like that?" Eva peered over Amanda's shoulder, visibly impressed. "And you looking a perfect little tramp, darling," she laughed. "We must convince him you can do better." She pointed to the nylon jersey. "Jason might like that."

The suppressed eagerness in Eva's voice caused Amanda to glance at her suspiciously. Surely they weren't hoping she would carry on where Veronica had left off? Unless Jason mentioned it himself, she had no intention of discussing the river. Richard must do his own negotiating in that direction.

Quickly—too quickly, she said, "What Jason thinks is not important, but I might run into town this afternoon and buy some shoes, if I could borrow the car? The shops were just closing when I brought this dress. I didn't have time to get any new ones."

She could borrow the car anytime, Eva assured her, and of course Amanda had to ask if she would like to come with her.

"Oh, that would be lovely!" Eva was delighted. "I do need a few things myself. We can shop together."

In Newton Abbot Amanda had her hair done. It was Eva's idea, but Amanda knew her hair needed cutting and shaping. Though it was growing nicely longer, there was bound to be a lot of split ends. Besides, it was nice to sit beneath the drier and dream, cocooned in a soft, warm world where no one could reach her.

Later Eva insisted firmly that Amanda must have a new wrap. "The one you have belonged to Veronica," she said keenly. "I recognized it. Don't you have anything of your own?"

"Of course," Amanda smiled lightly. "But Veronica leads a very social life. Lots of things are not even shabby when she throws them out."

"Your sister," retorted Eva, "can discard as she pleases, but you aren't obliged to accept everything she offers. You aren't the same size. You'd have to cut most of her things down."

"A little . . ." Amanda admitted.

"A lot!" Eva sniffed.

Finally Amanda went home with a lovely jacket in imitation mink, a present from Eva, along with a pair of silvery evening slippers and a new bag. She ought, she thought wryly, to look extremely smart. Smart enough to satisfy Jason, maybe? She pretended to be delighted, to please Eva, but her heart in no way reflected the sparkle in her eyes.

Jason arrived early the following evening. He had contacted her that morning by telephone and asked if she would accompany him after dinner to the house of a friend. There was some business that was suddenly important. Amanda had agreed, feeling she had little other option, but not at all sure she really wanted to go. For this one evening she hadn't wanted to share Jason with anyone, but then he was not to know.

There was a moon that evening, sailing high in the heavens—not a very full one, but enough to cast a romantic glow. Amanda saw it as she went to the door in answer to Jason's ring. Richard insisted she asked him in for a drink before they set off, and reluctantly she had agreed.

This evening Amanda wore her bluey green dress that suited her graceful figure, and reflected the blue of her eyes. The radiant image that her mirror reflected satisfied her that for this one night at least Jason should have no complaint. The colors enhanced the faint tan that she still had from her trip abroad, giving a fine glow to her skin that she hadn't previously noticed. Her hair looked wonderful. Eva's hairdresser was certainly expert! It was straight and heavy, long enough to coil into a knot at the nape of her neck, a simplicity of style that suited her regular features and showed the perfect shape of her head. As on that other evening when she had gone to Newton Hall, she applied a trace of eye shadow, a hint of color to her lips. A slight shiver ran through her as she had realized how much she was looking forward to dining alone with Jason. Not even the prospect of having to share him afterward could dim a glowing anticipation.

Jason in a dinner jacket was impressive, and when she opened the door and he saw her standing there, her dress gleaming against the shadows behind her, he stood quite still for a moment staring, while a slow fire kindled in his eyes.

Amanda evaded that brilliant glance as best she could, not ready to give way to a quiver of primitive awareness.

With a trace of breathlessness she dropped him a defiant curtsy, her lashes flickering onto lightly powdered cheeks. "Will I do?"

He came forward and took her arm. "Quite an improvement," he teased, "although you never were an ugly duckling."

"Nor am I yet a swan, I suppose," she answered sharply, freeing herself from his hold before his grip could tighten. The mocking tone in his voice hurt, as did his soft arrogance. "Richard would like you to have a drink before we go," she added hastily.

Richard looked tired and confessed that he felt a little weary. "I'm getting on, I'm afraid," he grinned ruefully. "I'm finding traveling more of a strain than I used to. One of these trips will have to be my last."

"That will be the day!" Eva laughed, but Amanda thought Eva might, underneath her lightheartedness, be rather worried. Richard was quiet, preoccupied, inclined to be forgetful. Nothing new in this, Amanda supposed, but one couldn't discount a subtle change in him.

She said as much to Jason as they left. Between them there existed some pretense of friendship, enough for her to mention Richard to him casually.

Jason replied briefly, but with some authority. 'Your father has always lived in a world of his own, and as he gets older he'll retreat further. Like many dedicated men he's totally absorbed in his work. You might be thankful for Eva. She bridges the gap between his world and ours. Otherwise he might lose touch altogether."

"I'm glad he's got Eva," Amanda said simply, but with absolute sincerity.

Momentarily he turned his head sideways, his vivid glance sliding over her. "You're full of concern, yet you never choose to come down here yourself. Your sister came, but you stayed in London. Once I remember wondering why?"

"I happened to be in America!" Stung, she retorted sharply. Suddenly she realized he had mentioned Veronica. Here was the opportunity she had waited for. It should be easy, now, to ask how well he had known Veronica, yet she found herself unable to do so. Perhaps she didn't want to know the answer that must surely fall from his lips. In order to cover a slight hesitation, she felt forced to explain further. "I was in Florida more than two years. Previous to that I was at school and stayed with Veronica during school holidays, and after I left."

"Two years was a long time."

Lulled by the light neutrality in his voice, Amanda went on, innocently satisfying his curiosity. "It didn't seem a long time. There was so much to do, and everything was different. I intended staying only for a short while to begin with, but the people I went with had twin boys, and I grew attached to them. Actually we had great fun. Their parents, like my father, were too busy to bother much, and the twins were used to me. I could never bring myself to leave them."

"But you did in the end."

"Yes, it was a sudden decision. . . ."

"There is usually a reason?"

She retorted stubbornly, "There doesn't always have to be." He would only laugh if she confessed to feeling that life was passing her by. She hoped her negative reply had dampened his interest.

But he persisted, if idly, "I believe you were returning to America with your sister. What was the attraction?"

In the darkness Amanda squirmed uncomfortably, though why she was not sure. It could have, she realized, something to do with Herman. She was well aware that in her own mind she had allowed the incident with Herman to assume unreasonable proportions. He hadn't touched her, even if that had been his intention, but now even to think of him made her feel besmirched in some way.

"There was no attraction," she said carefully. "You see, I'd lived with Veronica since daddy married again—we thought it best, at the time. But Veronica sold the flat after Herman finished his tour of duty. I had nowhere to go."

"Didn't you feel a bit de trop? After all, they'd only been married three months. Couldn't you have managed on your own?"

His voice had hardened again. Quite clearly he considered girls who couldn't fend for themselves spineless. Well, she didn't want his sympathy, but nor would she accept his contempt. She couldn't tell him the whole story, and, momentarily, she was glad, when he was being so disagreeable about the innocent little bit he knew. "Veronica begged me to go with her," she replied stiffly. "I found it impossible to refuse. Besides," she added tonelessly, "I hadn't enough money to find a flat of my own, and I had no job to help me get one."

"Veronica had money of her own," he said disagreeably.

"Yes, I know. But she had a good job, and money that our mother left her."

"Your mother?"

"Yes. . . . You see, she died, as you probably know, when I was born, and a few years previously she'd left everything she had to Veronica. I was a sort of surprise packet, you see, not expected. Daddy said afterward she probably intended to change her will later, but she didn't have time."

"And Veronica never offered you a share?"

"Not moneywise—but she did give me a home when I needed one, and was always good to me."

"And what made you change your mind about going to America again?" His voice slowed to a drawl, as if he sifted and assessed what she told him in his mind like a mathematical problem, sure of his ability to arrive at the correct answer.

Amanda clutched nervously at the edge of her seat, reminding herself to be careful. How easy it was, when traveling like this at night, to let one's tongue betray too many secrets! The road slid swiftly and smoothly by, the effect hypnotic. Jason was controlling her thoughts, his voice playing on her senses in a calculating, attractive fashion, and puppetlike she was responding. This was the hold he had over her, and she would do well to be aware of it. He wanted to know why she hadn't gone to America. It might be wise to satisfy his curiosity, but she hated him for probing. "I guess Veronica and I fell out," she sighed. "Nothing unusual in that—for sisters."

"But you'd already planned to go? You must have had one whale of a quarrel. What about?"

"I suddenly decided not to. Can't we leave it at that?" Her voice rose, slightly hysterical as the whole disturbing incident returned to haunt her. She could never tell Jason the truth, nor was it necessary. Surely he must realize she didn't want to talk about it? It wasn't as if it was interesting. She couldn't think why he bothered. Yet a few seconds later she thought she knew why.

"Do you think Veronica is happy?" he queried, ignoring her plea indifferently. "Herman appears a nice enough chap, but, I imagine, easily led astray."

Hot and cold Amanda went by turns. His sympathy was obviously with Veronica, and his summing up of Herman accurate to a degree. So accurate, in fact, that should Veronica ever relate the story of Amanda's fall from grace, Jason would have no difficulty at all in believing! He was worrying about Veronica's marriage. Why else would he inquire after her happiness? Amanda's lower lip trembled slightly and she bit on it. "I expect she's happy," she murmured, not very truthfully. "She certainly seems to be."

She fell silent after that and Jason, too, became preoccupied, the set of his mouth a little grim, he did not speak again until they ran into Torquay. Jason parked the car in

front of the hotel where they were to dine, but before
they went in he walked with her a little way until they
could see the sea. Even in the moonlight the setting was
panoramic. From where they stood among the high
wooded hills overlooking Tor Bay, the lights of the town
twinkled gaily. And below them anchored boats could
plainly be seen bobbing gently up and down on the water.
Amanda, who had never been here before, felt impressed. The subtropical trees and flowers in the garden
beside them could almost make her imagine she was back
in Florida, and she could smell the sea in the pine-scented
air about them.

Jason, by her side with a protective hand beneath her
elbow, added to the magic of the still, dark night, but confused her mind effectively. All she could think of to say
was, "In summer this must all be very attractive, almost
Continental."

Jason laughed. "Torquay's popularity as a holiday resort dates from the nineteenth century, when the Napole-
onic wars prevented many well-off people from taking a
holiday on the Continent. Times have changed slightly
since then, mostly, I imagine, because of our inclement
weather, but during a hot summer such as we've just had,
I think we might have been almost as busy as the south of
France."

"I must come and see for myself," she said.

He shrugged. "I think you would like it. It has everything to offer."

"Yet you go abroad." She glanced at him quickly.

"I do," he replied, his eyebrow quirking. "I suspect
you've been gossiping with Mrs. Drew?" He smiled again
as she felt a small tremor shoot through her, confirming
his suspicions. "I go to France and Spain chiefly because I
have property development out there. But I do have one
or two special spots, Amanda, that I might show you one
day."

As usual he was teasing. "I'd better see something of Devon first," she retorted, to hide the faster beating of her heart as he took her back to the hotel.

"Not many ever explore the county in which they live," he rejoined mildly, yet slanting her a wicked look as though he knew exactly how she was feeling.

If the appearance of the foyer was anything to go by, this hotel was just as luxurious as his other one on Dartmoor. Pretending great interest, she stared around, in order to hide her flushed cheeks, but his keen eyes noted her heightened color. "Am I rushing you, Amanda?" he queried softly. "Because I mean to—so you'd better be warned."

She tossed her head like an obstinate child, refusing to understand, pretending not to hear the veiled threat in his voice as he spoke, but finding it impossible to evade his gaze for long. Green eyes, faintly cynical, looked down, pinning her own with deliberate concentration. With a desperate effort she pulled herself together. "At times I find it difficult to understand you," she said frostily, and with as much dignity as she could muster.

For a moment his eyes darkened. It seemed he was about to add something more, then suddenly decided to let it go. It was time to eat, and there would be time—plenty of time, later. Some sensitive part of Amanda knew this and reacted strangely, not surprised when he muttered softly that a hotel foyer was scarcely the place to pursue such matters. Their dinner was waiting.

As on Dartmoor, the manager hovered in the background, along with a retinue of staff, all very unobstrusive, but there, nonetheless. Wistfully Amanda wished they could have gone somewhere quieter, where perhaps Jason wasn't so well known. The curious if discreet glances cast in her direction didn't appear to worry him, but she hated to feel herself the center of such interest, and felt resentful that he had subjected her to it.

Once they were seated, however, she forgot about the others and continued to look around her. After all, this was Jason's hotel; why should he go to the additional expense of taking her elsewhere? The place was busy, and when she expressed astonishment he assured her that if it wasn't busy, even at this time of the year, he would want to know the reason why.

"I thought you didn't work during the winter," she said.

"I don't," he agreed, "but I get around. Occasionally a crisis blows up."

"Such as yesterday morning?" she asked.

"Something like that," he nodded. "I might be at Merington, but I'm always available."

The meal Jason chose was delicious, but Amanda could never afterward remember exactly what she ate. She was too conscious of Jason sitting opposite her, and could not but be aware that he gave her his whole attention, rarely taking his eyes from her face. He even went so far as to cover her hand with his while they waited between courses.

As if he was perfectly aware of the effect he was having, his fingers tightened over her quivering ones as, startled, she tried to draw them away. Quickly, still holding her, he turned her hand over in his. "You have beautiful hands, Amanda," he said lazily, his eyes examining her smooth, delicate fingers. "With hands like these you ought to sit on a cushion and sew a fine seam all day."

"Hardly practical for a modern miss," she said in a soft, shaky voice. His hand was warm and hard and excitement thrummed along her veins.

"But you're not duty bound to be a modern miss, are you, Amanda? Although you certainly look one in that dress." His eyes slid over her, teasing yet intent on her slender figure, her silky skin. "You look quite beautiful this evening, Amanda," he said.

Despite the warmth of the room, for no definable reason that she could think of Amanda shivered, her heavy lashes falling even while she suddenly longed for the sophistication to hold his insistent glance. Her dress was a success, she was aware of it. It left her arms and shoulders bare and showed the alluring curve of her breast, the slender span of her waist. In it she felt she was someone quite different from her usual self. A faint sense of strain took possession of her. Perhaps she had had too much wine? She wasn't used to drinking a lot of wine, just a little of this or that occasionally. It had to be the wine, this floating, out of this world sensation that seemed to scatter the few remaining inhibitions she had left. In some ridiculous fashion she was even beginning to like the way he continued to hold her hand lightly, and allowed her own fingers to curl experimentally around his, not willing that this incredible magic should desert her, floating luminously on the tantalizing wave of her drifting emotions.

It was only as the waiter approached their table with the dessert that Jason spoke again in a gentle, tolerant voice, and she aroused herself, her wide blue eyes startled. Quickly breathless, she straightened, returning his smile, faintly apologetic, yet managing to retain an admirable cool in spite of the color that crept under her smooth skin. "I think I was almost asleep," she said lightly.

A glitter of something she could not put a name to crossed his dark watching face. "Well, at least your dreams appeared to be pleasant," he drawled, the quirk at the corner of his well-shaped mouth proclaiming him not the smallest bit impressed by her untruthfulness.

CHAPTER EIGHT

IT WAS VERY PLEASANT IN THE HOTEL, the food, service and decor all being first class, but they did not linger long after they had finished eating. They didn't in fact stay for coffee. Jason told her that his friend's house was some half-hour's drive away, and somehow Amanda sensed he was keen to be off. He wasn't a man to give much away, but this evening she was aware, or thought she was, of an underlying eagerness, slightly perplexing in a man who usually controlled his emotions to a fine degree.

Nor was she proved wrong. "David Hartley has a young mare," he explained as they drove out of Torquay. "She's only four years old and I've had my eye on her for some time, but he's always refused to sell. Now it seems that circumstances have forced him to change his mind. This is why he rang me this morning."

"Wouldn't he be better to sell at auction?" Amanda asked, glancing at Jason quickly but feeling a renewed stirring of interest. She had liked his horses, the atmosphere of his stables, and had found herself wishing more than once since she had left Merington that it might have been possible to have a horse of her own at Combe Farm. But, of course, the land there was all rented out, and besides, she could scarcely afford one. Jason had quite a number of horses and she wondered suddenly why he should want more. And why the subdued excitement about one particular mare? Something, a small flicker of she knew not what, went through her—an uneasy moment that she cast hastily aside. It wasn't possible to be jealous of a horse! She might have asked him to teach her

to ride, but this she realized would be far from practical.
Jason Meade was a busy man. If she had doubted it before, she had learned enough during the past few days to
convince her otherwise. He could not possibly have time
to spare for such idle pursuits as she had in mind.

Through the tangle of her wistful thoughts she heard
him answering her question. "He might get a better price
on the open market, but then again he might not. He
couldn't actually hope to better what I'm offering for the
horse, and I believe he wants to sell privately. There is,
however, another man who is interested. This is why I
should like to complete the deal this evening."

Amanda asked, greatly daring. "Why should you want
another horse? You can't surely ride them all."

"Do I detect a note of censure?" he laughed, but gently, turning his head to glance at her averted profile.

"Perhaps it's envy. . . ." She laughed lightly with him.
She didn't pretend to know anything about horses, but
she did know that when Jason talked about them he
seemed much more relaxed.

Steadily the car wound its way through the dark Devonshire lanes that stretched tunnellike before them, between
high hedges. The headlights flung strange, leaping shadows across the road, reminding Amanda once again of the
pagan tales of Dartmoor. An owl flew alongside the car,
then swooped away again silently. From a nearby field
came a fox, its long, bushy tail trailing behind it and with
what looked suspiciously like a pheasant or a chicken in
its mouth. Apparently not at all alarmed by the beam of
car lights, it turned to trot up the side of the road, waiting
it seemed for them to pass before continuing on its journey.

Jason said dryly, as if perfectly aware of her doubts, "I
don't just ride horses, Amanda, I breed and sell them.
Horses were my first line of business—they might even be
my last. At least they have never let me down."

There was some intangible quality in his voice not easily assimilated. A small frown passed quickly over Amanda's smooth forehead. If he had been anyone else but Jason Meade she might have concluded that some woman had been unfaithful. More likely, she thought cynically, it would be the other way around. Veronica, of course, according to Eva, had loved him and left him—high and dry! Yet somehow Amanda doubted this very much. When it came to loving and leaving it would be Jason who called the tune.

The thought filled her with a strange resentment, an unrealistic indignation that this should be so, and she felt oddly relieved when they turned in between high, pillared gates, arriving swiftly before the huge front door of a large, ivy-clad house. If Jason had expected some comment on his last remark he would have to be disappointed.

The house was far from the quiet country establishment she had been anticipating. Lights poured from every window along with the sound of gay music. "It looks as if they're having a party," Jason muttered. "Janetta, David's wife, is fond of them. Too fond," he added sourly, but again enigmatically, without explanation.

Leaving the car, Amanda followed him rather reluctantly inside, feeling, in spite of Jason's protective presense, something of a gatecrasher. The place seemed alive with people, all apparently having a good time, and after introducing her to their hostess, a petite blonde with a lively disposition, Jason left her with a drink in her hand and did not return again for well over an hour. And when he did come back, he chose not to stay any longer. Ignoring, with easy charm, the entreaties of the glamorous Janetta, he took Amanda away, the pressure of his fingers on her arm implying that it would be useless to plead she would have liked to remain for a while. She had danced a little, and, being young, had enjoyed it. It would have been nice to dance again with Jason, but obviously he had no such inclinations.

But if her own mood was despondent because of their swift departure, his was quite the opposite. "I've got her," he said with a quick grin as they drove away. "Come over to Merington tomorrow, Amanda, and see her. David promises to deliver in the morning. You'll like her; she's superb!"

There was no mistaking the enthusiasm in Jason's voice, but if Amanda felt impressed by his successful purchase she pretended not to be so. She ignored what he said about going to Merington. "You left me in a roomful of strangers," she retorted coolly. "You can't really expect congratulations!"

"Was it so unforgivable, Amanda?" He flashed her a quick look, his good mood still holding. "I'll admit I didn't expect to be gone so long, but these things take time, and I didn't think you would miss me. Besides," he added with a quirk at the side of his well-cut lips, "you did find one familiar face among the throng. Didn't I see Jeff Ronson making his way in your direction as I went out with David?"

"You don't know that I wanted to see him all that much," she protested. "I scarcely know him. But it was," she conceded with some bitterness, "a good job he was there."

"Well, at least you didn't come to any harm...."

"I'm not sure." Beneath her total disregard, Amanda moved fretfully, clinging stubbornly to a little feminine imperviousness. "I think I've had too much to drink. Jeff kept bringing me something that seemed fairly harmless at the time, but now I seem to feel a bit peculiar."

Jason laughed with seeming indifference. "I shouldn't think it's done irreparable harm, but all the more reason to be grateful that I rescued you. If you sit back and relax I think you'll soon find yourself returning to normal. And don't forget my invitation to Merington while you're dreaming of Jeff Ronson."

Jason could be impossible when he so chose! Yet somehow Amanda felt herself doing as she was told, although she found it impossible to relax completely. "I must see about a job," she was surprised to hear herself saying slowly. "Do you still have a vacancy in one of your hotels?"

"Right at this moment, no," he replied after a moment's silence. "For the time being I'd advise you to stay where you are."

"But you offered me one, if you remember?"

"When I imagined your circumstances were entirely different."

"But I can't stay at Combe Farm forever, doing nothing," she cried.

"You help Eva." The lightness had left his voice and his tone was discouraging.

She threw him a swift, frowning look through the darkness. How did he know about that, or was he only guessing? "Eva can get plenty of help. In fact, I believe I'm doing her daily out of a job, but I have to do something to justify my keep."

"I'm sure neither your father nor Eva would begrudge you that," he said firmly.

Something—some inflection in his voice, made Amanda see red. "I would like to be able to contribute toward general expenses, which is not what I'm doing now. Daddy is far from being a wealthy man." Turning in her seat, she stared at him tersely, as if trying to emphasize her point, a sick feeling welling in her throat. For no reason whatsoever she longed to get beneath the hard, protective veneer he wore so naturally. "Not everyone," she choked, "is as well endowed as yourself. It must be pleasant to be rich, but it rarely seems to make a man more sensitive."

"Amanda!" Suddenly impatient, he pressed his foot on the accelerator and the car leaped forward. Within seconds a side turning appeared and Jason pulled off the main road. There was a wide gravel verge beside a gateway and he drove onto it and stopped. There was little traffic about, none it seemed on this stretch of road, and the night was very still.

Amanda heard a faint click as he released his seat belt. It was too dark in the car to see his face, nor for a moment did she try. Blindly she stared in front of her, her eyes fixed on the distant hills whose shadowy silhouettes she could see through the wide wooden bars of the gate. Helplessly she concentrated on the blurred outlines, praying fervently that he couldn't hear the hard frantic beating of her heart. When a man stopped like this at this time of night it usually meant one thing. Not that Jason always followed the conventional pattern, but if he had wanted only to talk, he could quite easily have done so while he was driving. Perhaps it had been because he had been driving that she had dared to taunt him. Now regrets tore at her, but there seemed nothing she could say to put things right.

But when Jason spoke his voice was curiously even, and he made no attempt to touch her. "Amanda," he repeated dryly, his eyes penetrating the gloom, "we seem to be at cross purposes. I merely assumed your father to be well-off, that's all. A fairly innocent mistake, I can assure you."

"You assumed!" Distraught, Amanda raged bitterly, engaging any emotion that might hide the chaos within her. "How can you speak to glibly! You must have known he was short of money when he tried to sell you the river. You can't plead ignorance about that!"

For a moment he seemed struck into silence, and when he spoke again his voice had an increasing dryness. "I know he wanted to sell the river, my dear, but I was under no obligation to buy it."

"But you wanted it . . . ? You even discussed it."

"Naturally." He turned in his seat, easing his weight around so that he was able more clearly to see her dim profile. "That particular stretch of water would do the hotel no harm, but first and foremost I'm a businessman, Amanda. I have a fair idea what the fishing there is worth, and I'm not prepared to give more."

"But you might have done if . . . ." Nervously Amanda's voice trailed away. She had not intended to so much as mention the river, yet here she was going even further than that!

Through the utter confusion that smote her she heard him prompting silkily, "If what, Amanda?"

"If—if you'd wanted it badly enough," she managed, grateful that her wits hadn't deserted her completely.

From the derisive twist of his lips, there seemed little doubt he could see through her prevarication, but it became apparent that he wasn't going to challenge her immediately. He said softly, "There happen to be several reasons why I've done nothing yet about the river, but none of them, my dear, need concern you. And if your father can't afford to keep you, Amanda, then I can."

Surprise closed her throat, stopping all speech as she gazed back at him in helpless consternation. He was teasing her, she knew that, yet there was a look on his lean, dark face she couldn't define. Unless, of course, he was offering her a job after all—a salary? But before she could find the suitable words to ask, his hand went out to touch the fur of her jacket. "You wouldn't have to wear imitation mink; I would buy you the real thing. Doesn't that tempt you?" he said.

"The real thing . . . ?" Fright for a moment ran through her. If she hadn't taken him seriously before, something in his eyes contradicted this former impression. He didn't move, but she felt the change in him, a sort of complex tension. She heard what he was saying but wasn't at all sure what he was on about. It must be a job—surely he wasn't asking her to live with him! Her eyes, brilliant with shock, clung to his, trying to read an expression that should have warned her. There was a confident expectancy about his waiting stillness. She felt it, even if she could not clearly discern what lay behind it. If only her heart would stop thudding so desperately, her pulse refrain from breaking all records! She drew back from him a little, the silken mesh of her hair caught in the moonlight. Her voice, when it came, was weak. "Perhaps you could explain," she whispered.

He gave her an odd sort of smile, only half mocking, and moved one hand to her shoulder in one of his dominating gestures. With a quick flick he pushed aside her seat belt and pulled her nerveless body into his arms, burying his face against her hair. Nothing more—but his next words deepened the shock that already held her, bringing with it total disintegration!

"I've wanted you," he said slowly, "ever since I carried you into Merington that night and tucked you up in bed. I've wanted you and intend to have you, even if I have to buy the damned river to get you. Surely you realized I would never let you go?"

For one startling instant all Amanda's strength seemed to leave her, although she felt herself go rigid in his arms, the coolness of his voice along with what he said taking the breath almost forcibly from her. The way in which he phrased his words alarmed her, and because she didn't reply immediately she sensed his barely suppressed impatience.

"Amanda?" he prompted tersely.

The tension mounted. "I don't understand," her breath came unevenly. "You talk in riddles!"

"Riddles!" Jason echoed the word. His expression hardened. "Trust a woman to cling to a little mystery! I'm offering you everything you could ever want and you pretend not to understand."

"In heaven's name, then, why?" A fiery expression darkened her eyes as anger replaced the bewilderment within her. She could not analyze her feelings. He didn't speak of love, but there were so many different kinds of love; so many degrees. She remembered how after he had first discovered who she really was, he had denied having any designs on her person. Yet here he was now, almost admitting that he had had this in mind all the time. What did he expect her to do? Agree to go to Merington and live with him? Here her confused thoughts stopped. In spite of herself excitement touched her. Her own sensuous reaction to Jason Meade was not something entirely new, and her mind she found could not altogether control the instinctive impulses of her body.

The sudden silence brought a sensation of unreality as he stared at her, his dark brows drawn. She could feel his breath warm on her cheek as his head came nearer. "Don't you know the answer, Amanda?" he asked abruptly, his hand exploring her face, tracing the line of her throat.

His mouth was but inches from her own, and to her dismay she found it impossible to turn away, not realizing until this moment how much she had longed for his kisses. Helplessly, unable to stop herself, she turned her mouth up to his and only for a second did he hesitate before pulling her closer. Then, with a smothered exclamation, he held her to him, his arms hard, his lips hurting, expertly extracting the passionate response he relentlessly sought. His touch, his kiss, his nearness seemed to spark to blazing light some dormant fire within her, and she felt her hands creep up around his neck, her body melt into his, and had no thought of denying him anything.

She scarcely felt his hands pushing her fur wrap from her shoulders, until his lips left her mouth to trail down her cheek and rest firmly on her warm, bare skin. There their increased pressure played havoc with her starved senses as deliberately it seemed he sought to punish he for some misdemeanor—she knew not what.

But when at last he moved his head she felt bereft, no able to do without the positive magic of his arms. It wa like sailing among the stars, a mindless, crazy trip, playin with fire and not caring if she got burned. Convulsivel she moved against his shoulder, not aware of what sh was saying. "Jason," she whispered as his mouth cam back to her face, "please kiss me again."

Not needing a second bidding, he moved his hand gen tly up to grasp a handful of her hair, not heeding her sof gasp as her head came back onto his shoulder, as his lip descended unerringly again. "Are you begging, my lovel Amanda?" he asked with gentle mockery against he softly trembling mouth.

Amanda was past words—she was all mixed up. Th blood pounded through her veins and she felt suddenl full of a desperate yearning that made it impossible t fight her own turbulent desires. There seemed nothin she could do but wait until his lips crushed hers, this tim not playing with half measures, but subjecting her to hi hard, bruising strength, not prepared to treat her gentl anymore.

Tears of intensity forced their way between her tightl closed lids, finding their way to his mouth. She had know tentative, adolescent kisses. This evening, for a shor while on the terrace of the house where Jason had bough his mare, she had allowed Jeff to hold her. She had eve returned his kisses experimentally, mixing them up with sort of defiant indignation that Jason should have left he for such a time. Jeff's kisses had been pleasant, oddl comforting, and she had had no objection to staying in hi arms. But she had felt herself cold, too conscious of th noise about them, and it had been with a strange dissatis faction that she had turned away. None of this touched her when Jason held her. In his arms there was all the response from her body she could ever hope for, yet irrationally this filled her with a similar dismay. Her slender fragility, her innocence made one last stand of independence. Maybe she was not ready yet for total domination, such as she would be forced to accept in Jason's arms.

She heard the deep intake of his breath as his lips left hers abruptly, as the faint saltiness of her tears penetrated and he lifted his head.

He didn't let her go. His hand came up to brush the tears from her face, to smooth the hair back from her hot cheeks as if he was perfectly aware of the emotions he aroused in her but while prepared to be gentle was not willing that she should escape. "Marry me, Amanda," he said softly.

Amanda's eyes flew open, staring at him through the darkness, as shock tore through her. She had never expected to hear such words pass his lips, and startled, she drew away from him, a shiver of apprehension sobering her completely. He seemed to be asking her to marry him, but he hadn't said a word about love. Yet something must have prompted his proposal. Was it the river? Did he expect that by marrying her he might get it for nothing? No—this just didn't make sense; he had enough money to buy a dozen such rivers should he so choose. But there must be something—something that might have occurred to a man of his devious nature, which she wasn't aware of herself.

Maybe, she thought rather desperately, her tears had prompted those few impulsive words, this, and an undeniable attraction that seemed to lie between them. Men had been known to marry for less. She was tempted herself. In Jason's arms she found a searing excitement and the only security she had ever known, but not yet was she experienced enough to differentiate between two such incompatible emotions, nor was she prepared to try. That she was near to loving him in a davastating and wholly unpredictable way would be no excuse for agreeing to marry a man who didn't return her feelings.

Through a daze she heard him repeating his question as she remained silent in his arms. "Amanda," he asked tersely, "didn't you hear what I was saying?"

She recoiled from the hardness of his voice, retreating into some sensitive area of her subconsciousness. He sounded as if he was arranging some business transaction! She looked up at him with a mixture of resentment. "I couldn't marry you," she answered a little wildly. "Please, Jason, take me home."

"No!" His hands gripped her bare shoulders with unconcealed impatience, taking no notice of her pleading blue eyes. "Surely," he snapped harshly, "you realize what I'm offering? What more do you want?"

"Put like that, a whole lot more!" Anger surged as her head went back defiantly. She had never thought him insensitive. Obviously the women he had dealt with until now had never evoked his more protective emotions. Neither had she, for that matter! He wanted her, but he didn't love her—so much was clear, but that he only imagined she would consider him in the terms of his wealth hurt almost beyond endurance.

"Maybe," he taunted, his hand sliding across her silken skin, "maybe you're not interested in marriage. Another relationship might be easily arranged, but I wouldn't want to shock your sensibilities. I've thought of you as a charming little innocent, but I have a notion I might have been mistaken."

The silence that followed was fraught with a fine tension, the painful hurt of disillusion. Amanda felt herself go white and pulled forcibly out of his detaining arms. "It's none of your business, Jason Meade, what sort of a girl I am! I don't owe you a thing, not even an explanation."

"I saved your life. By every unwritten law you should

belong to me—with or without a marriage ceremony," he said coolly.

Fury smote her at that, rendering her speechless. She was well aware that for some reason he had deliberately intended to shock her. They had argued before. It was a debatable point whether he had saved her life or endangered it, but she refused to demean herself by pointing this out to him again. Her head throbbed with all the misery of shocked senses, and she sat mutely, staring at her hands.

"Amanda. . . ." Suddenly, with a startling suddenness, his mood changed, and before she could stop him he pulled her back into his arms, covering her tear-damp cheeks with gentle kisses. "Relax, girl." He spoke softly against her lips, his hands caressing. "Forget what we've said tonight. You're far from indifferent to me, I can sense it. I'm quite willing to wait a little longer. I'll give you all the time you could possibly want."

Long after Jason had driven her home, Amanda tried to remember why she hadn't turned him down completely. He had been too gently persuasive, too skilled in the arts of gentle seduction, too knowledgeable as to what made a girl respond almost completely. It had been a temptation beyond her control to stay in his arms a while longer. It had only been when Jason himself had released her abruptly, as a clock in some nearby church steeple had chimed the hour of midnight, that she had realized the limits he had set, though self-imposed, were only so far controllable. But when he had dropped her on her doorstep she had still been adamant about marrying him. Never, she had told him fervently, in a hundred years. There had been little comfort to be gained from the totally sardonic smile that he had given her as he had turned away.

Next morning, not surprisingly, her head ached badly and she felt distraught. So pale was she that when she went downstairs Eva insisted she went back to bed with aspirin and a cup of hot tea. And afterward, because she did as she was told, Amanda blamed herself for what happened.

She quite forgot that she had promised to take Richard into Exeter, and Eva didn't remind her. Eva said later she had been on her way to remind her, but Amanda had fallen asleep again and Richard, when consulted, had insisted on driving himself. After all, before Amanda had arrived he had done this all the time, and in London he had gone everywhere by car. Perhaps if there had been any fault at all, it lay in the fact that neither of them realized how much he had changed since his last trip to Nepal. And it was not until the police rang, an hour later, that the nightmare began.

The police refused to give much information over the phone, just that Richard had failed to stop at a crossing and a lorry had crashed into the side of his car. He was hurt and an ambulance had taken him to hospital, but apart from advising Eva to try to get there as soon as possible, they said little more.

Amanda felt horrified and filled with despair, but, strangely enough, after the first shock had passed found she was able to take control. A wave of unsteadiness came and went, and she prepared to subdue her own fright in order to help Eva.

Eva was distraught. "I should never have allowed him to go alone!" she kept repeating, her face white and full of regret.

Amanda did her best to reassure her, attempting to put on a brave front even while her heart was heavy with fear. There were things to be seen to before they got away, small things like Sam's biscuits to be topped up, and the kettle removed from the hot plate on the range. Thinking to distract Eva for a few minutes, she sent her upstairs for her outdoor things. "I'd better ring for a taxi," she said, exactly as Jason strode in through the front door.

"Amanda!" he exclaimed, his voice edged with a slight irritation. "I said I would pick you up. Didn't you hear me arrive?"

"I'm sorry, Jason," was all she could find to say as she stared at him blankly, not really seeing him as her stunned mind grappled with the problem of the taxi. To begin with she had quite forgotten they had only one car, which was now probably wrecked beyond repair, and the only available taxi would be the one that she had hired on that very first night during the storm. The driver would be sure to recognize her again! Yet it didn't seem possible that she should be worrying about this when it was imperative that they go to hospital immediately. With determination she reached for the receiver, only to find with startled dismay Jason's hand on top of her own, stopping her.

"My dear girl," he snapped, his fingers biting, "before you go any further will you kindly tell me what's wrong? You look as if you'd seen a ghost."

With another murmured apology she told him, for a moment letting her eyes rest on the dark height of him, renewing once more the feeling of security that the sight of him always seemed to give. "So we have to get a taxi," she finished flatly. "Eva is shocked—she couldn't possibly travel any other way."

For a split second the pressure of Jason's fingers tightened hurtfully. "You were going to ring for a taxi," he exploded softly, "while all you had to do was get in touch with me?"

Amanda flinched as he released her trapped fingers. "I'm afraid I didn't think about you—not after the police rang," she said unevenly. "In any case, you might have been busy."

"The horse arrived," he explained briefly. "I intended to fetch you to have a look at her. Remember, I did suggest it, and you agreed."

While he spoke he was picking up her coat from where

she had laid it on a nearby table. Helping her into it, he passed her a head scarf to tie around her hair. He didn't for the minute mention Richard at all. "The weather this morning is definitely colder," he remarked, his eyes keen on her numbed face. "We could be getting more snow. You'd better keep warm. I know where you keep your drinks. I'll go and get you something while you get Eva downstairs, then we'll be off right away."

It seemed to Amanda that from that moment Jason took charge. Afterward she couldn't imagine how she would have managed without him. He had made Eva have a drink, and calmed her down by using, it seemed, just the right amount of firmness and sympathy. By the time they arrived at the hospital she had managed to pull herself together remarkably well. Jason's big car ate up the miles as it carried them swiftly to Exeter.

Richard was gravely ill. He lay in a side ward, holding onto life by a slender thread, and in spite of her newly found calm Eva was horrified and upset. Richard's head and right arm were bandaged and he was unconscious. She stood gazing down at him as if she couldn't really believe he was the same man for whom she had cooked bacon and eggs just a few hours earlier. Amanda forgot her own grief at the expression on her face. Eva was obviously devoted to her father, and deeply shocked by what had happened. In a rather futile attempt to comfort her, Amanda put an arm around her shoulders and drew her close, feeling a surge of new affection blending with her pity.

The nurse said that a doctor would see them immediately. Jason came with them, and Amanda noticed the way in which the white-clad nurse glanced at him with some appreciation. It was strange, Amanda thought, that she should notice this when her father was so gravely ill. With another apprehensive look at Richard's still figure she followed the others from the room.

The doctor was exceedingly kind but could tell them little more than what they had already guessed. Richard had sustained multiple injuries. The crash had been a bad one and he was very ill, but, eventually, there was every chance of a recovery, although to what extent it was as yet impossible to say.

"In many ways your husband is fortunate to be alive," the man told Eva. "He has escaped relatively lightly, taking everything into consideration. No one injury is in itself very serious; it's his general condition that I'm rather doubtful about. Has he been ill lately?"

Eva replied. "Not ill exactly, doctor, but rather strange. Definitely not himself—tired, perhaps I should say. . . ." A little helplessly she glanced at Amanda, who nodded her head.

"My father has been out in Nepal," she explained briefly. "He's a biologist. He was in charge of an expedition. You may have heard of him."

"Professor Trent?" The doctor's fair eyebrows rose. "I've read many of his articles. He does good work, and he's just returned from Nepal, which could explain his symptoms very well. He's probably, unbeknown to himself, been suffering from exhaustion. Such pursuits can try a much younger man. When your husband recovers, Mrs. Trent, I should advise you to keep him nearer home."

It was reassuring that he didn't appear to doubt Richard's eventual recovery, but even so, Eva refused to leave her husband's bedside until he regained consciousness. Amanda stayed with her, extremely anxious herself about her father, in spite of what the doctor had said.

Jason, after making sure they had everything they needed, left to see the police and to sort out any official details. The accident had clearly been Richard's fault and, although the wagon involved and its driver were relatively unscathed, there would no doubt be some charge, even if only that of careless driving. The police took a dim view of those who apparently ignored the rules of the road completely. Richard's car, unfortunately, would never be a car again!

Some of this Jason related when he returned to the hospital, but not all. Eva thanked him, relieved to know that that side of things had been taken care of. It was late in the afternoon before Richard came around, and then only for a few minutes. But during that short time he did seem to recognize Eva and gain some comfort from knowing she was by his side. His head was swathed in bandages and the nurse told them that he had four stitches in his scalp and ten in his arm, together with bruised ribs. Until they were able to get him x-rayed it was impossible to assess the extent of any further damage.

"His color is improving," she said brightly, "but we must wait and see."

Later Jason returned to Combe Farm to collect Eva's dog and take him to Merington. Amanda stayed behind with Eva so that they should both be near should Richard need them. Jason found them a very comfortable hotel near the hospital, each bedroom with its own bath and telephone. It seemed expensive, but Amanda was too shocked at the time to give that point much consideration. Not until afterward did she learn that it was one of Jason's own, one of the three that he owned in Devonshire. She was even more dismayed when he refused to allow them to pay anything for the privilege of staying there. And when Eva accepted, thanking him with obvious gratitude, she remained silent, for the first time since she had known Eva annoyed with her.

"We don't want to be in Jason Meade's debt," she reproached her later. "We aren't yet reduced to having to beg, surely!"

Eva glanced quickly at Amanda's mutinous face as they set out for the hospital. "We might have to do more than that if Richard doesn't recover completely. Besides," she went on, with a slightly ironical smile, "it's quite clear that Jason is paying you a lot of attention. I'm not quite blind, my dear. And I shouldn't want to do anything that might offend him in any way."

Amanda gasped. They had stopped at a crossing, waiting for the lights to change to green, and she turned to Eva indignantly. "You're jumping to all the wrong conclusions," she began. "Richard's illness—"

"Oh, come off it, darling," Eva interrupted with a marked lack of finesse. "Richard's illness hasn't made me oblivious to everything else. Jason might concern himself with those in trouble, but in this case I'm convinced there's more to it than meets the eye. However," she conceded, "apart from this, I did think it a good idea to keep on the right side of him. I'm always hoping that eventually he might agree to buy the river."

"Which would mean an awful lot to you?" Amanda asked, her heart strangely heavy.

Eva nodded. The lights changed and they went across.

Richard's condition still gave rise to some anxiety and, although he improved daily, the outlook seemed far from reassuring. As the days went by it seemed quite clear that he would require much care and attention over the next few months and, at this stage, it was impossible to judge if he would ever work again as he used to. The doctor was still doubtful.

Another aspect filled Amanda with uneasiness. A telegram had been sent to Veronica, who sent word back that she would be over as soon as possible, just as soon as she could get away. She was, she said mysteriously, engaged in something very important, something that she alone could cope with, otherwise she would have caught the next plane. Somehow the prospect of seeing Veronica again didn't bring the comfort it ought to have done, and Amanda wondered why. Naturally Veronica would be worried about her father, it was quite normal that she should rush to his bedside. Yet something—something quite different, Amanda suspected, could be responsible for Veronica's visit. Richard might only be providing the excuse she'd been looking for.

Despite the fact that she knew her doubts to be unreasonable, Amanda found this inner apprehension almost unbearable and found small comfort in telling herself firmly to wait and see.

CHAPTER NINE

FOR AMANDA the next few days seemed haunted by a strange unreality, a feeling that much was to happen that could be momentous but nothing that she could in any way avoid. She tried to tell herself it was because she had nothing much to do, apart from visiting the hospital. Her nerves were merely playing with a too vivid imagination. The worst that could have happened had happened with Richard's accident. Fate could have nothing more traumatic in store for her than that.

Not until afterward did she realize how foolish she had been not to take her intuition seriously. The blow fell when Jason asked her again to marry him. Over the past week she had been lulled by a sense of false security into thinking that he had changed his mind about her. That, for all Eva's teasing, his watchful vigilance, his concern for their comfort was prompted by a feeling of compassion, nothing more. It was disconcerting to find she had been completely wrong.

He arrived early one afternoon and asked her to stay behind while he drove Eva to the hospital. She would have liked to refuse, aware of a slight uneasiness, but something in his face silenced the words of protest before she could utter them. So she remained in the lounge until he returned. She sat in one of the darker corners, trying unhappily to relax, yet finding it impossible to even touch the drink that Jason had ordered for her before he left.

When he returned he ordered beer for himself from the usual subservient waiter and slumped down beside her. He stretched his long legs as if he was a trifle weary and, apart from saying he had delivered Eva safely, he didn't speak again until the man came back. He wasn't apparently in a hurry. Nor did Amanda make any attempt to find out what he had on his mind. Perhaps her ever active sixth sense warned her that what she was about to hear would be in no way welcome and she sought, if only by silence, to prolong the moment when he might explain.

She didn't have long to wait. "I've arranged with Eva for you to spend the rest of the day at Merington," he began coolly. "But first we must talk."

Amanda blinked, gazing at him uncertainly. He took too much upon himself! "I can't leave Eva," she retorted, feeling she was being organized. "You know she needs me."

"And you, my dear girl, need a break. Have you looked at yourself lately?" His glance stayed on her too slim figure, her huge shadowed eyes.

Amanda might have told him that her appearance couldn't altogether be put down to Richard's illness, but she knew better than to confess her innermost doubts and fears to Jason Meade. "In a day or two," she replied, looking away from him carefully, "I expect to return to the farm. Someone ought to be there to keep the place aired. At this time of the year dampness soon creeps in. Eva is getting rather worried about it, especially as she thinks my father might be allowed home. As soon as I get back I'll come and collect Sam. I'll see your horse then."

Jason muttered something impolite about horses beneath his breath. "I'm not talking about horses, Amanda. And, as regards Combe Farm, Mrs. Drew can pop in and do all that's necessary. You can see Sam this afternoon at Merington, but first, as I've already said, I want to talk to you."

"What about?" Aware of a mounting nervousness, Amanda stared around her, looking anywhere but at his dark face. The lounge was empty. People, she supposed, rarely came to Exeter to sit in a hotel lounge, especially at this time of the year. She wished they did. Surrounded by people she might not have felt so conscious of Jason, might not have felt so certain that after she had listened to whatever he intended to say nothing would ever be quite the same again. She found herself swallowing some kind of primitive fear as his voice effectively jerked her to him.

He said smoothly, "It might be just as well to start with your father. You must know that in future he'll have to take medical advice and stay nearer home."

Amanda relaxed slightly, although her slim fingers still gripped the edge of her chair. Perhaps he just wanted to discuss Richard. Slowly she nodded her head.

"You realize this will limit his activities?" There was a harder note in Jason's voice.

"Maybe he should have done this before now," she murmured, not able to understand why Jason should be emphasizing the point.

"But he didn't."

"No—he would never listen to reason. This accident, should he be otherwise all right, might prove a blessing in disguise."

"Quite easily," Jason agreed suavely. "If he'd been blessed with a little more foresight. But as it is I gather he's always been a sight too independent. He has spent a great deal of his time and money on research unconnected with any specific job. Instead of sticking to a university career that would have supplied him with a suitable retirement pension, he could now find himself high and dry with barely enough to live on—certainly not enough to supply his immediate needs."

"How on earth do you know all this?" Stung, although unable to deny the truth of what he said, Amanda rounded on him fiercely, two patches of pink on her cheeks lighting her face up indignantly. "You must have been extra busy!"

"You could say that," he drawled, not in the least disturbed by her anger, giving the impression that her words were wasted, like cotton wool, without any impact. "To satisfy your curiosity, my dear Amanda, a lot of this I've known for some time, and the other day Eva and I talked."

"Talked?" Into a barely imperceptible pause she choked over the question.

"Don't worry," he mocked. "I don't think your step-mama betrayed any secrets. Together we went over a few things that were worrying her. She might just as easily have consulted her bank manager or solicitor. I merely happened to be on hand and, taking everything into consideration, was probably the best person to turn to."

Her voice was shaking. "I'm still not with you. . . ."

He grinned ironically at that. "I don't think you are, but you must have some idea. You can't be an ostrich forever, Amanda."

His laughter, low though it was, inflamed her. Icily she said, "You'd better try explaining."

He looked at her sardonically. "Hasn't it occurred to you that if Richard could sell his land and river his worries would be over? Definitely over in terms of hard cash."

"And you're going to buy it?" she asked tautly.

"That depends." He came very close to her, an intent look in his eyes.

"They don't have to depend on you, surely?" Amanda was suddenly furious—or frightened, she didn't know which. Suddenly she hated Jason for what she sensed was to come.

"Who else," he reminded her, "would be prepared to give more than what I'm offering? You'd have to look a long time, my dear. And you would also have to look a long time before finding anyone willing to buy the land without the house. And your father needs that house—especially now. It might almost kill him to leave it."

"The neighbors?"

"Certainly none of your immediate neighbors are interested, even if they could afford it, which I doubt."

She remembered how he had been confident of his ability to outbid another buyer to get the horse he fancied, and she knew a flare of resentment. "And you could," she taunted. "How nice to have money!"

"You've said that before, Amanda. I warn you to be careful."

Was there a threatening note in his voice? She took a deep gulp of air, feeling suddenly that she was drowning. Her pulse missed a beat, then continued painfully. "You said it depends?" her mind backtracked uneasily.

He didn't keep her in suspense any longer. "It depends whether you'll marry me or not," he said.

"Marry you!" Her eyes widened and her voice trailed off on the last syllable as she swallowed abruptly. She felt herself go white.

His tone was hard and goading. "Don't pretend to be surprised. I've asked you before."

"I do remember, Mr. Meade," she replied tersely, straightening her shoulders.

"Well, then?" he pointed out, his eyes with the glint of steel in them not at all her idea of a man proposing.

Rather desperately Amanda lowered her gaze and looked down at an empty ashtray, as if expecting it to provide inspiration. "You make it sound like another of your business propositions!"

"Maybe because you choose to look at it that way," he suggested.

She glanced at him briefly, shaking her head, breaking away from his sardonic stare, not knowing why she couldn't bear the way he looked at her. Her heart thumped and her mouth felt dry. She might have been something he had seen in a shop window. Something he fancied, but not for any particular reason. But surely there had to be a reason?

She asked stubbornly, "What other way would you expect me to look at it? I'm merely applying my own interpretation. People don't marry for no reason whatsoever."

"I have a reason all right," he countered, his eyes narrowing. "You can take it I feel a certain attraction. Besides, I could do with a wife. Maybe I feel a need to settle down and have a family. A son and heir has some appeal to a man in my position."

Amanda felt her cheeks grow hot as a strange perverse excitement ran through her. He taunted, but his words defeated her against her will. Jason was an attractive man; she accepted that. His features were rugged, his mouth determined. Sitting beside her in a blue town suit, his darkness accentuated by his crisp white collar, he had the power just by looking at her to make her heart beat faster. And because she loved him she could be in danger of grabbing what crumbs he offered, gratefully. It could be wiser to refuse him—if she had any choice?

Perversely she strove to keep her voice even, to ignore his last remarks to some degree. He made it quite plain what would be expected of her! He didn't believe in beating about the bush— Well, for that matter, neither did she. "If I agree to what you ask," she began recklessly, "you will pay my father exactly what he wants for what he has to sell?"

"Every penny," he agreed coolly. "He'll have my check right away. Just as soon as you're wearing my engagement ring."

"And if not...?"

A crooked smile played about his mouth, not quite reaching his eyes. "I don't think we need consider that point, Amanda. You wouldn't care to have me mention the week you spent with me during the storm. If not your parents, there are others who would undoubtedly be interested. Perhaps you would enjoy a local scandal?"

The definite threat in his voice made her go cold all

over, even while a wild fury shook her. If she ever doubted he was adamant she didn't now. It seemed he would
stop at nothing in order to have his own way. "You're
detestable!" she spluttered.

"Merely stating facts." His tone grew detached, as if
the conversation was beginning to bore him. "I wouldn't
be a good businessman if I didn't know when to apply a
little pressure."

Her lip caught painfully between small white teeth. Jason meant what he said, she knew it. Helplessly she
looked away from his hard green gaze. She didn't really
believe that he would broadcast that week of indiscretion,
but he might tell Richard and Eva, and that she could
never bear! Dully she heard herself saying, "Okay, you
win," and wished the hardness of her voice could be
reflected in her heart.

"You won't regret it." The quirk at the side of his
mouth belied the formality of his words. "You don't feel
particularly gracious, but that will come later. You must
be glad for your father's sake, at least."

Her eyes gleamed like ice crystals. "I mustn't think of
myself!"

"Let's say that for the moment I'll do your thinking for
you," he responded, still taunting, his eyes alive on her
rebellious face. "I'm quite aware of a degree of immatu-
rity so far as your emotions are concerned, but I don't
think you're afraid of marriage and all it involves, Amanda."

She stopped abruptly at the hard edge in his voice. She
dared not fling another remark at him, yet all of a sudden
she didn't want to. Nothing she said could help her at this
moment. Later perhaps her turn would come. In the
meantime she must exercise patience. It could do no
harm. Better this than that Jason should guess how much
his indifference hurt.

Demurely, and apparently with a proper confusion, her

lashes swept down onto her cheeks. "I've always thought of marrying one day," she admitted.

"Of course you have!" Now his tones matched her own, although his expression remained dark and immobile; curiously watchful. If he was pleased with himself it only showed in the gleam of his eyes as they rested on her small, delicate features. "Like most women you like making a great ado about nothing, but we must get this thing settled right away."

From his pocket he drew a box and opened it reflectively. Nerves strung to breaking point, Amanda saw it contained a ring—a beautiful, sparkling diamond engagement ring, seemingly a clear indication that he hadn't doubted her ultimate surrender.

"Yours," Jason said smoothly, and with some satisfaction as she stared wordlessly. From the arm of her chair he took her hand, slipping the ring onto her third finger. "Every girl should have diamonds," he said firmly as he lifted her hand to his lips.

Her hand moved convulsively in his and his grip tightened with a fine flare to his nostrils as his head came up. "I hope you like it?"

Appreciate it, he means, Amanda thought a trifle wildly as feeling surged from the touch of his lips. The ring gleamed on her finger, sparkling against the light—a thing of beauty, worth probably, she hazarded, more money than she had ever possessed. Dazed, her glance shifted from the ring to his face, meeting his eyes. "It's very nice," she said slowly.

"Very nice!" For a second his dark eyebrows rose impatiently as he flicked her hand on which the huge diamond flashed ostentatiously. Then he sighed with a shrug of his broad shoulders. "You're not exactly enthusiastic."

"This is hardly the place . . ." she began, then stopped uncertainly. How could she tell him that she wished he had waited until they had arrived at Merington? To become engaged in a hotel lounge was so impersonal, in fact totally inhibiting with a member of the staff hovering, if discreetly, in the background. Of course, if she was rash enough to point this out, he might only retort that theirs was no ordinary engagement, that the usual betrothal endearments belonged to an intimacy they didn't share.

Flushed with the confusion of her thoughts, Amanda jumped quickly to her feet. "I'd rather go now, please, if you don't mind." Her former sentence she left unfinished.

Jason rose abruptly, only a split second behind her. His hand dropped to her shoulder, gripping, bruising as if perfectly aware of all the things she left unsaid. His expression was a compound of no-nonsense and alertness. "On our way to Merington we'll call at the hospital," he told her. "And remember, my darling, you're supposed to be in love with me. I shouldn't like your father to get the wrong impression."

The only impression Amanda noticed at the hospital was one of delight. Eva threw her arms around them, and Richard, with transparent relief that he made no attempt to hide, wished them well. As they left, Amanda reflected bitterly on how much she appeared to have risen in her father's estimation—especially when Jason openly promised him a check in the morning.

At Merington she accompanied Jason to the stables, still feeling she was living in some dreamworld quite divorced from reality, not even the heavy ring on her finger giving her dream much substance. Jason showed her his new mare, a horse full of singular grace and beauty, and for a while Amanda wandered, finding pleasure in renewing old acquaintances among the other animals in their stalls.

The Drews offered their congratulations, Tom Drew saying very little but Mrs. Drew adding that she hoped they would both be very happy. On the way there Amanda had been anxious about the Drews and not really relieved when Jason had told her to leave the Drews to him.

"I've told them all they need to know," he had assured her. "You don't have to worry. The Drews have an excellent position, one that I hardly think they would be keen to jeopardize in a hurry, as I've told you before."

All the same, Amanda decided unhappily, they must be thinking it a very unusual situation, and she had found herself wishing, as she had done so often lately, that she could have met Jason under more normal circumstances.

But, in spite of her doubts, the momentous day continued as if everything was exactly as it should be. Jason opened a bottle of champagne, insisting that they all had a drink. Tom Drew, mellowing after his second glass, beamed, and Mrs. Drew smiled in her usual friendly fashion and asked Amanda about her father. She was pleased, she said, to hear he was so much better, and that the little dog, Sam, would no doubt be delighted when he was home again. Of course he was no bother.

She was pleasantly talkative, but never once indicated by a word or glance that Miranda Smith had ever existed. It was both comforting and disquieting, if two such emotions could be felt at the same time. Jason, however, appeared to have no such qualms, and Amanda was silently aware that he would have little sympathy with her uneasiness.

Later in the evening, after they had eaten the very good dinner that Mrs. Drew had prepared, he said, "We'll be married in about two weeks—just as soon as I can arrange it. Your father will be home and I'll see to it that Eva has plenty of help."

Amanda looked at him, attempting to think coherently. His expression was steady but enigmatical, despite the straightforward statement. Two weeks! Her pulse raced, then settled to an erratic beat. She couldn't possibly marry him so soon. And why should he be in such a hurry? It wasn't as though he was madly in love! If he had been she might have been tempted to agree, but although she did realize that eventually she would have to go through with it, a one-sided union had little appeal.

"I'm afraid I would need more time," she declared woodenly.

He sighed deeply as if praying for patience. "You were falling over yourself to find a job only a week or two ago!"

Hastily she lowered her lashes. "That isn't quite the same thing."

"You can say that again!" Amanda could feel he was appraising her as she stared down at her hands. His voice was determined. "But you were prepared to start work immediately."

"I don't think I was," she retaliated, "and the same thing applies now."

"Surely, Amanda," he protested, "you're not comparing marriage to me with a job? Although," his voice teased, "I do expect to be in command—in more ways than one."

A quiver of fear and something else—some totally unpredictable feeling, ran through her. She had no illusions about marriage with Jason. He wouldn't want to know anything about the emancipation of women, not in his own home. He would expect to rule the roost, and he would expect her to be suitably amenable. There might be much, she acknowledged, that she would receive in return, but what she really longed for he would deny her. And her life would be wholly barren without his love. A slick sickness washed over her, making her cold and shivery, and her heart ached.

Ruthlessly he took her silence for acquiescence, refusing to apply any other construction. He studied her a little unnervingly, yet there seemed a new gentleness about him, an unwillingness to throw the sheer weight of his more dominant personality against her less robust strength.

"Come here, Amanda," he said quietly, and when reluctantly she joined him on the huge leather settee before the fire he put his arms around her, drawing her softly against him. "Stop worrying, girl," he smiled. "Leave everything to me. Perhaps we're doing things the wrong way around. Don't you know you haven't kissed me since we became engaged?"

Their eyes met as she stared at him, startled. A little mutiny stirred. "You don't expect me to anticipate your every mood? I wasn't to know what was expected of me!"

Jason's grip tightened. His smile deepened to low laughter as he surveyed her flushed face. "I should like you to be clear on that point at least."

He drew her closer and kissed her, very softly on her lips, but not in quite the same way as he had done previously. There seemed to be about his arms and mouth a tenderness that had been missing on those other occasions. Amanda felt surprise, and a little disappointment touch her. Yet, after a moment, she found his new approach equally satisfying. Her own lips responded to the insidious restraint of his, and she found herself curling up against him, her body soft and boneless, her hands creeping around his wide waist, yielding herself to the hard masculinity of him. When he lifted his head she had a dreamy, half-satisfied look on her face as she stirred against his shoulder.

Together they lingered until it grew late, watching the firelight. They didn't speak, and Amanda felt a new drowsiness overtake her, subtly dangerous but utterly irresistible. Jason's hands, she found, could charm as surely as his lips ever did. . . . Together they stayed and watched the firelight, hearing only the sound of crackling wood and November wind against the window. And with the same wind came strange sounds in the old chimney, a vague suggestion of long-lost, long-dead travelers, still wandering the moor, still pleading to be in. Or was it Jason's lips against her cheek with their soft murmurings that almost, if not quite, succeeded in sending her to sleep?

Almost! The man, as if sensing the danger Amanda wasn't wholly aware of, put her gently away from him and rose to his feet. "I'm taking you home now, my darling," he said abruptly, but almost as if he meant the endearment.

For one long, heart-stopping moment, Amanda almost thought he did!

After four whole days Amanda began to feel that, given time, all would be well with her world. It wasn't a definite feeling so much as a nebulous one. Something instinctive, like knowing it was spring before the calendar said so; like knowing the flowers would bloom because a bud was on the tree. It was a lightening of spirits that made her realize she was young and in love, even if not entirely satisfactorily.

If Jason had the air of a man prepared to bide his time she pretended not to notice. For reasons, perhaps as he had stated, he wanted to marry her, and had been ready to resort to blackmail to achieve his ends. But as the days went by none of this seemed to register anymore. He didn't ask her again to Merington, although she knew he intended they should live there, and after they were married she could, he said, refurbish in any way she liked. If it came to her imperceptibly that there were advantages in being a wealthy man's fiancée, it struck her forcibly what it would mean to be his wife.

But if he was completely attentive and willing to humor her in every way, he remained adamant about the date of their wedding, and Amanda's halfhearted attempts to make him change his mind met with little success.

"A trousseau isn't necessary," he told her firmly. "After we're married you can shop. I'll buy you anything you like. On our honeymoon we stop at Paris first."

He was ready, she thought wistfully, to give her luxuries when all she longed for was one word of love. The pattern was all too familiar. As he had said, he needed a wife and she would adorn his table and be rewarded accordingly. Apart from the odd moments of sexual attraction her feelings were not returned. Amanda's face softened and saddened. It was like being near to heaven but separated by a thin glass wall. A flick of humiliation touched her but couldn't altogether kill a quiver of hope. Maybe, if she was patient, it might all come right? In the meantime there seemed little else she could do but fall in with his wishes. Half a loaf could be better than no bread. Just to live with Jason might be better than not having him at all.

Eva said, "I think we shall all be worn out before your wedding day, darling. What with Richard's accident, your marriage, and Christmas so near! I almost envy your father his inability to move."

About Richard this wasn't strictly true, but Amanda knew what she meant and sympathized. There was so much to do.

Richard was home. He had been discharged sooner than they had expected, and while able to move around the house unaided, still needed much care and attention. Still, it was lovely to have him back, and his continuing delight over the now healthy state of his bank balance more than compensated Amanda for her heartache.

Altogether the few days following her visit to Merington passed pleasantly enough. There was nothing whatsoever to prepare her for the chaos that was to come.

VERONICA ARRIVED one stormy December night when the wind blew so hard they scarcely heard her taxi. They hadn't known when to expect her and were quite startled when she walked in the door. Eva and Richard were sitting by the fire. Amanda was making after-dinner coffee in the kitchen.

She had been to Exeter with Jason. While Richard had been there in hospital there had been little time to explore the beautiful old city. Jason and she hadn't exactly done this, this afternoon. They had just wandered around, because, as he said, the winter days were really too short and dull for proper sight-seeing. He had shown her the cathedral with its two famous Norman towers, and the magnificent west front with the carved figures. And inside he had pointed out the fifty-nine-foot-high Bishop's Throne, the minstrel's gallery and the astronomical clock in the north transept. Just opposite the cathedral, in the Close, he had taken her to see Mol's coffeehouse, a building where Elizabethan sea captains used to drink. There were many other places to see, he had told her—the university, museums and art galleries; the River Exe, only five minutes' walk from the High Street, but he had a meeting that evening with some of his hotel managers and didn't want to be late. It seemed to Amanda that he made a point of being busy in the evenings, and in a fit of pique she had asked him why.

"You wouldn't appreciate the answer to that one," he had laughed as he kissed her goodbye.

But only gently. As the percolator bubbled she thought of the way he kissed her nowadays with a strange, unsatisfied yearning. He didn't see her in the evenings; he kept her at arm's length when he did take her out. Could he, she wondered with a decided drooping of spirits, be regretting his hasty proposal? It was only when she considered his new tenderness, her own growing sense of happiness, that she got on with the coffee, telling herself not to be so silly.

Then in came Veronica, sweeping aside Amanda's newly acquired tranquillity. She was beautifully dressed in the latest fashion and hadn't yet discarded the smart little fur hat that sat smoothly on top of her sleek dark head. The slight twist of her lips could have passed for a smile.

"That coffee smells super," she said, surveying the steaming percolator greedily. "I'm ravenous, as I've just been telling Eva. I don't think I've eaten much all day."

For no reason she could think of Amanda's heart sank. It was as if she and Veronica had parted only yesterday, and on the best of terms—instead of the reverse. Uncertainly she gazed at her sister, trying to gauge her mood. Veronica, she knew from experience, was rarely as she appeared to be.

"Have you nothing to say, darling?" Veronica prompted.

"Oh, yes, of course. I'm sorry..." Amanda exclaimed. "You startled me, that's all. For a moment I thought I was seeing a ghost."

"Or wishing I was one?"

"Why, no, certainly not. Don't be silly. We were expecting you," Amanda quivered, unable to define the cool note in Veronica's voice.

But before she could utter another word Eva appeared, almost, it seemed, to the rescue. "Were you as surprised as I was to see Veronica, darling?" She addressed Amanda, her air protective, making it quite clear she was prepared to stand between the two sisters if need be.

Amanda nodded, forcing herself to smile. She asked Veronica, deliberately casual, "How did you manage to get here at this time of night?"

Veronica shrugged. "I got a taxi, sweetie pie. The man was very obliging. He told me he hadn't been to Combe Farm since the recent storm when he dropped someone off in the snow."

Color surged beneath Amanda's skin, and she knew Veronica was aware of it as she turned away abruptly. "You must be relieved to see daddy so much better," she stammered.

Veronica hadn't missed the color. She shrugged again, but her eyes were keen. "Richard was always lucky," she said lightly. "I should have been surprised to find him otherwise than greatly improved."

Why then did you come, Amanda almost cried, restraining herself just in time. Veronica would only consider her impertinent. Instead she said stoically, "Daddy will be pleased to have you here." Yet as she spoke she wondered if this would still be true. Hadn't Richard told her himself that he had almost quarreled with Veronica, although none of them had ever known him to bear a grudge? Still, there was always a first time, although for Veronica's sake in this instance, she hoped not.

From a distance, it seemed, she heard Eva saying that Richard was always pleased to see any of his family. If there was just the faintest hint of reproach in her voice at Veronica's somewhat critical demeanor, then Veronica chose not to notice. "How is Herman?" Eva went on, filling a small gap of silence. "He hasn't come over with you?"

"He did," Veronica frowned. "As a matter of fact he's been returned to London for a week or two by the embassy. This is why I didn't come sooner—I felt I couldn't leave him on his own."

An admirable sentiment, if one that didn't ring quite true. Not as Veronica said it—she seemed curiously evasive. Amanda bit her lip nervously, suddenly finding herself reluctant to mention Herman's name. He still left a nasty taste in her mouth, a reminder of something she would rather forget.

Eva smiled quickly, sensing undercurrents. She turned to Veronica. "You won't have heard yet about Amanda's engagement. We didn't send you a wire in case you were on your way."

"Engagement?" Veronica looked surprised. "Why, she's been home only a few weeks!"

Veronica talked over Amanda's head, almost as if she didn't exist, and Amanda remembered with some apprehension that her sister had been friendly with Jason herself! More than friendly, according to Eva, and even if she hadn't wanted him herself, Veronica was not prone to be generous with her castoffs.

"Amanda has been home long enough," Eva said firmly. "She's now engaged to Jason Meade. I'm sure you'll be pleased about it. Richard and I are delighted."

Veronica was not! "Jason Meade! Good heavens—you must be joking!" She stared at Eva with patent dislike, her face a study of startled emotions. "Why, she doesn't even know him!"

"Your sister does happen to be standing behind you," Eva pointed out sharply. "And she is wearing Jason's ring. Why don't you look and see for yourself?"

Slowly, feeling rather like a puppet on a string, Amanda lifted her hand. The faint touch of triumph in Eva's voice blending unhappily with Veronica's ill-concealed antagonism. On her finger Jason's diamond seemed to flash with a challenging brightness.

Amanda heard Veronica's breath catch in her throat, a raw kind of sound, and her color heightened. After that first incredulous glance she didn't look at the ring again. Her eyes, returning to Amanda's pale face, held a glittering kind of anger. "Jason's too old for you," she cried coldly.

"He's only in his thirties," Eva pointed out when Amanda refused to answer.

"Just!" Veronica retorted.

"You exaggerate," Eva rejoined, but with something in her manner that must have warned Veronica she was going too far. Eva prided herself on her tolerance, but she would only put up with so much.

Amanda, making a supreme effort, stirred, attempting to shake off a peculiar lethargy. Veronica always had this effect, but she couldn't go on sheltering behind Eva. "I suppose," she said, "this is rather sudden, but these things happen."

"I should be interested to know how," Veronica replied enigmatically, her expression proclaiming louder than words her opinion of Amanda's naive little speech. "However," she added with apparent caution, "I suppose you know your own business best. When is the wedding to be?"

This last seemed tacked on merely as an afterthought, without any real conviction that such an event was ever likely to take place. "Before Christmas," Amanda retorted, more sharply than she otherwise might have done.

"So it's lovely that you and Herman will be here," Eva put in sweetly.

Amanda was well aware of Eva's protective instincts, but knew it was time she fought her own battles. Her skirmish with Veronica, before Veronica had gone to America, seemed to have given her courage. Now she tilted her chin and said with cool dignity, "As Eva has just said, it will be lovely to have you. Jason and I are to be married at the end of next week, which should work in with your plans very well."

Afterward Amanda realized that her new composure had not achieved the desired effect. Veronica, while still looking annoyed, had obviously been restrained by some inbred caution. Her lips stretching in the slightest of smiles, she had quickly left the room, murmuring abruptly that she was going back to talk to Richard. Eva, after throwing Amanda a wry grimace, had promptly followed.

At this rate Eva would be worn out long before the wedding day, Amanda thought distractedly. Veronica's tongue could be cruel as well as kind, and Eva was quite aware of it. That was just it, Amanda decided, as she set about preparing Veronica a light supper. Just when Veronica said something spiteful, and one was beginning to hate her, she cleverly reversed the trend by saying something nice. But such an atmosphere was not comfortable to live in, and Amanda, in an enlightened moment, breathed a gentle sigh of relief at having escaped in time. Whatever happened, she vowed she would never again live with Veronica, no matter what anyone might say. If only she could get through the next few days without mishap, all might be well.

But in spite of her optimism the vindictive expression on Veronica's face continued to make her uneasy—this, and a growing awareness that Jason had meant something in Veronica's life, whether she was prepared to admit it or not. Amanda sighed a little as she picked up the percolator and a plate of ham sandwiches, placing them on a tray. Would it be unsisterly, she wondered, to wish that Veronica, like bad weather, had never arrived? Or again, like bad weather, that she might simply go away!

CHAPTER TEN

OF LATE when Amanda had woken in the mornings she had known, before full consciousness came, a feeling of happy anticipation. This morning there was nothing but a curious sense of foreboding, some vague notion that all was not well with her world and that she would be better to go back to sleep. This feeling of apprehension, she realized, must have something to do with Veronica being here.

The night before, just as she had been getting into bed, Veronica had come to her room and talked. She had chatted lightly about living in Washington, D.C. She didn't really care for it, she had said, although it had possibilities. Herman was out a lot, she didn't see much of him. If Amanda had been there she wouldn't have been so very lonely. And so on....

To all this Amanda had listened, simulating interest, her wariness in no way lulled by Veronica's easy manner. Veronica, however, never once mentioned Jason or, even casually, Amanda's engagement. She had only asked why Amanda had disappeared so completely in London after she had left the flat.

"I tried to find you," she explained with a reproachful yawn, "but you seemed to have disappeared. I looked everywhere—I even rang Merington in case you'd come down here. But of course you hadn't."

Once again that evening Amanda had found herself flushing and unable to hide the hot color in her cheeks because of the bright light above her head. And again, although Veronica's eyes narrowed, she had made no comment. Not even when Amanda rejoined with nervous uncertainty, "I stayed in a hotel."

"Really, darling," Veronica had drawled, "you might have told me. It was such a silly little quarrel, after all." Her tone of voice had clearly indicated that she was quite prepared to forgive and forget the whole incident if Amanda was willing to do the same. But in spite of a feeling of relief, Amanda had been glad when at last Veronica had said good-night and retired to her own bed. Her whole body felt taut, in no way relaxed as she was struck by the sudden conviction that things were to happen over which she might have little control.

Now she stirred with a dismal kind of sigh, then sitting up quickly, glanced at her watch, seeing to her horror that it was well after nine o'clock. She had overslept, which came of talking into the early hours. All the hustle and activities of the last few days topped by Veronica's arrival must have proved exhausting. Not, Amanda chided herself as she hurriedly scrambled out of bed and threw on some clothes, that this was any excuse. She ought to have been up ages ago helping Eva. The daily help wasn't coming this morning and there would be a lot to do.

A few minutes later she stood in the kitchen pouring herself a cup of tea. Eva walked in, a bright smile on her face as she saw Amanda.

"Richard insisted on getting up early," she said. "He heard Veronica leave and I think it disturbed him."

"Veronica?" Startled, Amanda shot a quick glance at Eva as she put down the pot. "You mean...?"

"Oh, nothing like that—she hasn't gone for good. She's only gone to Ashburton for cigarettes. She forgot to bring a supply, and I'm afraid I couldn't help, and I knew no one else could either."

"Oh, yes. I see...." Amanda turned away, tidying the kitchen table while her tea cooled. Veronica had only gone for cigarettes, certainly nothing that might account for the quiver of apprehension that shot through her now. Yet it was rather strange that Veronica should dash off at this hour of the day. Amanda never could remember her smoking much in the mornings.

Eva was shrugging her elegantly clad shoulders, almost as if she guessed something of what her younger step-daughter was thinking. "Being in the country makes your sister restless. She often went off like this when she stayed before. The cigarettes might only be an excuse."

Which ought to have been comforting but somehow was not, and did little to dispel the nervousness in Amanda's heart. Nor did it help when Veronica rang later to say she had met an old friend and wouldn't be home for lunch. And when this call was followed almost immediately by one from Jason, who said abruptly that he wanted to see her right away, Amanda stared at the receiver with anxious dismay. That something was wrong seemed obvious from his tone of voice. Rather wearily she smoothed her hot forehead with impatient fingers. Maybe it was nothing? Perhaps his meeting the previous evening with his directors hadn't gone according to plan? Such things did happen, especially nowadays when so many companies were running into trouble. But before she could give more than her brief assent the line went dead, and she was left holding the receiver with the distinct feeling that her fingers had been burned.

Jason had said he would send Tom Drew over for her in the car, but in spite of his request for haste it was after one before Tom arrived, just as she was beginning to think he wasn't coming at all.

She hadn't bothered to dress, but kept on a pair of blue slacks, pulling a pullover over a thin blouse. Jason, she thought, applying a little optimism, might be busy in the stables and permit her to help.

The car arrived, Tom apologizing for being late. Nothing had gone according to plan that morning, he grumbled; he would be behind all day. On top of this Mr. Jason had been in a foul mood. "Begging your pardon, miss," he said.

Glancing at him uncertainly, Amanda made no reply. His reference to Jason's mood was not encouraging, but it probably had to do with the stables, not herself. Tom told her that he was taking Mrs. Drew into town to do some Christmas shopping after he dropped Amanda.

"She says there won't be anything left if we don't get there soon," he grinned, if not very enthusiastically, and Amanda smiled back. But her smile faded for no reason that she could think of when he added, "Of course, when Mr. Jason is away on his honeymoon I won't be able to leave the place, so he suggested I go this afternoon."

Mrs. Drew was waiting on the doorstep, smartly dressed for her shopping expedition. When the car drew up, Amanda got out and she got in. "I expect you'll find Mr. Jason in the library," she said cheerfully, "He told me to tell you he would be there."

Amanda gazed for a moment after the swiftly disappearing car, her winged brows drawn, renewed dread in her heart. It wasn't like Jason to be so offhand, of late he had been more than attentive. But perhaps she was getting spoiled! She couldn't expect him to be at her beck and call all the time. Besides, in some ways their relationship wasn't exactly a normal one. Jason, for all his attentiveness, had never pretended to be in love with her. Still, it didn't do to dwell too much on that. Brushing the tumbled hair from her eyes with an impatient sigh, she turned and ran quickly into the house.

As Mrs. Drew had told her she found Jason in the library. He stood with his back to the fire, facing her as she came in through the door. There was a half-empty glass in his hand, and something about his expression pulled her up short.

"Come in, Amanda," he invited politely, but his voice

was so stony that the impact hurt, driving the color from her wind-flushed cheeks, lighting her eyes with apprehension.

"Jason—" she began uncertainly as she took another step into the room.

But before she could go on he cut her short, his eyes ruthless on her nervous face. "I had Veronica here this morning," he stated abruptly, "and she enlightened me about several things. I thought it was time we had a frank talk, you and I." His tone was bleak and uncompromising, blending darkly with the winter's afternoon.

"Veronica!" Amanda was stunned. Her voice came in a horrified whisper, and her face paled. "But she's only just arrived! She came last night."

"I'm quite aware of that. Sit down, Amanda." His mouth tightened grimly. He had the appearance of a man holding himself on a tight leash, only the habits of a lifetime restraining his more primitive impulses. "I'll get you a drink," he added coldly, without reassurance. "Perhaps you're going to need it!"

Helplessly Amanda sank into the nearest chair, clutching at her scattered senses. Numbly she stared at him. Even before Jason said anything more she knew what was to come, and she felt herself tremble. Veronica had obviously, in a fit of jealous rage, told him about Herman. She must have intended doing so all along—she probably had been unable to help herself. The cigarettes had only provided an excuse to leave the farm so early. In that instance Amanda knew intense regret, a despairing remorse that she hadn't told Jason herself, yet in retrospect it hadn't seemed feasible. She hadn't been sure that Jason would understand, and she hadn't wanted to be the cause of any ill feeling between the two men. She had reasoned that if they were to be brothers-in-law, the less said the better. Veronica, too, she had concluded, would much rather forget the whole thing. It wasn't as if anything had actually happened.

Or had she—Amanda considered her own motives with a painful honesty—merely been using these evasions as a means of avoiding something unpleasant, something that in telling might only have reflected badly on herself? It was confusing, this turmoil of uncertainty. Unhappily she continued to stare at Jason's broad back. Small wonder he had made no attempt to kiss her as she came in, and was pouring himself another liberal measure of whiskey. And from the hardness of his expression it seemed clear that he had allowed himself time to think things over, to form his already obvious conclusions, none of which seemed favorably disposed toward his fiancée.

Amanda shuddered, dragging her eyes away from his silk-clad shoulders to stare about her with half-seeing eyes. The afternoon was rapidly darkening, the gray clouds outside bringing a spatter of rain against the window. Inside the room was dim, the heavy curtains half-drawn to keep out the cold. But it was warm in the room, in spite of a fire that only smoldered, as if reflecting the mood of the man who stood beside it. He had given her a drink, setting it down on the table by her side without asking, as he usually did, what she preferred, or even if she had wanted anything at all. All of which seemed a clear indication that he was prepared to treat her with contempt.

For the first time since she had arrived Amanda felt a stir of anger. Her conscience was clear, whatever he thought! He had no right to judge her without even waiting to hear her side of the story. Her rounded chin lifted, indignation forcing a sparkle to her eyes where a second ago she had felt the prickle of defenseless tears. "You were about to say?" she prompted coolly.

He drank off half his whiskey in one quick swig before he drew nearer, placing his glass on the table beside her own. As he stared down at her his face was grim. "What I'm about to say, Amanda, might not make pleasant hearing."

She waited, not breathing.

"Veronica said—" his voice hardened "—that you'd been having some sort of affair with Herman, which was why you took off in such an almighty hurry and came down here—after she'd almost caught you in the act."

"And you believed her?" Amanda's breath released added a trembling emphasis to her words.

He ignored this. "She seems to have a good idea as to where you spent the following days. Maybe you told her—proud, no doubt, of the habit you seem to have acquired of collecting scalps."

"I didn't tell her any such thing!" Furiously Amanda jumped to her feet, her face scarlet. "What do you take me for!"

"I'm beginning to wonder! She found you and Herman in the bathroom." His voice was cold with distaste. "What do you expect me to make of that?"

Blankly she stared up at him, her dark blue eyes almost black with emotion. "That would surely depend on the amount of trust you have in me, but already you appear to believe the worst."

"Oh, come off it, Amanda," he laughed ruthlessly. "All this innocent pretense seems a bit dated. We live in a fairly permissive society. It's beginning to be the accepted thing. The mistake I made was in thinking you were different. We could have wasted a lot of time."

The ironical coldness in his voice didn't deceive her for one minute. She sensed that he wanted to hurt her, hurt her badly. She could have told him that already she was mortally wounded because of his lost faith, of the way in which he condemned her. And because of this she could have cried.

With some effort she controlled herself—after all, a girl must hang on to her pride. She went back to his second-last sentence, saying tersely, "And because Veronica chose to tell you some tale, a complete fabrication, you assume I'm not?"

"It's not your fault I put you on a pedestal," he said belligerently.

"Well, it was flattering while it lasted! Actually—" her voice cracked "—I never put you on one at all."

"You could try explaining." His eyes glittered with a fury to match her own.

Yet there was also a dangerous calm about him that ought to have warned her—that might have if she hadn't been past caution of any kind. Her voice rose. "You encouraged Veronica, hoping to get the river on the cheap. She was half in love with you. Probably she married Herman on the rebound, although it was nice of you to allow the story that she'd turned you down."

His eyes were icy, for a moment frightening her into silence. "This is none of your business," he grated, his jaw tight. "And it won't help your cause to throw insults in my direction. The fact remains—when you stayed here you stayed under false pretenses. You weren't what you made yourself out to be."

Amanda heard herself asking shrilly, "Whatever do you mean?" Her whole body felt hot and trembling and her voice somehow out of control.

His mouth twisted with curt contempt. "Oh, I was the fool, my dear, I'm quite ready to admit it. I put myself out to protect your reputation from the big bad world outside. I believed that if I treated you kindly you might come to care for me. I imagined you were innocent, when in reality you had little virtue left. . . . ."

Unable to stop herself, Amanda shot her hand out, making contact with his scornful face. Aghast, she stared at the spreading red mark on the granite-carved cheek, yet she felt no real regret. There was only hatred in her heart and a primitive desire to hurt more.

It was then that his arms went out, as with a muttered oath he dragged her to him, hurting with his hard, virile strength as he caught and held her soft, pliant body to his own. Desperately she tried to escape as her head fell back against his shoulder. She was aware of his barely controlled violence, aware that the only thought in his heart was of revenge. If she had ever regretted the gentleness of his recent kisses she thought wistfully of them now, in the split second before his lips crushed down on hers and she knew no more.

He kissed her possessively, his lips claiming hers with a sensual abandonment, without restraint, intent it seemed on arousing a flame of desire within her to match his own. And as response came, yearning became uncontrollable passion, a flame and surge of ecstasy transcending place and time.

He lifted her, sweeping her up in his arms and carrying her out through the door, up the wide staircase to his room. She had never been here before. He threw her down on the bed and she felt herself pinned beneath the weight of his heavy body. She had no idea how lovely she looked with her hair loosened and disheveled, her tremulous lips, the high flush on her soft white skin. She heard Jason's breath drawn sharply above the thudding beat of her heart. And then his lips were on hers again, his hands sliding to the warm skin on her back, up and around. She was lost, submerged, floating in a world where time ceased to count.

Then, with a suddenness that was like a douche of cold water, he lifted his mouth from her face, wrenching her arms from where they clung tightly around his neck and leaving her lying crushed against the white sheets. He halted just one moment beside the door, his back toward her, not apparently willing to spare her another glance. "Anytime you're ready you can go," he said curtly. "You can leave my ring or keep it, whichever you choose. There seems little sense in prolonging an engagement that has become meaningless."

Long after he had gone Amanda lay as if unable to

move. She was limp, numbed, depleted by a soaring rapture. She felt weak, emptied of emotion. Her lips hurt, and her body where his hands had touched, yet she scarcely noticed. Little by little she was beginning to realize how much Jason meant to her, and unable to visualize the devastation of her life without him. She was even ready to confess, if only to herself, that whatever he might have demanded of her a few minutes ago she would have been more than willing to give. She had no defenses to stop him, nor had she wanted to; her total submission must have been obvious in the responsive warmth of her own lips and arms as he had held her to him.

Why—why, she moaned almost aloud, burying her hot face against the pillow, had he left her so abruptly? Why, when his opinion of her was so low, hadn't he finished what he had so ruthlessly begun? From the pillow came the faint scent of the cologne he used, and for an impulsive moment, she clasped it to her, closing her tear-wet eyes, imagining it was the man.

Then, just as suddenly as he had done, she slid off the bed. Hurriedly groping for her pullover and shoes, she swiftly left the room, tearing down the stairs out the front door as if the devil himself was after her. A new panic mixed up with a sense of shame seemed to propel her unconsciously, a sure knowledge that if she stayed any longer she would find herself searching for Jason, begging him with ignominious humiliation to give her another chance. Whatever the heartache, no matter how bleak the future might appear to be, she must never stoop so low as that.

There was no one around as she went out. Of course the Drews were in town; she had forgotten. She saw now that Jason must have deliberately arranged it, and bitterness welled with relief. He had thought of everything, his actions obviously premeditated to ensure that no one would witness his final act of revenge. But that which hurt most was not his anger or even his subsequent rejection, but the fact that he had so utterly believed everything Veronica had told him.

Almost four miles lay between Merington and Combe Farm, but Amanda, having walked it before, didn't hesitate now. There was, after all, no alternative. She had no other means of getting home, being willing to brave the elements rather than beg Jason for a lift, even if she had the courage to face him. And to wait until the Drews returned was unthinkable. The wind buffeted her, whipping her long hair behind her as she ran, and the rain came down, draining over her face, but somehow she didn't feel the discomfort. If she hurried she might just catch the evening train to London. She made plans. Tomorrow she would get in touch with the Randalls. They were keen to have her back anytime—she had had a letter. She had only, they had said, to let them know—they would arrange everything. It was a means of escape and she meant to take it. In a very few days she could be out of the country, and away from Jason forever.

Veronica hadn't returned when she reached the farm, and Amanda was relieved. But this also meant there was no car available, so she rang for a taxi. The man promised to be there in half an hour. She ran straight upstairs. Richard was having a nap, something for which she was thankful, but she met Eva on the landing.

Eva considered her stepdaughter's drenched state with startled eyes. "Where on earth have you been, darling?" she exclaimed. "Where is Jason?"

"At Merington," Amanda explained briefly, while throwing off her wet clothes. "Look, darling," she said, and there was a trembling note in her voice, "this is going to be a shock, but our engagement is off. Which reminds me—I'd like you to give Jason this." Hastily she pulled off her ring, almost thrusting it into Eva's hand. "He asked me to leave it, but somehow I forgot."

Aghast, Eva looked from the glittering ring to Amanda's still, white face, her own face stunned. "I just refuse to believe it!" she gasped.

Amanda carefully ignored this. "I'm going to London," she went on as if Eva had never spoken. "I've arranged for a taxi; it won't be long. I shall probably go back to the Randalls, so you don't need to worry. I shall miss you, but of course daddy should be all right now. And the agreement about the river is completed and signed up. Jason couldn't do anything about that, even if he should want to."

"Amanda!" Eva half shouted, alarmed by the wild rush of words. With some exasperation she continued as Amanda fell silent, "I'm not bothered about the river, or whether your father and I can manage. Will you tell me, please, what's happened? You come in half-drowned and as white as a sheet and expect me not to ask questions. Surely, all things taken into consideration, I have some right to know?"

Amanda was busy zipping herself into a pair of dry trousers, prior to throwing a few things into a suitcase. She half turned, glancing at Eva with heavy weariness. "There's nothing really to tell, darling. We found out we weren't suited, that's all."

Eva frowned, but only slightly. Her eyes still retained a flicker of hope. "Only a lovers' quarrel, perhaps?"

"Never that!" Amanda sounded so vehement that Eva started, shocked, her face crumpling suddenly as if she were about to cry.

About to lock her suitcase, Amanda left it to come over and put her arms around her. "Eva, dear," she said, "I'm sorry, truly I am—about you, the preparations and—well, just everything, but please, can't we leave it at that? None of this was ever any fault of yours. Don't ever think so."

Something, something tense in Amanda's pale, ex-

hausted face must have warned Eva against saying anymore. After a moment she composed herself, asking
instead, "Where will you be staying in London? Have you
made any plans? Don't you think it would be better to
wait a few days before rushing off like this?"

Emphatically Amanda shook her head. She thought of
her father's old cousin who used to keep house. "I'll probably stay with Rebecca," she replied. "At least for tonight. She doesn't have much room, but I can always
sleep on a cushion. But please, Eva, I want you to promise not to mention this to anyone, Not," she added bitterly, "that anyone is likely to inquire, but just in case."

It was only when she was sitting in the taxi on the way
to the station that she realized that neither of them had
spoken of Veronica. Deliberately she had tried not to
think of Veronica herself, and of course Eva would have
no idea what Veronica had been up to. Amanda frowned;
she had yet to try to work it out. Apart from jealousy,
what other reason could Veronica have had for acting as
she had? In going to see Jason, in telling him a completely
fictitious story, she had intentionally or otherwise spoiled
any chance of happiness her sister might have hoped for.
Even with some basis for such a tale, much of it, as she
had tried to explain to Jason, was complete fabrication,
and Veronica was well aware of it. But surely, somewhere, there must have been something, something beyond her own knowledge, Amanda decided with a sense
of growing misery. Something in which Jason had been
personally involved. She remembered his anger, his refusal to talk about it, and shuddered. Yet in spite of her
unhappiness she was glad she hadn't said anything to Eva
or Richard. Veronica would return to the farm and be
company for them, helping to tide them over her own departure, and no one need be any the wiser. Besides, what
use to any girl was a man without even a modicum of
trust?

It was almost eight when she arrived at Paddington and, for a few minutes after leaving the train, stood gazing about her, only half-conscious of the hurrying crowds. Leaving Combe Farm had proved a greater wrench than she could ever have imagined it would be, and she tried unsuccessfully to put it from her mind. It was one thing, she discovered, to decide what to do, and quite another to put those same conclusions into practice. But the fact remained that Jason didn't want her. He considered she had made a fool of him, and deliberately planned his revenge. Why, then, was she finding it difficult to realize she had had a fortunate escape? To be married to a man with so little faith, who was prepared to doubt one's every word, could only lead to misery!

In time, Amanda assured herself, she would forget. Must forget! It would be impossible to live forever with such intolerable pain; with such a feeling of loneliness, such an inner conviction that she might never love again. Never in the same way! This afternoon Jason, by some devious trick of fate, might have left her whole, but she knew, with aching certainty, that he had spoiled her for any other man.

A wave of weariness overtook her as, with some effort, she left the station, and a nervous headache began to niggle at her temples and over her eyes. She knew she had had about enough, knew she was almost physically as well as mentally exhausted, and for this one night, at any rate, not fit to start looking for a hotel. She had better stick to her former plan and visit Rebecca. Rebecca might grumble, but she couldn't possibly turn her away.

She hailed a taxi. It seemed to be becoming a habit. It was also probably wildly extravagant considering the rather doubtful state of her finances, but right at that moment, tired, and with the chill December wind penetrating her thin coat, she felt she couldn't face the journey by any other means.

Rebecca answered the door herself and appeared in no way surprised to see who stood on her doorstep. A half-smile curved her thin mouth, but it was quite something in one who seldom smiled at all. Amanda was positively startled by it. It surprised her still more when Rebecca stepped back, beckoning her by a wave of her hand to come inside. "I suppose you'll be after a bed for the night," she commented as she closed the door and fixed the lock before ushering Amanda through into her sitting room.

"Not a bed, exactly." Amanda, reverting to a habit from childhood, smiled pleadingly. "A cushion would do, Rebecca; in fact I'd rather sleep on your settee, if you wouldn't mind?" Somehow the thought of a bed did things to her pulse, accelerating the beat of her heart uncomfortably.

"Well, just as you like," the old woman was saying as Amanda followed her in. "It's either that or sharing a room with my friend, and she went to bed an hour ago. She hasn't been feeling so good today."

"I'll stick with the settee," Amanda answered with a wry smile. Then, politely, "I'm sorry about your friend."

"Her own fault," Rebecca grumbled. "She went out without a hat. She deserves all she gets." Thus disposed of, the friend was not mentioned again. With some semblance of hospitality Rebecca stirred the fire, removed Amanda's coat and went out to make some tea. "I'll be back in a minute," she said.

Amanda waited, sinking into a chair with a sigh of relief. Rebecca fussed a lot, but then she always had, and she couldn't be expected to change now.

She was almost asleep when Rebecca returned with a tray containing two cups and a plate of biscuits. "I suppose," she said as she poured out, "you're here to do some shopping for your wedding?"

"Wedding!" Amanda stared at her bent head, aghast.

But of course, Eva had naturally sent an invitation. This surely explained why Rebecca's mood was mellow.

"Yes, your wedding, dear." Impatiently Rebecca looked up. "Although you must know I shan't be able to come. The journey would be too much for me, especially at this time of year. I posted a letter to your dear stepmama only this afternoon."

With a quick gulp Amanda glanced for a moment into the fire, not able to find the right words with which to tell Rebecca of her broken engagement, but before she could speak Rebecca continued with a nod of approval.

"I believe your fiancé is a wealthy man. And you're a very wise girl to settle for an Englishman. Not like your sister and her American. Little wonder she's lonely, over there on her own."

For the first time in her life, so far as Amanda could recall, she was one up on Veronica in Rebecca's estimation. Not that it mattered, she told herself, looking at Rebecca helplessly. It wouldn't last long. She would have to confess that the wedding was off. It was then she decided to wait until morning. She would tell Rebecca before she went. She couldn't bear all the questions, the recriminations that would result from such news.

So she just smiled again gently, murmured something, which obviously carried no weight, about Veronica's being happy and listened awhile, while Rebecca rambled on. But she felt grateful when a few minutes later Rebecca heaved herself to her feet, announcing without apology that she was going to bed, and would advise Amanda to do the same.

"And don't try to waken me, my dear," she warned. "I take a sleeping pill and sleep like a log."

Which was just as well, Amanda mused later when she first heard the sharp rap on the outer door. It was almost midnight. Too tired and numb to feel really worried, she glanced at the clock. Maybe someone had lost his way or needed help? It must be a man—it could even be a policeman at this time of night. Anxiously she tumbled off the settee. After Rebecca had gone to bed she hadn't bothered to undress, but had sat in a dispirited sort of daze, staring into the fire, seeing in the flames a filmlike sequence of the past weeks. She hadn't wanted to see, not even in her mind's eye, but the pictures had kept floating by, each one more somber than the other. The happiness, the heartache, had all been there, but more condemning than all, her own folly.

The knock on the door, though startling, proved a welcome release. The second knock, when it came, propelled her into immediate action. Rebecca had taken a pill, but that was enough to waken the dead!

In the small hallway she switched on the light and called, "Who's there?" all in one breath. Better to be safe than sorry!

"Amanda, for God's sake open this door before I knock it down or freeze to the step!"

It was Jason. For one terror-stricken moment Amanda stopped short, then, driven by a compulsion stronger than herself, she did as she was told, with fingers that shook so much that the simple task took much longer than it ought to have done. "Jason," she said through the awful constriction in her throat, and could say no more.

He stepped inside, not waiting a further invitation, his face grim as his eyes flashed over her, as he grasped her arm. "Are you alone?" he asked harshly. "Can we talk?" And as she nodded, still speechless, the door closed significantly behind him.

"Rebecca has gone to bed," she managed as he almost thrust her back into the dimly lighted sitting room with fingers that were none too gentle.

"Long may she stay there," he ground out, sweeping her around to face him, his terse glance penetrating her white face, her huge shadowed eyes, the tremor he could feel running through her slight body. "Thank heavens I've found you!" he muttered, pulling her into his arms.

It wasn't until a long time later that Amanda began to be conscious once again of time. All she was aware of was Jason's voice, murmuring that he loved her, that he couldn't live without her, as he cradled her against him, kissing her cheeks, her eyes, her throat before at last her lips, his own as warm and passionate as she could ever wish for. It was an avalanche of feeling, a dream materializing, just having him there, being able to hold and feel him. It was a flare of emotion that left her clinging to him blindly so that she would have fallen if he had not held her.

"Jason," she pleaded on a trembling breath against his mouth, "please tell me why you are here?"

"I thought I'd done that already, my darling." His lips trailed fire over her cheek.

"You haven't," she muttered somewhat incoherently. Impossible to think clearly as his arms pressed her closer, as his lips explored the throbbing pulse at the base of her throat.

Reluctantly, it seemed, he raised his head. "I have only an urgent desire to make love to you," he said. "Heaven after the sheer hell of the last few hours! You'll have to forgive me, Amanda, there's no other way."

"How do you mean?" she asked, her heart in her blue eyes. "You didn't want to see me again."

"Amanda!" Taut pressure lines formed beside his chiseled mouth. His hands slid away from her body, catching her wrists, still holding her. "After you'd gone I think I went berserk. I'm not too proud to admit it. You don't know how badly I wanted you. It took me about a couple of hours to come to my senses, to realize exactly how much I loved you, but by the time I got to the farm you were well on your way. Eva would only tell me that you were going to London. I managed to wheedle this address out of Richard, but had no idea if you would be here. Richard wasn't sure. Anyway, long before I reached the station your train had gone, and I was left to cool my heels, waiting for the next one."

"But surely—" she protested, but he cut her off.

"Just listen," he said with a little of his old authority, touching a finger to the tiny frown between her fine dark brows. "I was there, pacing the station with fine ill humor, when who should get off an incoming train but Herman. I'd been cursing myself for listening to the story that Veronica had told me, for refusing to believe you when all my instincts told me you were telling the truth. In any case, my darling, I was past caring. I only wanted to find you, to find out if you cared at all, if you would forgive me. Nothing else was important. Then along came Allen. I could cheerfully have knocked him down!"

Amanda's eyes stayed on his dark face. "But you didn't!" she breathed in some despair.

"I felt like it," Jason returned dryly. "I even took a step toward him, only to change my mind. I wasn't going to speak to him, but he spotted me before I could disappear. I don't know your brother-in-law all that well, Amanda, but well enough to be able to see that he'd been imbibing too freely on the train. I decided, rather reluctantly, that I'd better sober him up a bit, otherwise your parents might get a shock if he arrived at Combe Farm the way he was."

"Then what happened?"

"Nothing much," Jason said tersely. "Actually he wasn't as bad as I'd thought, or perhaps the black coffee did the trick. He was soon okay, but he started to talk and I couldn't shut him up. He said he'd been recalled unexpectedly and was rushing down to Devon to spend the weekend with Veronica and her family before they went. Veronica wouldn't hear of his going back alone. It was then that he started telling me about Veronica's jealous little ways. He had a vague idea, he said, that Veronica's sister was at the farm, and he'd been drinking to bolster himself up. Then it all came out, in one long self-pitying ramble, and I don't think he had the faintest notion that I knew you at all. He confessed to having surprised you in your bathrobe—a kind of a joke, he said, that had just fizzled out. How you were about to brain him with a candlestick when Veronica appeared. How he hadn't even managed to get near you, but how Veronica had refused to listen to reason. When I told him, my darling, that he'd been talking about my fiancée, you should have seen his face!"

"Jason—" unable to think coherently, Amanda was shaking "—were you ever in love with Veronica yourself?"

"No, never that!" he grunted decisively. "She started coming to Merington quite a lot. I rather enjoyed her company until she began to get too possessive, but completely without justification."

"Eva though you quarreled because of the river."

"The river—" he shook his dark head emphatically "—had nothing to do with it. I didn't explain to anyone why I didn't buy it. You see, I didn't really want it. I intend to put most of my hotels on the market. I'll keep the property that I have abroad, and Merington, and concentrate, I think, on breeding and training horses, as I used to. If you'll help me, Amanda, and you'd better say yes!"

"Darling," Amanda murmured sometime later as if the thought had just occurred, "but you did buy the river, after all?"

"Of course I did, young woman." His hand curved her soft chin possessively. "Everything seemed weighted against me. I had some fixed idea that I was about to lose you. I had to stop that happening, and the river seemed all I had to hold over your head."

"When you only needed yourself." The color came beneath her skin as she evaded his fingers and buried her head against his chest. "I loved you so much, Jason, almost at once, and you never guessed."

"Amanda!" Urgently his hand returned to her throat, lifting her mouth to his and there was a long silence as his lips crushed hers again, drowning her words. She was almost without breath as his head lifted, his heavy eyes dwelling with some satisfaction on her flowerlike face. "I tried to restrain myself, young woman. I thought if I treated you gently you might come to care for me. You had me well-nigh distracted, that night when you first came to Merington, soaked with snow and rain. You were unconscious, but I thought I'd never seen anything so lovely, so desirable. At first, I confess, it was just plain desire—until you ran away. I could cheerfully have murdered you, my darling, but it was then that I began to realize I must have you for my wife. I've never asked anyone before, Amanda, not even you. Not in the right way, with love in my heart, no bribes, no threats, nothing else!"

"Jason!" She smiled up at him, aware with everything within her that what he said was true. There was no barrier anymore, and nothing between herself and paradise but this man who would walk with her. "Darling," she murmured, her smile fading even as she teased him, "you can have me for the rest of my life, if that won't be too long."

"And beyond," he threatened, his eyes going over her with soft menace as he pulled her closer. "Nobody or nothing will ever trouble you again, I'll see to that. But you'll never escape me, and you'd better not try!"

"Who would want to?" she protested before his lips stopped all speech, blotting out the firelight, all conscious reality, leaving only his arms and a wild sweet singing through her heart.

Greek Bridal
Henrietta Reid

"Take my tip – be wary of Nicholas Martinos," Christine was told. "He's a Greek Lothario if ever there was one, and I'd pity the girl who lost her heart to him."

That being the case, Christine was the girl to be pitied. Nick had come to her rescue after all her money had been stolen; he even found her a job so she didn't have to return to England right away. Christine had tried very hard not to, but she'd fallen in love with him in spite of herself.

But Nick was betrothed to Mariga Tracos. He might flirt with Christine, but deep down she knew he would marry the Greek girl. . . .

CHAPTER ONE

CHRISTINE HUTTON turned out of the bustling square with its luxury shops filled with expensive items. It had been fun window-shopping, but she was well aware that most of the opulent contents of those gleaming windows were wildly beyond the modest sum she had earmarked for purchasing souvenirs.

She glanced at her guidebook. Her next visit must be to the Acropolis, she decided. It would be impossible, when she returned home, to have to confess to Valerie, who loved all things Greek, that while she was in Athens she had not viewed the Parthenon.

She could see it now, perched on top of the Acropolis, its marble columns starkly beautiful against the incredibly blue sky. From where she stood it did not seem far away, but she was deceived by the strangely brilliant, clear light of Athens, and by the time she reached her destination she felt hot and weary.

Scores of sightseers bearing cameras wended their way up the steps; coaches disgorged excited, chattering crowds who were continually harried by peddlers selling postcards, sponges, local embroidery and cheap little replicas of classical Greek statues.

When at last she reached the Parthenon with its soaring columns and bleak, classical beauty, Christine had to admit to herself that in spite of its awe-inspiring loveliness she felt a vague sense of disappointment. To begin with, the marble had not the icy whiteness of a wedding cake, and Christine had to admit to herself that, to be unromantically precise, it was the color of underdone toast.

She felt a faint sense of disappointment as she glanced down over the town of Athens, thinking that although she was in Greece at last, on the holiday she had dreamed of for so many years, yet much was missing! She had, reluctantly, to admit to herself that she wasn't enjoying her holiday; something elusive and intangible was not there.

Of course, everything would have been different if Valerie had been able to come.

Valerie was quite an old campaigner when it came to Greece. She knew her way around this enchanted land, knew the tavernas where the music and dancing were the genuine article, could speak knowledgeably of the restaurants that served the best seafoods, including—to Christine's well-disguised revulsion—her favorite fried octopus, and could even pass herself off with a few useful phrases of the language.

How often they had discussed in detail the wonderful excursions they would make! They had closed their eyes and pictured the hills covered with wild flowers, the air intoxicatingly scented with orange and lilac blossom. Christine had giggled like a schoolgirl when Valerie, volatile and fun-loving, had launched into a mock-serious description of the handsome Greek boys who would be immediately smitten by their charms.

Of course, it hadn't altogether been in fun, Christine had to admit to herself, a little shamefacedly: somehow, deep down, she had felt that Greece and romance went together. It had seemed as if it would be a part of the mood conjured up by the clear crystalline air, the aquamarine sea, the intoxicating scents of herbs—sage, lavender and thyme—that covered the mountainsides.

But although scenically Greece had fulfilled all her dreams, she had to admit to herself that things hadn't gone to plan.

Just a few days before they were to set off, Valerie's mother had been stricken by a serious illness. Naturally, all thoughts of the long-anticipated holiday had flown from Valerie's mind, and Christine, although bitterly disappointed, had made up her mind not to go alone.

But Valerie in her robust, forthright way had talked her into continuing. "You mustn't think of backing out," she had urged. "If you let this chance go, it may never come again. The best time to see Greece is early in the year. It can be unbearably hot in summer. Anyway," she had added with a shadow of her former gay banter, "you'll probably meet a handsome Greek god who will take you up to see the Parthenon in the moonlight and you won't miss me a bit."

At length Christine had reluctantly agreed to carry on with her plans. But of course, without Valerie nothing had been the same.

The hostel where they had arranged to stay was reasonably comfortable, but there was no Valerie to share the funny little incidents. In her small bedroom tucked under the roof there was no one to talk things over with at the end of a day's sight-seeing.

Now as she stood beneath the soaring columns of the Parthenon, the austerely beautiful monument to the goddess Athena, Christine felt no sense of elation and wondered bleakly if she had made a dreadful mistake in coming alone to Greece. It was almost with a sense of panic that she realized how intolerable the rest of her stay was going to be if this horrible feeling of isolation and disinterest should persist.

She hurried down the steps, suddenly eager to join the crowds of chattering tourists and touts who milled about the platform beneath.

The *evzone* soldiers in their quaint skirts that looked like ballet dancers' tutus, and pom-pomed shoes that appeared so unmilitary, were posing proudly for their photographs, and small boys were racing through the milling throngs.

Christine gave a gasp of alarm as two brown-skinned children of about twelve darted toward her so that she staggered and almost fell. Then, with a muttered word of apology, they rushed back into the crowds and were lost to view. Immediately she dismissed the small encounter from her mind, little realizing how devastating it would prove to have been later on.

She slowly descended the long flight of steps and wandered aimlessly through a jumble of little streets at the foot of the Acropolis. She saw tables outside a rather seedy-looking café and suddenly realized that she was extremely tired and thirsty. It was time, she decided, for a portion of the delicious iced watermelon that had been one of her happiest discoveries since her arrival in Greece.

Gratefully she sat down at a little table set inside the entrance. Nearly all the other tables were occupied, she noticed, by parties of voluble Greeks, gesturing excitedly or busily clicking strings of beads between their fingers. Through an open door at the back she could see an elderly peasant woman, a black scarf tied over her head, presiding over a vast array of cooking pots. For a moment the woman glanced up and stared at her enigmatically, before once again bending to her cooking.

Should she have come here alone, Christine wondered, suddenly uneasy as she noted that, apart from the old peasant, she was the only woman in the café. Perhaps it wasn't customary for unaccompanied girls to wander into cafés.

She was made even more uneasy when a gigantic man with small suspicious eyes lumbered forward and stood staring down at her with an air of antagonism. The thought crossed Christine's mind that he looked more like a mustachioed bandit in an operetta than the keeper of a restaurant.

However, she clearly and distinctly asked for *karpouzi*,

which she had carefully learned was the magic word to be used when one desired watermelon.

But the brigand was not deceived by her efforts to speak his native tongue. A broad grin creased his dark, leathery skin. "I speak English," he announced proudly, then ambled off and returned with a large portion of delicious pink melon, juicy and icy cold.

Christine ate it slowly. She had not realized quite how arduous sightseeing could be or how welcome the dark, shadowed café, after the clear, brilliant light that seemed to accentuate color and outline each building and temple with dramatic sharpness.

As she was finishing her portion of melon, a group of young men surged into the café, laughing and gesturing and talking with the velocity and animation that Christine had already discovered was characteristic of the Greeks. They took their places at an empty table adjacent to her own.

When they had settled down and given their orders, Christine became uncomfortably aware that she was the object of their undivided attention. Embarrassed, she began to study her guidebook with an air of absorbed interest, but out of the corner of her eye she saw that they had called the brigandlike proprietor to their table and with glances and smiles in her direction appeared to be giving him orders.

Whatever they demanded seemed to meet with his approval, for, chuckling, he retired into the recesses of the kitchen, then returned with a flagon of wine that, together with a glass, he placed in front of her with a triumphant flourish.

"But I didn't order this," Christine protested.

"It is a present," he beamed, indicating the group of young men, who were observing her reactions with an air of eager interest.

"But . . . but I can't accept it," she told him, her voice sharp with surprise and embarrassment.

"But you must. It is the custom of the country," the brigand informed her with a great deal of disarming shrugs and gestures. "What is the harm? You are a stranger in Athens. The wine will help to make you welcome. They think you are very beautiful," he added insinuatingly, evidently sure that this assertion would weigh the scales in their favor.

"I . . . I . . . oh, no," Christine replied, flustered and uncertain. And for a moment she tried to visualize how Valerie, gay and extravert, would have dealt tactfully and graciously with this situation.

The proprietor frowned, and Christine realized that he considered her reaction rude and ill-bred.

"Then drink a glass of wine before you go, to let them know that you accept and are not offended," he insisted.

And before she could protest further, he filled the glass to the brim, and Christine reluctantly raised it to her lips and sipped, forcing a smile of appreciation.

As soon as she tasted the wine she coughed and had a hard job to keep her smile from turning into a grimace of revulsion, for it tasted disgustingly of turpentine.

Immediately she realized that this must be retsina, a wine tasting of resin that the Greeks find palatable, but that, according to her guidebook, is an acquired taste for foreigners.

This, Christine decided, was an understatement, for it was a taste that she, at least, was unlikely ever to acquire. She repressed a shudder as she firmly resolved to make this first sip her last.

The proprietor, however, seemed to find her efforts completely satisfactory. His face was wreathed in smiles as he nodded in the direction of the young men as though assuring them that his mission had now been accomplished to his complete satisfaction.

As she put down the glass, Christine was acutely aware that she was being observed closely by a broad-shouldered man who was seated at a table against the wall facing her.

He must have taken his place while she was ostensibly perusing her guidebook, for she had not seen him enter the café. She had a quick impression of glossy dark curls, a lean olive-brown face. And the fact did not escape her that he was now grinning broadly at her evident discomposure, his teeth a band of even, glittering white against his swarthy skin. It was only too clear that he realized how nauseating she found the native wine and was amused by her efforts to conceal her reactions.

She gave him a swift and what she hoped was a withering glance, before opening the flap of her capacious shoulder bag to pay the proprietor for the *karpouzi*. Then, as her fingers failed to meet the familiar outlines of her leather purse, she began to scrabble frantically in its interior.

She put the bag on the table and began feverishly to take out its contents. But there was no doubt about it, her purse was missing.

"My purse . . . it must have been stolen," she faltered. Panic-stricken, she gazed up at the proprietor.

Gone was the bonhomie of a moment ago! Instead, to her agitation, he was regarding her with a suspicious and ugly frown that, to Christine's dismay, held a hint of ferocity.

"So your purse! It must have been stolen," he repeated derisively. "Do you think I am so stupid as to believe that? You are not the first person to try to trick me."

He crashed his huge fist down on the small table so that every object on it rattled and trembled.

This sudden violence brought a halt to the chatter and clicking of beads. Every eye was turned toward Christine and the furious man, who had now burst into a spate of abuse in Greek.

She sprang to her feet, drawing in her breath in alarm

as she caught the words *astinomikon tmima. That means police station,* she thought wildly, and gazed about the café in the desperate hope of rescue. But the faces that regarded her held only amusement or absorbed interest in the spectacle—as though, Christine thought in despair, they were looking at a play and were merely curious at the outcome. No one seemed to realize the misery of her situation.

And then her eyes, still searching desperately, met those of the man sitting by himself in the shadows against the whitewashed wall. Now he no longer showed the band of even teeth. Instead, his face was grave, almost stern in its lines, but his eyes held hers steadily and comfortingly.

Forgetting her former hauteur, Christine regarded him in desperate entreaty.

Then, as though having come to a considered opinion, he slowly stood up and crossed to her table, and in a voice even more stentorian than the bandit's began to harangue him in a spate of Greek.

Bewildered, Christine looked on until her rescuer, with a final furious exclamation, dramatically tossed some drachmas onto the table.

Immediately, as though a tap had been turned off, the bandit ceased his furious tirade, calmly swept the coins into his enormous hand, and, to Christine's surprise, began to attend to the wants of another customer with every sign of good humor.

Christine slumped into her chair, weak with relief.

"That's right," her rescuer remarked approvingly in accentless English. "You look as if you could do with a nice sit-down. Meanwhile I'll order coffee and see if we can bring the roses back to your cheeks. As a matter of fact, I could do with some myself. I had quite a long drive into Athens and the truck's a bit of a bone-shaker."

And, without waiting for her reply, he pulled out a chair opposite her and calmly sat down.

He signaled to the bandit who, now smiling broadly, took his order and swiftly reappeared with two tiny cups of strong, sweet coffee.

Christine sipped it cautiously. Perhaps in time she might have become accustomed to Greek foods and drinks, but without money, she wouldn't be able to stay on. Her holiday would come to an abrupt termination.

It was only now that the significance of her loss began to penetrate. The brigand's violent histrionics had frightened her so much that she had not realized just how desperate her situation was.

She was aware that her companion was regarding her closely.

"By the way, it's true, I suppose, that you actually did lose your money?"

Christine laid down her cup and gazed at him in bewilderment. "What on earth do you mean?"

He grinned again, showing those extraordinarily white square teeth. "You weren't trying to save a few drachmas at my host's expense? People on holiday usually spend too much on souvenirs and that type of thing, then find, by the time they're due to go home, that there's practically nothing left."

Christine felt herself stiffen with anger and her eyes flashed as she said hotly, "You don't seriously think I'd do such a despicable thing simply to save a few drachmas, do you?"

"No, actually I don't," he returned calmly. "I said it for the pleasure of seeing you cast me one of those imperious looks, like the one you bestowed on me before I came to your rescue."

"I don't know what you mean," Christine returned stiffly. Somehow or other this man had the ability to place her in the wrong.

"Don't you know you're very beautiful when you're haughty?" he said softly.

Christine's lips tightened. It was time she put him firmly in his place, she decided.

"Do you imagine that, just because you pay me a rather ridiculous compliment, I've forgotten that you've as good as accused me of trying to rob that horrible man?"

But her companion was maddeningly unchastened by her remarks.

"To begin with, he's not a horrible man. He's simply trying to earn an honest living. I often come here for coffee after market, so I know him pretty well. But may I ask what you're doing in this part of Athens? What am I to think when I find an apparently prim and proper English girl seated by herself in the Plaka district, eating a provocative iced melon?"

In spite of herself, Christine couldn't restrain a smile. "I don't see why I shouldn't be allowed to eat an iced melon—provocative or otherwise."

"Because, my dear girl, the Plaka district is considered slightly unsavory."

"How was I to know?" Christine protested. "I was visiting the Parthenon—"

"Visiting the Parthenon," her companion interrupted. "Tell me, how were you impressed?"

"Well . . . ." Christine hesitated, reluctant to reveal herself a philistine by admitting that she had been disappointed.

He nodded wisely. "I know. You needn't tell me—you were disappointed. Isn't that it?"

"Well . . . yes," she admitted. "Although everyone says how wonderful it is."

"And so it is! Especially by moonlight! And with the right man by your side!"

Christine looked at him suspiciously and discovered, to her surprise, that his eyes were not brown, as she had thought them, but a dark and penetrating blue. And now they were gazing at her in a most disconcerting fashion. It was time she extricated herself from this encounter, she decided hurriedly. After all, this man was a complete stranger to her.

"You must give me your name," she said with prim formality, "so that I can return whatever you spent in paying my bill. I'll get in touch with the British counsul just as soon as I can, and forward the money."

He shook his head. "There's no need to repay me. It was a small outlay for getting to know you. Actually I had been considering various ways of effecting an introduction. I had the feeling that my usual forthright technique would not cut much ice with you, so the contretemps over the bill was a heaven-sent opportunity. By the way, my name is Nicholas Martinos and I run a farm in the country outside Athens. Now, in exchange, you must tell me your name."

As she hesitated, he continued, "You must realize we Greeks are insatiably curious and I have the national reputation to uphold. I should have failed in my duty as a Greek were I not to learn even the most minute details of your life. For example, are you married? Single? What do you work at? What is your favorite type of man? Must he be dark, fair, or in between?"

Christine regarded him warily. He was gently poking fun at her English reticence, she suspected. Yet there was something extremely disturbing about those dark blue eyes beneath the close, glossy curls that fell loosely on his brown, broad forehead. His features, she decided, were as perfect as those on an old coin. She glanced away in case her expression should give a hint of her thoughts.

"I don't believe you're really Greek," she said lamely.

He raised his eyebrows. "Indeed! Now why should you have come to that conclusion? I should have thought my nationality was fairly obvious."

"But you speak English perfectly! You haven't even the faintest trace of a foreign accent."

"Why should I? My mother was English. She came to Greece as a governess to the wealthy Panos family, who were big landowners. She fell in love with Pericles Martinos, who ran a fruit and vegetable farm in the valley, and never returned to England again. And now you must tell me your name, and what you're doing in Athens all by yourself."

Well, perhaps she did owe him an explanation, Christine thought. After all, her holiday had come to an abrupt end. There was nothing to be lost by confiding in him, because when she left Athens their paths would never cross again.

He listened closely as she told him how she and her friend Valerie had planned for years to visit Greece together; how they had saved out of their salaries as typists in the same typing pool; of her disappointment when, at the last moment, Valerie had been unable to come, and of how her friend had talked her into going ahead alone.

"If Valerie had been with me, I'm sure I shouldn't have lost my money," she concluded. "She's much cleverer than I am and knows her way around. I think, looking back on it, that I was robbed as I was coming down from the Parthenon."

When she described to him how the two small boys had apparently accidentally crashed into her, Nicholas Martinos nodded. "Yes, that's when it happened. It's a well-known technique. While you were confused and off balance, one of them slipped his hand into your bag and it was all over in a few seconds. Young as they are they're experts at relieving tourists of their possessions."

"Yes, but if Valerie had been with me, she'd probably have been wise to such a maneuver and have taken proper precautions. It makes me feel so stupid and inept when I realize I was robbed so easily."

Nicholas Martinos laughed. "No, not so easily! It takes quite a bit of practice and one has to begin young. But now that this has happened and you haven't the sagacious Valerie by your side, why don't you let me take her place? In future, you'll see all the sights in perfect safety. I promise to make a most reliable guide."

"In the future!" Christine echoed. "But don't you see, this has changed everything! All I'll be able to do, I suppose, is to ask the British consul to give me assistance to get home again. But it looks as though my holiday in Greece is not going to turn out as planned."

He frowned, and stared thoughtfully ahead for a few moments. Then, as though coming to a conclusion, he said quickly, "Do you realize you haven't told me your name yet?"

"But what difference does it make?" she asked crossly. "The fact remains that I'll probably be leaving Athens as soon as I've seen the consul and made arrangements."

"But, my dear girl, it makes all the difference in the world," he retorted blandly. "Do you realize how difficult it is to make a proposition to a girl without even knowing her name?"

"Make a proposition?" Christine queried cautiously. "What on earth do you mean?"

He shook his head decisively. "Not until I get your name."

"Oh, all right! I'm Christine Hutton."

"Married or single?"

"Single. And I can't see what difference that makes, either...."

"I shall call you Tina and you must call me Nick. Agreed?"

"Agreed," she conceded. It was really more trouble than it was worth to spar with this very determined person. "And what exactly is this proposition of yours?" she asked dryly.

"I know by the sound of your voice that you're not overconfident in my intentions," he informed her chidingly.

"Naturally not! I meet you in a café that as you yourself have told me, is situated in what is not exactly a respectable district. Why should I not be suspicious of you?"

He waved his hands in parody of typical Greek denial. "But I saved you from jail! Are we not on Christian-name terms? What more can I do to prove that my motives are strictly honorable?"

Christine found herself dissolving into giggles as, with a wealth of dramatic gestures, he registered extreme despair, "Oh, all right, let's hear your proposition, as you call it."

"That's better!"

Immediately he grew serious and, leaning forward on his elbows, fixed her compellingly with his dark blue eyes. "What would you say to staying on in Greece?"

She stared at him blankly. "But I've already told you, I've no money."

"You've told me you're a typist. Would you consider a working holiday? I know a very charming English lady who keeps a guest-house near my place. She caters mostly for archaeologists—preferably English—who are at work on a nearby dig. She's a terrific cook, but she has no head for business. In fact, she's rather a character, if you know what I mean. I've often heard her bemoan the fact that she knows no one to keep her affairs in order. What's more, you're British. That would appeal to her, because she suspects, rightly, that we local Greeks are as slapdash as herself."

Christine was silent, confused by this surprising suggestion. She had resigned herself to returning home and she found it difficult to adapt herself to the idea of remaining. Gradually she felt a growing excitement at the idea.

"Suppose she doesn't want me?" she hazarded. "Even if I were able to help her out, it wouldn't follow that she would care to have me actually living under her roof."

"I haven't the smallest doubt that she'll like you. After

all, Tina, I do, and I assure you I'm very hard to please," he informed her blandly.

"Thanks!" Christine returned dryly. "But I don't feel particularly flattered."

He sighed. "Most girls would be eating out of my hand after a compliment like that."

"Perhaps it's because I'm not like most girls," Christine retorted loftily, then immediately regretted her words as she saw his eyes twinkle with amusement.

"But to get back to your proposition," she continued hastily. "Suppose your friend and I discover, when we meet, that we're just not compatible?"

"Then you can return to Athens, and no harm done," he assured her.

"But how would I find my way?" she objected. "I don't know any Greek."

"Except *karpouzi,* meaning watermelon," he put in slyly.

"I'm afraid that won't get me very far," Christine said ruefully.

"My dear girl, why must you keep raising objections? It's all very simple. It will take only a few hours. I'll drive you out to Ruby's. And drive you back again, should you take a violent dislike to one another. By the way, how are you fixed? I mean, will you have somewhere to stay if you decide against this job? If you haven't I'll be only too glad to advance you what you need until you get your affairs fixed up. Actually this would be an excellent time to touch me for a few drachmas, as I sold my first truckload of early vegetables only this morning."

"Oh, no," Christine returned hastily. "I've paid in advance at the hostel, so I've no worries in that direction."

He raised his eyebrows quizzically. "It seems to me you're a very worrying sort of person. It looks to me as if I'll have to get you some *komboloi.*" Then, as Christine looked puzzled, he went on, "Look about you. Do you see all the clicking of beads? They are known as *komboloi*, or worry beads. They give you something to do with your hands, and help to keep blood pressure down."

Christine laughed. "I must say it looks extraordinary to see hefty men clicking away at their beads! Although I must say some of the beads are really beautiful, especially the amber ones."

"Now you're getting away from the subject," he said severely. "Think of the advantage of working for Ruby. The Villa Helena has a terrific view of the sea. It's just up the hill from my place. There will be plenty of opportunity for you to fall in love with me before you go home. And don't look at me with that disapproving gleam in your eye. You must learn to laugh while you are in Greece. Well, what do you say? Shall we set off right away? I suppose you won't mind riding in my fruit truck? You see, I didn't guess I'd meet a charming English girl in the Plaka, or I'd have come by car."

Christine turned her spoon thoughtfully between her fingers. She was torn by indecision. There was something extremely persuasive about Nicholas Martinos—yet suppose no such person as Ruby existed? Apart from saying she was an Englishwoman running a boarding house for archaeologists, Nicholas had not been particularly forthcoming concerning the lady. It would not take a particularly imaginative person to dream her up.

"Well?"

"Yes...I suppose I could try it," Christine said slowly. "But I'd better return to the hostel first. There's ... there's something I must do."

He grinned. "Such as making a few discreet inquiries about Miss Ruby Jackson, no doubt, just in case the lady is a figment of my wicked imagination."

"That's exactly what I intend to do. I suppose you've no objections?" Christine demanded scathingly.

"Not at all! And I can assure you, you'll find that Miss

Ruby Jackson does, in fact, exist and, what is more, is fairly well-known. After all, she has been here for years and we Greeks are inveterate gossips. Now, are you satisfied?"

But Christine would only nod noncommittally, before changing the subject.

CHAPTER TWO

However, when Christine returned to the hostel, tucked away in a narrow side street, she discovered that in replying to her questions the manageress was anything but forthcoming concerning Miss Ruby Jackson.

As she tidied up in her room, Christine was thinking that she had detected a tight-lipped disapproval in the manageress's manner. However, she had agreed that at the Villa Helena an English lady did exist, who catered for archaeologists, some of whom had worked during the previous season on a site in the district. Apart from this piece of information, she had shown a severe reserve concerning Miss Jackson and her affairs, and Christine had got the impression that disapproval was tacitly being conveyed. When she had probed further, all that had been vouchsafed was that Miss Jackson was *xene*—a foreigner.

On an impulse Christine packed a few necessities in an overnight bag. Were she to be delayed in any way in connection with this trip, she would at least be able to spend the night at the Villa Helena—now that she had been assured that this Ruby Jackson did indeed exist.

When she emerged into the street she found her rescuer awaiting her at the wheel of an extremely dirty pale blue truck.

"You followed me!" she accused. "I thought we arranged I should meet you outside the café."

He grinned down on her disarmingly. "It occurred to me, Tina, that you might lose your way, so I followed at a discreet distance. And, now that I'm here, what about hopping up? It's time we were on our way, just in case I have to take you back to Athens again."

He stowed away her bag and she climbed up beside him, to find that a clean rug had been spread over the sagging seat.

"You see, I haven't forgotten the welcoming touch. We Greeks are renowned for our hospitality. Did you know that?" he queried blandly, as they set off through the streets of Athens.

"You mean the rug, I assume?" Christine returned stiffly. "It wasn't really necessary, you know."

Perched in the cabin of the truck beside him, she felt at a distinct disadvantage. What on earth was she doing here anyway, she asked herself confusedly, driving out of Athens into the countryside, to an unknown destination with the equally unknown and disconcertingly self-possessed Nicholas Martinos?

He seemed, however, unaware of any constraint in her manner. His eyes fixed on the streets as he skillfully weaved through the traffic, he said cheerfully, "Oh, but you'll find it was necessary when we get into the countryside. When it is dry, dust rises in clouds everywhere you go. That is why the first thing we Greek country boys do when we arrive in Athens, early in the morning, is to have a shoe-shine. That way, people won't take us for country hicks and we can stroll about the city with perfect self-confidence."

"I should have thought *you're* not lacking in self-confidence," Christine told him dryly.

"Oh, but you're wrong," he assured her solemnly. "For instance, I was extremely doubtful if you'd accept my suggestion of a working holiday, and was fully expecting that you'd flounce out of the café at the very idea."

"Perhaps it would have been better if I had," Christine replied flatly.

He raised his eyebrows. "But why? I expect you've already made inquiries and have found that everything is completely aboveboard and that the lady does, in fact, exist."

"That's not what I mean."

Nicholas sighed. "And what, may I ask, do you mean?"

"I mean there's something you haven't told me about Ruby Jackson. There's a catch somewhere. Isn't there?"

"Well . . ." he began cautiously, then paused, his whole attention seeming to be engaged on negotiating a sharp corner. "Let's say Ruby's a bit of an eccentric. It's not everyone who can get along with her; she can be pretty intimidating at times."

Christine gazed at him in exasperation. "Really, do you imagine I'm the type of girl who wilts at a cross word?"

"No, I shouldn't think so," he grinned. "But Ruby can be horribly outspoken. During her years in Greece she has acquired the national characteristic of asking direct and extremely personal questions."

"But I thought you described her as charming!"

"*I* happen to find her charming, but then I'm half-Greek. Perhaps a girl like you would find her a bit disconcerting."

"A girl like me!" Christine repeated. "But you don't know anything about me! After all, we met only a short time ago!"

"Which makes it all the more extraordinary that we're sitting side by side in my truck, driving into the Greek countryside," he returned. "It's not every girl who'd have the nerve to agree to such a plan."

It was true, Christine thought blankly. But instead of feeling flattered, she felt dismayed and faintly guilty. Even the volatile and easygoing Valerie would not have agreed to such an imprudent and harebrained scheme.

To conceal her reaction, she said with what she hoped was an air of jaunty confidence, "I certainly shan't allow her to bully *me*. Anyway, I'll be here only a fortnight and, from what I gather, I'll be kept busy bringing order into Miss Jackson's correspondence. But what on earth made her think of opening a guest-house if she's such a haphazard and unconventional sort of person?"

"She came here years ago, to help out on a dig, and fell in love with Greece, and when the Villa Helena came up for sale she bought it. She's extremely popular among the archaeologists, for apart from being a great cook, she doesn't regiment her customers." He chuckled. "What's more, she's rather an eccentric, and we Greeks love an individualist."

"*You* seem to like her, at any rate," Christine told him a little acidly.

He glanced at her swiftly, then gave a roar of laughter. "Why don't you stay on and save me from the enchantress? After all, you and I will be close neighbors. There is no reason why we shouldn't see a lot of each other."

Christine said, through set teeth, "Thanks, but I expect to be kept pretty busy and I'm quite sure you will be, too. After all, you have a farm to run, haven't you?" she added sarcastically.

He nodded, and she guessed from his expression that he was proud of his farm.

"It's called after Daphne, daughter of the river god, who turned her into a laurel tree when she was pursued by Apollo."

"Oh, yes," Christine exclaimed in pleased surprise. "We have a small reproduction of the statue at my parents' house."

"Do you live with your parents?" he asked.

"Now you're being thoroughly Greek, and asking personal questions," Christine told him severely.

"But why shouldn't you tell me? We're practically old friends by now."

Christine smiled. "Oh, very well! But I see I'm going to have a hard time keeping any sort of privacy. No, I don't live with my parents. My father has a weak heart, so he has retired with my mother to a small seaside town in the south of England. I live in London with my friend Valerie—the one who couldn't manage to come with me."

"Do you mind if I say I'm glad she didn't accompany you? Had she been here, I shouldn't have had the chance of coming to your rescue, because the competent Valerie would have steered you through the hazards of your first visit to Greece."

"You sound as if you disapprove of competent people," Christine remarked in an effort to cover the sudden and disconcerting rush of pleasure she felt at his words.

"Perhaps I like them a little goofy, like yourself."

"Or Ruby Jackson," Christine put in slyly, and for a moment, she wondered what Ruby looked like, and what sort of person she really was.

"Now you're jealous," he told her. "But don't worry, you've nothing to fear. Ruby's just not my type."

"Thanks, you've taken a weight off my mind," Christine said tartly and, to her exasperation, heard him snort with laughter.

Athens was behind them now and for the next few miles they drove in silence, Nicholas wrapped in his own thoughts, and Christine eagerly watching the passing scenery, overwhelmed by the beauty of the Attic countryside.

Beneath the translucent blue sky with its strange luminous clarity were hillsides thick with wild flowers. In the folds were silvery green olive groves, and Christine felt a thrill of delight as they passed a taverna where among shrubs of rosemary and myrtle were tables with gaily checked cloths. Surrounding it were fields of milk-white narcissi.

Nicholas seemed pleased at her reaction to the scene. "That is the best taverna in this part of the country. Some day you and I must dine there and I'll introduce you to *dolmades*. I don't know any other taverna that makes them so well."

"*Dolmades?*" Christine repeated doubtfully.

He nodded. "Yes. They're vine leaves folded around a

stuffing of spiced minced meat and rice. You may not like the sound of it, but I assure you, once you've tasted it, you'll become an addict."

"Perhaps," Christine said cautiously. "But so far, apart from a few dishes, I'm not terribly keen on Greek cooking."

"That's because you've been wandering around on your own, going to all the wrong places and selecting the wrong dishes. With me as your guide, things will be completely different."

He sounded proprietorial and, for a moment, Christine didn't know whether to be pleased or resentful at his casual assumption that she would allow him to take her affairs in hand. But as she was silently composing a suitable retort Nicholas began to hum quietly to himself, and to her chagrin she realized that he wasn't even aware that she might resent such possessiveness on his part.

He seemed to be concentrating completely on the melody, which to Christine's unaccustomed ears had a tuneless Oriental sound.

She turned and resumed her study of the passing countryside. She would ignore him, she decided, not let him have the satisfaction of thinking his words had impinged on her sufficiently.

But after a few miles her resolve was shattered.

The truck had swept around a bend and before them lay a village climbing the hillside on one hand, while on the other side the land curved down to a sea of aquamarine blue. The houses were washed shades of palest gray, pink and blue, and at a point where the land dipped into a hollow she caught a glimpse of a lovely valley in which masses of blossoming trees stretched. Set a little apart and apparently perched on a ledge of rock was a large snow-white house with rose-red shutters.

"How lovely!" she exclaimed.

Nicholas gave a theatrical wave of his hand. "Yes, I thought you'd approve. That's the Villa Helena."

As he turned the truck into a white, dusty side road, Christine felt her heart beat with excitement. Now that she was actually to meet the formidable Ruby Jackson, she began to feel more than a little apprehensive. Would they immediately detest each other, she wondered, and would the excursion end in her ignominious return to Athens?

The air was filled with the scent of blossoming lilac that grew in tubs set about the large flagged patio. Tiny blossoming creepers grew in the crevices and in the center stood a fountain in the shape of a spouting dolphin. But no water poured into the white basin, and Christine could see from the patches of green that stained the marble that quite a long time had passed since cool water had poured from the fish's open mouth.

She stood entranced and took great breaths of the intoxicating air.

"What a heavenly scent!" she exclaimed.

Nicholas, who was pulling her bag out of the truck, turned with mock indignation. "Don't give the lilac of the villa all the credit. Most of that heavenly scent, as you call it, is wafted up from my lemon trees in the valley."

"Oh, is that it? Yes, I forgot you're a landowner," Christine said demurely.

"Well, in future you won't forget it," he said evenly. "Every time you open your windows you will get a breath from my lemon groves. It will be an excellent way to keep me in mind."

It was hard to know if Nicholas Martinos was in earnest or if he was quietly making fun of her as an overromantic English girl on her first visit to Greece, and Christine, to be on the safe side, said airily, "I think you're taking too much for granted. If Miss Jackson doesn't approve of your scheme, I'll be on my way back to Athens fairly soon."

"Well, you're on the point of being put to the test," he said quietly, "for here comes Ruby Jackson in person."

In spite of Nicholas's warning hints that Ruby was anything but conventional, nevertheless Christine found herself gaping in stunned surprise at the extraordinary figure that now emerged from a side door and advanced toward them across the patio.

Ruby Jackson was much smaller than Christine had imagined and her stringy figure was dressed in a pantsuit of mauve velvet. Above it, a small, white, heavily made-up face was slashed with crimson lipstick. From her ears hung heavy pendant earrings studded with multicolored stones that glittered in the brilliant air and were all too obviously fake. Surmounting all this was a mop of frizzy, faded red hair, and as the apparition drew near, Christine could see that Ruby's eyes were the pale green color of unripe gooseberries.

Ignoring Christine completely, the bizarre apparition faced Nicholas arms akimbo and said in a furious voice, "You have your nerve, Nicholas Martinos! I thought it was arranged that you were to repair the fountain. Instead of that I find you—" here the green eyes darted toward Christine with a basilisk glare "—I find you gallivanting about with one of your girl friends!"

Christine, momentarily stunned by the waspish ferocity of the attack, was on the point of splutteringly coming to her own defense, when Nicholas, unmoved by his reception, put in smoothly, "Now, now, Ruby, keep your hair on! Has it occurred to you that I've my own affairs to attend to? And, apart from that, I shan't be paid a single drachma for my efforts."

Ruby seemed genuinely surprised by his reaction. "But you're half-English! Why shouldn't you help me out?"

Nick sighed resignedly. "Oh, all right! I'll fix it as soon as I have a free moment. But why the rush? After all, it hasn't been operating for some time."

To Christine's amazement the redheaded termagant showed signs of coyness. "I've had word that Professor Harvey is coming."

"Oh, indeed!"

Christine could see that Nick was having difficulty in re-straining his amusement. "Then we must certainly get the fountain fixed," he said gravely. "After all, Professor Harvey is a very special sort of person."

"Yes, indeed he is," Ruby agreed tartly, and Christine got the impression that this bizarre-looking little woman was embarrassed by his remark. She swung around to view Christine, eyeing her up and down. "And who is this?"

"This is a young lady I found wandering in the Plaka without her typewriter," Nick informed her.

"Ha! A typist, in other words!" Ruby interpreted this speech. "And what, may I ask, was she doing wandering in the Plaka?"

"It's an involved story," Nick told her, "but to put it shortly, she had been relieved of her money by a couple of young rascals while she was inspecting the beauties of classical Greece."

"A lame duck, in other words!" Ruby told him dryly.

"Yes, my heart bled for her," he assured her.

"I'm sure it did!" Ruby retorted sardonically. "If she weren't so pretty would you have been quite so sympathetic? Those big, big eyes set in a tiny face appealed to you, didn't they? A wistful little waif, wandering about the Plaka! What an opportunity for you to play the hero! I can see it only too clearly."

"Oh, come, Ruby! You make me sound—"

"I make you sound what you are: the most irritating, unpredictable, complex, unreasonable, susceptible—and yes, I will admit it—the most charming man in Greece. There, I've said it, and now you'll have a worse swelled head than ever," Ruby concluded.

"It's not likely to remain swelled for long," he grinned. "Not while you're around to cut me down to size! But, to return to Christine, she's looking for a job, now that she's short of cash, and –"

"And you thought I'd be the perfect person to foist her off on," Ruby continued. "Well, let me tell you right away, I've no intention of doing any such thing. She doesn't look to me as if she'd be good for anything. She's much too pretty, for one thing. You can see at a glance she's the type of girl who sits about all day, filing her nails and powdering her nose and generally expecting to be paid for nothing."

"That's not true," Christine interjected, stung beyond endurance. "I'm very efficient. I . . . well, anyway, I wouldn't take a job with you, not if you paid me a thousand pounds a week. And I think you're very rude—both of you—to discuss me as if I weren't here. I'm going back to Athens immediately, and—"

But Ruby was completely unimpressed. "Nonsense, girl!" she broke in. "You'll do nothing of the kind. And if we're to get along you'll have to learn not to be so touchy. You'll just have to take the rough with the smooth. I'm used to speaking my mind, and I've no intention of changing my ways now."

"But . . . but it's obvious you've no job for me," Christine returned feebly, the wind quite taken out of her sails. Ruby was so obviously unmoved by her show of resentment.

"Wrong again," Ruby told her, almost triumphantly. "I've a desk full of unanswered letters, not to speak of bills, waiting to be sorted out and suitable replies sent out. You're used to secretarial work, aren't you? It should be no trouble to you."

"I wasn't a secretary, exactly," Christine admitted honestly. "I was in the typing pool, and—"

"Well, you'd better come up out of that pool," Ruby told her with a hoot of raucous laughter. "We'll dignify you with the title of secretary while you're here."

"You have a typewriter, I suppose?" Christine began, feeling that events were moving rather more quickly than was comfortable.

"Oh, yes," Ruby assured her. "I got one in an auction. I don't know if it's working. Come to think of it, the last girl said it was out of order—but then she complained of everything! You'd better come in and have a look at it."

"In that case, I'll be off," Nick said with a grin as he handed Christine her bag. "But I'll be back tomorrow to see how you're getting along. After all, you're my protégée and I must keep in touch...."

"And as for you, Nicholas Martinos—" Ruby swung on him with a voice heightened in tone by well-simulated rage "—don't you dare to show your face here unless you arrive with Stavros and a bag of tools and get that fountain going again!"

"Oh, very well." With simulated contrition, Nick climbed into the cab of his truck and with a wink to Christine disappeared into the narrow road in a cloud of dust.

Christine stood looking after him, her heart sinking. He had been annoying and maddening, but after all, he was the only link she had with recent events. Now she suddenly found herself left alone in the Greek countryside in a strange house with a woman who, although she was English, was unnervingly eccentric and given to unpredictable changes of mood—someone, it was clear, with whom it would be very difficult to get along.

Without noticing where she was going, she followed Ruby into the house and soon found herself in a small whitewashed room, regarding with a sinking heart an enormous old-fashioned typewriter in what was obviously very bad condition. She sat down, rolled in a sheet of paper and gently tried the keys. "It doesn't seem to be in very good condition," she told Ruby reluctantly, "but perhaps all it needs is oiling."

"Well, don't bother about that now," Ruby replied. "I want to show you your room. You can have a look at the typewriter in the morning. And I'm not a bit surprised it isn't going. The last girl I had was completely hopeless—which just shows you, you should never do a good turn. It's not appreciated. She was a girl from the village, who went to secretarial college to better herself. Told me she was learning English! I gave her a job to give her a bit of encouragement, but the girl couldn't spell for toffee."

Christine's heart was sinking as she followed Ruby up the white scrubbed stairs. At every moment it was becoming clearer that working at the Villa Helena would be no joyride.

But her thoughts were diverted as Ruby threw open a door and she found herself in a scrupulously clean room with a plain plank floor. This had been polished to a shining amber and strewn with native hand-loomed woolen rugs of bright blue, yellow and red. The curtains and bedspread were of matching material. It was austerely furnished, but the wide brass bed glittered in the sunlight and its snowy white frilled valances stirred in the soft breeze from the open window.

Outside, she could see the ground sloping upward, carpeted with flowers, and at the top, outlined against the incredibly blue sky, were two white pillars glowing with a faint warm biscuit tint, reminding her of the pillars of the Parthenon. They were obviously the remains of what had at one time been a temple.

Seeing her look of admiration, Ruby said gruffly, "All that remains of a temple to Aphrodite, the goddess of love. The slope behind the house used to be a great center of worship in pagan days."

Then Ruby left her with an abruptness that was typical of her disregard for conventional behavior.

Christine unpacked her small bag, and when she had washed and had brushed her hair she went downstairs and found a meal ready at a table on the patio. Whatever Ruby's shortcomings, she obviously had an unerring eye for the beautiful: tubs of lilac and orange trees in blossom were grouped behind the wrought-iron table, which was surmounted by an enormous red and white umbrella.

They were served by a tall girl with long, straight, raven-black hair and smoldering eyes set in a face of smooth classical features. Unsmilingly she acknowledged Ruby's introduction and stared at Christine with open suspicion and dislike.

"Mariga is really a treasure," Ruby said when the girl had returned to the kitchen quarters. "Her English is pretty good, and, what is more important, she understands it when it is spoken to her. I really don't know what I'd do without her. The trouble is she only comes in 'to oblige.' Her family, the Tracoses, were well-off at one time, but her father is dead now, and for the past few years she and her brother have had to shift as best they can. They have a small holding in the valley, but the brother is an idle layabout and the place is run down. In spite of that, Mariga is very proud and touchy. I only hope I'll be able to keep her for the summer. I'm the sort of person who speaks her mind and lets the chips fall where they may. I'd certainly hate to lose her, now that I've taught her English cooking; roast beef, Yorkshire pudding, steak-and-kidney pie, jam roly-poly, all that sort of thing. It's really ridiculous to think that great big grown-up archaeologists come here demanding ye olde Englishe cooking! But they do! And I make it my business to give it to them. At the Villa Helena my guests find everything just as it was at home. That's the way they want it. It's silly, of course, but there it is. But that's one of the reasons why my house is full when others are empty.

"You'll find Mariga a bit moody, I don't deny. But then I'm not particularly even-tempered myself. So far we've pulled along pretty well. I only hope it continues."

Christine could not but be aware that this was a none-too-subtle hint that she must tread carefully where Mariga was concerned. It was, she thought dryly, all too obvious that if by any chance she were to quarrel with the girl,

Ruby would have no hesitation in deciding which of them was dispensable.

When the meal was over Ruby, crossing her short, skinny legs, lighted a Turkish cigarette and narrowing her heavily mascaraed green eyes, regarded Christine challengingly.

"And now tell me exactly how you met Nick. You haven't fallen for him, by any chance, have you?"

For a moment Christine was speechless with surprise, then she found herself stammering, "But...but of course not. Anyway, I met him this afternoon for the first time. Why, the...idea is ridiculous—"

But with a dry laugh, Ruby broke in, "I've seen girls fall for him quicker than that. But, take my tip, be wary of Nicholas Martinos, for he's a Greek Lothario, if ever there was one, and I'd pity the girl who'd lose her heart to him."

"I haven't the smallest intention of losing my heart to him—or to anyone else, for that matter!" Christine said stiffly.

Ruby snorted. "Don't give me that stuff! What's a girl like you doing wandering about the Plaka alone unless she's on the lookout for romance?"

"I had lost my way. I'd just come down from the Acropolis," Christine informed her defensively.

"Very cultural, I'm sure! I suppose you'd read all about it before you left England: how romantic the Parthenon looks in the moonlight, et cetera, et cetera!"

Christine flushed a little. It was true, of course, that some of the more lush descriptions in the travel books had set her dreaming.

"Ha, so I was right!" Ruby declared triumphantly. "You came here, like every other young girl, looking for romance. Well, you'll find it won't last long with Nicholas Martinos, so, if you'll take my advice, you'll put him out of your mind. I don't want to have a disillusioned young girl on my hands, who's good for nothing but moping and self-pity. I'd hate to see you winding up on the beach with the hippies when you find your dreams of romance have come to nothing."

"But I've told you," Christine said in exasperation, "I haven't fallen in love with Nick, and I haven't the remotest intention of turning into a hippie. I've a perfectly good job and when my holiday here is over I'll return to England."

Ruby blew out a cloud of smoke and said broodingly, "Don't be too sure! I came here years ago to help on a dig and have never returned. This country gets hold of you after a time, so be careful: don't let it catch you the way it did me."

"But you're happy here, aren't you?" Christine asked.

Ruby shrugged. "Oh, it's all right while I've guests, but after they're gone it can be lonely. I begin to wonder why I don't pack up and clear out, but each year it becomes harder."

Ruby relapsed into a gloomy silence, and Christine, a little embarrassed at this revelation from the apparently hard-boiled woman, said diffidently, "Well, I expect I'd better begin to earn my keep right away. I could help with the dishes, I suppose."

"If you like," Ruby returned indifferently. "But don't expect any gratitude from Mariga, for you won't get it, I can assure you."

Yawning, Ruby reluctantly got to her feet and gathered up her pack of cigarettes and lighter. "I'll begin checking through the bedrooms, while you're helping Mariga."

Before going upstairs she indicated the kitchen, which lay off a narrow whitewashed passage to the side of the house. And Christine, a pile of dishes in her hands, carefully walked along it until she came to a door behind which she could hear the clatter of someone poking a stove.

She pushed against the swing door with her shoulder and edged her way into the room. This meant that she was in the kitchen before the other girl was aware of it.

But at the sound of the door creaking shut, Mariga swung around with a startled exclamation and, to Christine's amazement, there was in her fathomless dark eyes an expression of bitter anger.

She advanced on Christine, who stood paralyzed, the pile of dishes still clutched in her hands. "Get out of here!" she hissed.

"I . . . I only wanted to help with the washing up," Christine faltered.

"Go away," Mariga cried. "Go away! Go back to England! You are not wanted here!"

Christine's hands were trembling as she carefully placed the dishes upon a table. She was telling herself that Ruby had warned her that Mariga was temperamental, but somehow she had not expected this inexplicable burst of anger. She would also have to make allowances for the vehement way in which Greeks expressed themselves. Already she knew that they could show a violent, almost murderous rage one moment and the next moment be suddenly calm and smiling. Perhaps it would be this way with Mariga.

She could see now that the feet showing under the cotton skirt were bare. Obviously, Mariga had merely slipped her feet into shoes while she was serving at table. Perhaps the reason for her resentment lay in her being discovered in this way—she, a Tracos, once well-to-do, now walking barefoot like a peasant.

Forcing herself to meet the girl's dark, furious gaze Christine said with a smile, "You really must let me help with the dishes, Mariga. After all, I'm here to help and. . . ."

But a moment later she was backing toward the door, a cold chill striking her as Mariga advanced on her, her

CHAPTER THREE

ON THE FOLLOWING MORNING Christine awoke early, to find the sun blazing through the window of her room. Everything seemed spotlessly clean and glittering in the brilliant, pure Greek light. Dew sparkled on the wild flowers that grew thickly on the hillside; the two pillars on the crest of the slope were touched with the faintest hint of flamingo pink as though the colors of the rising sun still lingered on them.

It was hard now to believe that her strange encounter with Mariga had ever taken place.

And it was harder still to credit it when she went down to breakfast and found Ruby, comfortably informal in a floral dressing gown, her bright red hair rather tousled, planking a plate of croissants and a sensibly large coffeepot on the table, meanwhile announcing crossly that Mariga hadn't turned up that morning. Had she only imagined the dark-haired girl's strange behavior, Christine wondered.

She put the incident out of her mind as Ruby, helping herself to a spoonful of a strange white sticky-looking jam, said abruptly, "Well, how do you feel about staying on at the Villa Helena, now that you've had time to draw your breath and consider things?"

Christine, a little bewildered by this sudden challenge, hesitated, and Ruby, with one of her raucous laughs, said, "Perhaps the Villa Helena is to your taste, but its owner isn't? Is that it? Oh, don't bother about polite denials," she added, raising a repressive hand, as Christine attempted to mutter a reply. "I'm well aware I'm thoroughly disliked hereabouts. They're a good-for-nothing lot. They'd rather laze about in the sun than do an honest day's work. That is," she added grudgingly, "with the exception of Nick. But then he's half-English."

Christine smiled. "I expect you wouldn't have stayed on if you really disliked them as much as that."

Ruby grinned grudgingly. "You may be right. There's something about the Greeks that gets you after a while. Anyway, I simply couldn't face the English weather after this. I'm one of those skinny people who love to soak in the sun. But we're getting away from the subject! How do you feel about staying on and putting up with my moods?"

"I think I'll manage," Christine smiled. "I expect your bark is worse than your bite," she added mischievously.

And, to her surprise, she saw that the heavily made-up green eyes that smiled back at her had, for the moment, lost their hardness.

But immediately, as though regretting a momentary weakness, Ruby said quickly, "Very well, that's settled! Here, try some of this jam. It's something you'll taste only in Greece."

A little reluctantly Christine helped herself to a spoonful, thinking that this was Ruby's way of intimating that she intended to be as amiable as possible.

As soon as she had tasted it she was hard put to it to prevent herself showing revulsion, for the jam was horribly sweet and sticky and had a strange perfumed flavor.

Ruby was watching her closely. "You don't like it!" she announced. "Lots of people don't. But I can assure you it's considered a great delicacy. It's made of a sort of mastic that oozes from trees that grow on the island of Hios. In the old days the entire output used to be sent to Turkey for the making of Turkish delight, and the jam is highly prized here. At the beginning I didn't particularly like it myself, but you'd be surprised how quickly you become adapted to native customs. In fact, strange as it may sound, I now actually like retsina wine, though most of the tourists abhor it. Who knows, perhaps you'll marry a nice Greek boy and settle down here, like myself!"

"That's extremely unlikely," Christine laughed, but she could see that the energetic Ruby's mind was already on the work that lay ahead.

This was the beginning of the season for her and she wanted everything spick-and-span for her guests.

It was only in her business methods that Ruby displayed a remarkable lack of method, Christine was thinking later, as she gazed around in dismay at the disorder in the little whitewashed study. The desk was covered with odds and ends obviously deposited there for lack of a better place to put them. In the dark cupboards she found bundles of neglected papers and in the drawers she discovered a jumble of unanswered correspondence. But, worst of all, the typewriter was covered in dust and seemed in parts to be rusty.

She rooted through the cupboards and several drawers and eventually found some brushes and, at the bottom of a bottle, a little oil. For the next hour she brushed and dusted and oiled the typewriter and carefully swept out the gritty particles of rubber that the previous typist had carelessly allowed to accumulate and jam up the works.

When she had given the carriage a final polish, she stood back and reviewed her handiwork with satisfaction. The typewriter had taken on a new lease of life and in its own old-fashioned way was quite capable of dealing with the type of work that she would have to do at the Villa Helena.

Her next job was filing the jumble of correspondence that had been piled in haphazard bundles here and there throughout the small room. She rather enjoyed this: there was something creative in making order out of chaos. The letters in themselves were not particularly interesting, simply business letters inquiring about accommodation and charges, the dry, austere sort of letters that one would expect from archaeologists!

It was only when she came to one signed Clive Harvey that she found her interest quicken. Apart from the fact that she remembered that it was a Professor Harvey who was to be the first of Ruby's guests, she noted that the letter had a much warmer and more intimate tone than the others. Was this the reason, she wondered, for Nick's sly reference to him on the previous day, and Ruby's bridling embarrassment? Friendly as the professor's letter was, there was nothing to suggest a loverlike attitude, and Christine felt a momentary stab of pity for the strange, gnomelike little woman with the frizzy hair and the heavily made-up eyes. Did she perhaps see romance where none existed, and was the hard-boiled Ruby as vulnerable as the rest of womankind?

But she had no time to dwell on the subject. She was fully determined to get her little sanctum into shipshape order before settling down to work and did not notice how the morning was slipping by.

When at last she was satisfied, she stood back to survey the room.

The papers were neatly filed in the green japanned drawers intended for the purpose. In the center of the desk, which she had polished vigorously, stood the high, old-fashioned typewriter gleaming bravely in spite of the fact that the black enamel was chipped in places.

But she felt a certain disappointment dilute her pride in her achievement. Now that order had been introduced, the little room looked austere and cell-like. Pretty, brightly colored curtains and a few vases of flowers distributed here and there would make all the difference, she decided. On her first trip into Athens she would purchase some cheap native cottons. As to the flowers—well, the garden of the Villa Helena was a mass of blossom—narcissi, hyacinth and heavy purple and white lilac.

Christine was still studying the room thoughtfully when the door opened and Ruby entered. Around her frizzy hair she wore a bandanna, and between her bony fingers was one of her favorite Turkish cigarettes. She looked hot and dusty and seemed not to be in too good a humor, having spent the morning putting the finishing touches to the bedrooms.

She gave a whistle of surprise as she gazed about. "Well, you *have* made a difference! I must say it looks a lot better. But come along. Lunch is ready, and there's something I want you to do for me afterward."

Christine found that Ruby's cooking fully lived up to the reputation Nick had given it. But Ruby was not very talkative during the meal and as soon as it was over she said briskly, "If you're finished I wonder if you'd go down to Nick's place. Now that Professor Harvey's arriving I want to stock up my freezer with vegetables, and Nick grows the finest in this part of the country. But don't tell him I said so!"

So she was to encounter Nick Martinos once again!

Christine found herself for some reason or other both elated and dismayed by the prospect. There was something about the man that put her on the defensive, yet the challenging, direct gaze of those dark blue eyes set in the sharp-boned, olive-skinned face had the power to give her an exciting sense of danger.

She glanced across the table at Ruby, hoping that she had not detected her reaction in her expression. But Ruby, her green eyes narrowed against the smoke of her after-lunch cigarette, was gloomily absorbed by the fact that Mariga was still absent.

"The wretched girl hasn't turned up yet! On your way to Nick's, call in at the Tracos place and find out what she intends doing. You can go up the slope at the back of the house. There's a track leading on into the valley. You can't miss the Tracos place—it's fairly big. Ask as tactfully as possible if Mariga is going to turn up for the afternoon."

Ruby ground out her cigarette on a saucer with an air of angry frustration. "If I didn't need her so badly, I'd take great pleasure in telling that sulky beauty just where she gets off!"

"You'd think she'd have enough to do keeping house for her brother without taking outside work," Christine ventured.

It seemed strange to her that a girl so proud and resentful of what she considered a comedown in the world should work for Ruby Jackson.

"She hasn't much choice," Ruby returned dryly. "The Tracos family have hit bad times. Her brother, Stavros, prefers to spend his time sitting in a taverna in the village drinking retsina to cultivating his olive groves. Mariga is like a lot of girls hereabouts: her only hope of escape is to marry."

"She'll hardly have any problems where that's concerned," Christine smiled. "She's so very beautiful!"

Ruby nodded. "Half the young men in the village are crazy about her, but Mariga's not easy to please. She has her own ideas about whom she intends to take as a husband and she'll fight like a tigress for the man she wants. No second best will do for her."

"Yes, she strikes one as the sort of girl who would be fiercely possessive if she set her heart on someone," Christine agreed.

"Let's hope, for her sake, that the man she has set her heart on returns her ardor," Ruby concluded darkly.

But she was no longer really interested in the subject. With a sigh she got to her feet. "Well, back to the treadmill! Oh, by the way, hadn't you better get in touch with the authorities in Athens about your stolen money? You could go in on the bus this afternoon."

"Yes, and I could call along to the hostel and collect the rest of my things," Christine agreed.

"I suppose, until you get things fixed up, you'll need some cash," Ruby said with a gruff awkwardness that Christine was to discover always accompanied any show of kindness. Then, before Christine could thank her, she hurried from the room.

Christine went upstairs and slipped into a jersey dress of orchid pink and kingfisher blue. She had pushed it into the corner of the overnight bag she had packed at the hostel. True to the assurances she had received when she bought it, it had emerged without a wrinkle and now fell about her slim figure in smooth, creaseless folds. The only makeup she applied was a touch of honey-pink lipstick.

Slinging her white linen bag over her shoulder, Christine began to climb the slope behind the house, following a narrow goat track that led through bushes of juniper and thyme. When she reached the top she found that the ground had been leveled, obviously for the building of the temple.

She stopped to survey the spot that had intrigued her since her arrival and sat down on a broken column of marble that lay on the paved ground. Before her lay the aquamarine blue sea with islands shimmering in the distance. Beneath her, gleaming ice-white in the pellucid light, was the Villa Helena with its rose-red shutters.

She sat there dreamily, a soft warm breeze stirring the strands of hair that had fallen on her forehead. Only the sound of seabirds broke the silence, and gradually a sense of unease began unaccountably to steal over her. There was something strange and eerie about the spot, she felt. It was as though spirits from ancient Greece that thousands of years ago had come to this place to worship the goddess Aphrodite still lingered about the stark, crumbling pillars and jumble of marble shards that lay scattered about the broken, weed-grown pavement.

She jumped to her feet and, feeling a little ashamed of her unaccountable nervousness, hurried down the track that led into the valley.

It was easy to recognize the Tracos home. It was a large dilapidated building from the windows of which hung broken shutters that at one time appeared to have been painted a bright ocher yellow but were now faded and blistered. But it was obvious that the large gloomy-looking house had, at one time, been the prosperous home of well-to-do farmers. Now the outbuildings were repaired with odd bits of wood and strips of galvanized iron. About the weed-grown yard were scattered pieces of rusty farm machinery and rotting harness. To one side grew a few straggling olive trees, and even to Christine's untutored eye they looked barren and neglected.

Before the house was parked an ancient, battered car, and as she approached, Christine saw the door of the house being thrown open; there Mariga appeared. For an instant Christine hardly recognized the girl. She was wearing a smartly cut suit of pale almond green. Her thick, straight hair was caught back in a rhinestone clip; her shoes and stockings were of a warm golden tan and the bag slung over the crook of her arm was of the same color.

She took a few steps toward the car, then stopped as she caught sight of Christine.

Immediately her face resumed her usual withdrawn and antagonistic expression. "Well?" she demanded. "What are you doing here? What do you want?"

Her tone was openly insolent and Christine, in spite of herself, found that Mariga, as usual, had the power to ruffle her. But she was determined not to let the girl have the satisfaction of seeing her lose her temper. "I'm not here by choice," she said stiffly. "Miss Jackson sent me."

"And what does dear Miss Jackson want?" asked Mariga derisively.

For an instant Ruby's admonition to approach Mariga tactfully on the subject of her absence flashed through Christine's mind, but she could not prevent herself blurting out, "I should think it's fairly obvious why she sent me! She wants to know why you didn't come this morning and if you intend to turn up this afternoon."

"She does, does she?" Mariga's voice became shrill. "Well, you can tell Miss Ruby Jackson that I'm not coming to work this afternoon because I'm going into Athens shopping." Then with dramatic intensity, she declaimed, "I am Mariga Tracos—not a slave!"

There was something so incongruous about the girl's unrestrained manner and her well-groomed and sophisticated appearance that Christine could find no reply.

Then, satisfied that she had vanquished the intruder, Mariga got into the car and slammed the battered door triumphantly. But before she could drive off, Christine, recovering herself, hurried forward. "Just a moment!" she said urgently, putting her hand on the door. "Before you go, will you direct me to Nick Martinos's house?"

Immediately Mariga's hand dropped from the wheel. Slowly she turned her head toward Christine, her eyes narrowing suspiciously. "And why should you want to know the way to his house, may I ask?"

Christine drew in her breath impatiently. Really, the girl was impossible!

"Because Miss Jackson has sent me to order vegetables for her deep-freeze—not that it's any of your business!" she retorted hotly.

She knew she was ignoring Ruby's injunctions in allowing herself to be riled by Mariga's manner, yet she couldn't help herself. There was something between this girl and herself that made her bristle with antagonism. They never would be friends, of this she felt certain; no effort on her part could dissipate the ferocity that lay beneath Mariga's superficial veneer of sophistication.

Mariga gave vent to a loud and unamused burst of laughter. "Of course, there was no one to send but you!" she sneered. "She couldn't have sent me, for instance, who lives so close to him! Oh, no, she wouldn't do anything like that, would she? We might talk of more than eggplants and tomatoes. Sometimes," Mariga added sibilantly, "I think she's jealous, because the man she wants doesn't even know she exists. To him she's only the owner of the Villa Helena. Why does she not realize that, for her, the time for love is past?"

"What do you mean?" Christine asked, puzzled.

Was the girl, by any chance, hinting that Ruby was infatuated by Nick Martinos? The idea seemed bizarre. But recollecting Ruby's heavily made-up face and exotic hairstyles, Christine wondered doubtfully if it was possible.

It was out of the question, of course, that, curious as she was, she could discuss this with Mariga. Instead she said, "It is not my business to tell Miss Jackson whom she should send on errands. Remember, like yourself, I am employed by her."

"Perhaps!" Mariga shrugged. "But just remember that when *you* return to England the Villa Helena will still be there. But should *I* choose to leave it would be finished. Miss Jackson is a silly and absurd old woman, but she knows how valuable I am to her. You will find that she will put up with my absence and be glad to welcome me back. And now, if you are so keen to visit Nick, he lives in that direction."

She pointed to a narrow path that led off to one side through the grove of straggly olive trees, and without another word started the car and drove off as swiftly as the ancient vehicle would allow.

As Christine turned to follow her direction, her eye caught a movement from one of the tumbledown outbuildings that were attached to one side of the big house, and discovered that she was being watched intently by a man who stared at her from the shadowed interior.

Under an ancient cap, dark eyes smoldered in a nut-brown face, and his hair hung down on each side of his face in a thick thatch. This must be Stavros Tracos, she decided, for there was a distinct resemblance to Mariga, although he conspicuously lacked her striking good looks.

A little discomfited that she had been unconsciously under his scrutiny, Christine nodded a little awkwardly, but he stood motionless, staring at her unblinkingly. And as she moved away she was conscious of his absorbed, inimical gaze, which she found vaguely disturbing.

She had not gone far along the winding dusty track when she found herself in a grove of handsome well-kept olive trees and immediately guessed she was now in the grounds of Nick's farm. Apart from that, there could be no mistaking that familiar intoxicating scent of lemon blossom.

It was just then she saw Nick coming toward her through the silvery green of the olive grove. In spite of herself, she found her heart giving a strange, disconcerting little lurch as she saw that he was smiling at her, his teeth a gleaming band of white against his evenly tanned skin.

"So you have come! Just as I thought, you couldn't resist me! I have been making little bets with myself as to what day you would turn up, but I didn't flatter myself you would make it the very first day."

Christine stopped in her tracks and drew herself up haughtily and was on the point of delivering a scathing rejoinder when she realized that he was having difficulty in suppressing his laughter.

"Why must you take life so seriously? You're in Greece now. You must not go around with a solemn face. Let me see you smile," he urged.

He was close to her now and Christine could see that the dark blue eyes beneath the thick straight brows were touched with flecks of light that seemed to dance and flicker as motes do in sunlight.

In spite of herself she felt her mouth curve into a smile.

"That's better!" he nodded approvingly. "You know, you've a dimple in your left cheek that I find most intriguing. I have known girls with dimples in both cheeks," he added as though giving the question serious thought, "but having only one dimple makes you rather unique."

He was making fun of her again, Christine realized. A little primly, she said, "I hate to disappoint you, but it wasn't my idea to come here. Ruby wants to know if you can supply her with vegetables. Professor Harvey is coming soon and she wants to have everything in order before his arrival."

"Professor Harvey," Nick repeated. And she could see that again, for some reason or another, he was amused. "In that case, we mustn't let her down. After all, only the best is good enough for Clive Harvey!"

"What do you mean?" Christine asked, curiosity making her forget that she had intended to keep Nick Martinos at arm's length.

He grinned. "Surely Ruby has given her secret away by now!"

"What secret?" Christine asked in exasperation.

"That she's madly in love with him, of course! It was the same last year—she went into a tremendous flap when he was due to arrive. But she seems to be under the impression that no one knows that she's badly smitten, although the whole village is abuzz with the subject."

Instantly Christine's mind flashed back to the letter she had filed away in the little office in the Villa Helena. It was signed "Clive Harvey" and dealt only with details concerning accommodation, although there had been something especially friendly in its tone. But not by any stretch of the imagination could it be considered lover-like.

So this was what lay behind Mariga's sneering remarks about Ruby! "The man she wants doesn't even know she exists," the girl had said. It was Clive Harvey she had been referring to, not Nick Martinos! Poor Ruby! Christine felt a pang of compassion. There was something poignant in the fact that the eccentric little woman was unaware that what she regarded as her secret was common knowledge.

"Well, it's not funny," Christine protested hotly.

Nick raised his eyebrows. "Did I say it was?" he asked.

"No . . . no, not exactly!" Christine found herself stumbling over the words, the wind rather taken out of her sails by his rejoinder. "But I can see by your attitude that . . . that you think it's amusing."

"Let's be sensible and face the facts! Ruby isn't as young as she used to be and from what I've seen of him I've got the distinct impression that Clive Harvey just isn't interested. It seems to me that he's completely unaware that Ruby's crazy about him. Otherwise he'd steer well away from the Villa Helena."

"All the same, you think love is only for the young," Christine persisted.

"Let's say it seems to me that you and I are more like the ideal couple. Don't you think it would be a good idea if we fell in love?"

"Oh, why can't you be serious?" Christine demanded exasperatedly.

"But I am," he rejoined blandly. "Oh, no doubt, at present, you are not feeling particularly romantic! But give me a little time! I'll grow on you, I assure you . . . ."

"If you're quite finished, perhaps you'd let me know what message I'm to bring back to Ruby," Christine interjected coldly. "I've better things to do than to stand here and listen to your nonsense."

"What better things could you possibly have to do than to visit a lone bachelor and admiring neighbor?" he asked with an air of shocked surprise.

"Well, for one thing," Christine told him, "I've got to go into Athens and report my loss, and then I must collect the rest of my things from the hostel."

"You mean you intend to go this afternoon?" he asked in genuine surprise.

"Yes, of course. Why not?"

"But the afternoons are no time to conduct business. Even at this time of the year they are too hot. I suggest you wait until later and let me drive you in so that I can show you the famous violet light that falls over Athens when the sun goes down."

Christine drew breath to reply, but before she could speak Nick continued smoothly, "And now you must come in for a cup of coffee. You can inspect my little abode and decide for yourself if the housekeeping is up to scratch."

And before Christine could gather her wits together she found herself hustled through a lemon grove toward a large, substantial square house, the walls washed a pale dove gray against which the inevitable shutters stood out a startling geranium red.

Inside it was deliciously cool and Christine was pleasantly surprised to see how tidy the large kitchen was, with its polished stove and orderly array of gleaming pottery and cooking utensils. The large table in the center of the bare floor was scrubbed to a snowy whiteness, and glancing about at the gaily patterned curtains that so exactly matched the tones of the geranium shutters, she had a growing suspicion that the pristine cleanliness of the kitchen had not been achieved by the slapdash methods of a man as obviously undomesticated as Nick Martinos.

"Well, what do you think of my housekeeping?" he inquired gravely.

"I certainly don't believe it's you who keeps things in such order," she informed him flatly.

He registered shocked protest. "Really, you have the most suspicious mind. Are you determined to give me credit for nothing?"

But Christine, noting the bowl of grape hyacinths that

stood on the deep windowsill, was more than ever convinced that this was the work of a woman's hand.

"I suppose it was you who tastefully arranged the flowers," she remarked dryly.

"All right, you win," he conceded. "You see, Mariga takes a dim view of my domestic arrangements and any time she has an hour to spare she drops in and sets to."

CHAPTER FOUR

THERE WAS A LONG MOMENT of silence in the large kitchen.

Embarrassed, Christine was thinking that Nick must be aware that even she, with her slight knowledge of Mariga, must know that she was not the type of girl gratuitously to fuss over a man in a purely platonic relationship.

"I'm sorry," she said in a small voice.

"Sorry for what?"

She was aware that he was regarding her intently as though a little puzzled by her obvious confusion.

"After all, it's none of my business."

"But I'd like you to make me your business," he told her quietly. "After all, it's not every day of the week that pretty visitors from England pay me a call."

But Christine had crossed to the open deal cupboard and was now making a great show of studying the pretty peasant pottery mugs that were set out, evenly spaced along the shelves. "What lovely colors!" she exclaimed. "Are they made locally?"

She was aware that Nick was smiling slightly as though aware that her interest in Greek ceramics was simply a ruse to cover her embarrassment.

"And now you must drink some coffee out of our delightful native pottery," he invited, echoing her words in a slightly ironic tone.

With a competence that surprised her, he set about producing a steaming pot of fragrant coffee. While Christine gingerly sipped at the coffee, Nick clapped a small striped cloth on the table, upon which he placed a plate of cakes.

The coffee, although thick and spicy, was refreshing, and Nick, watching her reactions closely, remarked, "So at least you approve of our coffee!"

"Yes," she agreed. "I must admit it has rather an unusual flavor, but I'm sure one could become rather an addict."

He laughed aloud at her air of pleased surprise. "It's evident you don't altogether approve of our Greek cuisine. We acquired our tastes in coffee and cakes from the Turks, but not everyone likes them. I'll be interested to know what you think of our *baklava*," he remarked as he offered the rather appetizing-looking cakes.

But one nibble was enough to convince Christine that this was one form of Greek confectionery she would not become addicted to. The cake, she discovered, was composed of a wedge of pastry, drenched in honey and sprinkled with cinnamon.

"So you disapprove of our delightful *baklava*," Nick said reproachfully.

"Much too sweet," she pronounced, "although I must say I love Turkish delight. But on the whole Greek food is not my cup of tea."

"That's because you haven't tasted some of our really delicious dishes," he protested. "I intend to make it my business to convert you to our way of life."

"But why?" she queried. "After all, I shan't be here very long."

For a moment he sipped from his thick pottery mug, then laying it down on the table, he said quietly, "Who knows? Like other Englishwomen before you, you may fall in love with Greece. Or, better still, with a Greek!"

Avoiding those piercingly blue eyes, Christine said lightly, "I don't imagine so! Anyway, although I think Greece can be very beautiful, there's something dreadfully melancholy about its ruins. I expect I'd need to be an archaeologist really to understand and appreciate the Acropolis."

"And do you feel that way about the ruins of the temple of Aphrodite behind the Villa Helena?" he asked. "Remember, she was the goddess of love. Surely when you looked out from your bedroom window and saw the stars glittering between its marble pillars something stirred in your heart!"

"How do you know my room looks toward the temple?" she asked sharply.

He chuckled. "A simple deduction, my dear girl! Until your arrival, when in the evenings I strolled through the lemon groves and climbed the slope to gaze down toward the sea, not as much as a glimmer of light showed from that window in the Villa Helena. You can't imagine how cheerful it was to see it flooding through the darkness while amidst the ruins of the temple I smoked a pensive pipe."

Was he making fun of her again, Christine wondered. It was hard to tell with a man like Nick Martinos. Somehow he was an enigma—at times thoroughly English and at others wholly Greek, with all the Greek's love of discussion and argument.

"But you haven't answered my question," he added.

"But why should I feel romantic about a couple of pillars and piles of chipped marble?" she protested.

"Because, my dear girl," he assured her solemnly, "Aphrodite, who as you know is the goddess of love, might take revenge for your indifference."

"And would that be very terrible?" she asked demurely.

He considered her thoughtfully. "It depends! Depends upon the type of girl you are! You see, should you offend Aphrodite she will order her son, Eros, to shoot a golden arrow at you."

"That doesn't sound very terrible, either," Christine countered.

"You say that because you haven't realized that Eros is

Cupid under another name. Should you be struck by one of his golden arrows you will fall in love instantly. Now do you realize the dangers of taking Aphrodite lightly?"

"Very well," Christine assured him laughingly, "in future I'll be more circumspect and make sure Cupid doesn't aim any of his arrows in my direction!"

She saw that he was eyeing her thoughtfully and decided that the conversation was straying in dangerous directions. It was high time she led it into very different channels, she determined.

"Have you always lived here?" she asked, glancing about the kitchen with an air of well-simulated interest.

"Now you're deliberately changing the subject!" he accused. "I'm afraid there's nothing very exciting to tell. My parents died when I was fairly young. After that, I felt I had to get away from things for a while until I made up my mind if I really wanted to carry on as a farmer. My father's wish was that I should keep the place and follow in his footsteps. After all, it had been in the Martinos family for centuries! But I wasn't so sure. I wanted to see a bit of the world before I decided whether this was the life for me, so I got a neighbor to run the farm for me and joined a ship trading along the coast between Marseilles and Naples. Well, it was fun for a while, but somehow it began to seem an unsatisfying sort of life, with no assured future. I wanted to do something that would bring me results, something I could build with my own hands."

He gazed frowningly through the open kitchen door and Christine guessed he was reliving those moments of indecision.

"So you decided you'd rather return to farming?" she ventured.

"Yes, after a few trips, I decided it was time to begin creating some sort of life for myself. Farming was the life I understood and I had all sorts of plans for expansion. For instance, we had always grown figs, olives and citrus, but I wanted a vineyard, too. So I've started one, at any rate. No doubt my children, if I ever do have any, will benefit."

Then, as though conscious that the conversation had taken on a very personal tone, he turned to her with the familiar mocking grin. "But why this interest in my past? Most girls, I have found, are more concerned with the present or the future. For instance, a typical feminine question concerning this new venture would have been, 'Will it succeed? Will it be financially profitable, et cetera?'"

"In that case most of the girls you have known must have been extremely mercenary!" Christine said severely.

He considered her answer, his blue eyes now faintly puzzled as well as amused.

"Do you mean you wouldn't be at all interested in whether my activities were successful or not?"

"No. Why on earth should I be? After all, it's no concern of mine," Christine said carefully.

"All right! But let us pretend for a moment that you are a local girl interested in acquiring an eligible husband! Don't you agree that she is justified in demanding that he should be financially successful?"

Christine considered this proposition carefully. "If I were a girl on the lookout for an eligible husband . . . which, of course, I'm not," she added hastily.

"Of course, I understand perfectly," Nick said gravely.

"Well, I think," Christine pursued, "it would be more important to me that he should be successful—but not particularly financially."

"Now what on earth do you mean by that?"

"Simply that I'd like my husband to feel happy and contented in what he is doing. Then it wouldn't matter particularly whether he was financially successful or not. Surely success can be measured in something more than money?"

Nick leaned back in his chair and considered her quizzically for a long moment. "Do you know, Tina, that in spite of not being Greek, you are quite the little philosopher."

There was something in the tone of his voice that gave her a strange sensation of confusion that wasn't altogether unpleasant. She shrugged with an assumption of nonchalance. "I should think most girls feel the same way."

"You're wrong, Tina. Most girls don't think that way at all—at least, the local variety don't. Romance takes a very secondary place in their estimation when it comes to marriage."

"Perhaps," Christine said lightly, "they believe in the old saying that without money love flies out the window."

"Perhaps," he conceded dryly, "but in my opinion there's usually mighty little love in the first place to fly anywhere."

"Then you'll have to be very particular whom you pick," Christine informed him mischievously, then waited for his reply with a tenseness that surprised herself.

He leaned forward, his bare brown arms folded on the table, and considered her closely with those dark blue eyes. "I think I'll take your advice. Before committing myself to any girl I shall submit a questionnaire, and unless her answers are completely satisfactory concerning love, money, et cetera, I shall without hesitation cross her off my list of probable brides."

Christine bit her lip. Had he been aware, she wondered, of the eagerness with which she had awaited his reply? She would, she decided, impress upon him that she was taking no more than a passing interest in his affairs.

"I should have thought that in your case no questionnaire would be necessary. You seem quite capable of taking care of yourself."

"Now that's just where you're wrong. I'm putty in the hands of a pretty and designing female. I think it might be a good idea if you'd drop in now and then to keep me on the straight and narrow."

His voice was light, but the blue eyes were watching her carefully and Christine felt a sense of exasperated frustration. How difficult it was to understand just what was going on in the mind of this enigmatic man! How to guess when he was quietly mocking or when there was an underlying vein of harsh reality behind his words. Surely he must be aware that Mariga Tracos loved him with all the violence and possessiveness of her nature. She was obviously a girl who scorned to hide her feelings when she loved a man. Surely on those housecleaning forays she made to the farm she had revealed the depths of her feelings! But she felt that no matter how she framed her questions Nick would instantly balk any attempt to extract information. She would ask Ruby about it, she decided. Ruby with her sharp, discerning green eyes would have gauged to a nicety exactly how matters stood between Nick and Mariga.

She got to her feet and with an air of limpid innocence said demurely, "Well, it's time I was getting back. I'm just getting things into order before I settle down to work."

"Knowing Ruby, I expect a great many things will have to be got into order," he grinned. "But remember I'm taking you into Athens later this afternoon, so be ready in your best bib and tucker when I arrive."

"I'm afraid I'm wearing my best bib and tucker," Christine told him a little ruefully. "I couldn't fit another single thing into my bag."

For a moment his eyes traveled over her slim, graceful figure. The delicate shades of blue and pink in her dress were a perfect complement to her small features and mane of soft dark hair.

"I'd like to think of you always as you are now," he said slowly.

Suddenly shy, she laughed unevenly. "Sorry, I can't oblige. I'm afraid it will be necessary to ring a few changes."

He sighed. "Oh, very well, we'll call at the hostel and collect the rest of your gear—but that's as far as I'm prepared to go where business is concerned. After that, you and I are going to enjoy ourselves. I'm determined you'll see Athens at its very best, and not as a mere tourist."

Christine walked across the kitchen toward the door, glad that he was following her and could not see in her face the startled pleasure she felt in his words.

He went with her toward the track. "Tell Ruby I'll fill her freezer to capacity, not forgetting the eggplants."

"I've seen them on sale," Christine told him, "but strangely I've never tasted them. They're such a beautiful color, I wish one could buy fabric of exactly the same shade. Ruby must like them very much."

"Not Ruby! They're for Clive Harvey. I think she'd scour every island in Greece to get the plumpest eggplants for her beloved Clive. You can see to what lengths true love can go, Christine."

Nick laughed gently and without the faint derision she had previously detected in his attitude to Ruby's infatuation for the professor.

As she walked quickly up the rough, flinty path she was aware that he was standing watching her until she reached the bend that led toward the Tracos farm.

Gradually she slowed her pace to a saunter. It was an exquisite day, the sky a clear forget-me-not blue; the air balmy with an amalgam of delicious scents. Hedges of myrtle and thyme grew on the slopes. And Christine, wrapped in her own thoughts, was barely aware that she was passing through the thin plantation of sparse olive trees near the Tracos house.

However, she was to get a rude awakening.

She had emerged from the olive trees and had gone

only a few yards when a heavy stone thudded at her feet and a spray of pebbles and dust showered over her shoes. With a start of alarm she looked about, bewildered. But the countryside seemed deserted, nor was there cover enough to conceal anyone hiding in the bushes of juniper and myrtle. On the height the ruined columns of the temple of Aphrodite stood stark and deserted against the sky. She seemed to be alone on the narrow track with no other living soul to be seen in the surrounding countryside.

Then she realized that a little back from the track stood an outhouse, the gable of which was turned toward the track. It too shared the general air of decay and dilapidation. In the mortared walls were gaping gray patches and only in places could signs be detected that at one time it had received a coat of whitewash. High up near the roof was the square, dark opening to a loft.

More curious than alarmed, Christine retraced her steps and gazed up, trying to pierce the velvety darkness that lay behind the gaping opening.

For a moment she saw nothing, then there was a flurry of movement and she found herself gazing up at Stavros Tracos; his mahogany-brown face was unmistakable beneath the tattered cap. For an instant he glared down at her and then as suddenly seemed to be swallowed up and merged in the shadowed background.

Christine stood gazing up uncertainly. She was now quite certain that the stone had been hurled by Stavros Tracos. From the direction in which it had come it must have been flung from his vantage point near the roof.

But why on earth should he do such an extraordinary thing? After all, he was not a mischievous small boy, but a grown man! Perhaps she should call out to him, demand an explanation! But she felt sure that silence would be her only answer. Apart from that there had been something fierce and unrestrained about the dark face with its beetling black brows that made her reluctant to insist on a confrontation.

Slowly she walked on, wondering if she should describe the encounter to Ruby. Then she decided against it. Even in the short time she had been at the Villa Helena she had learned that with Ruby Jackson one could never be quite certain how she would react. There was every chance that her story would be received with derision, or even with downright disbelief.

But she had not counted on the little woman's sharp observant eye.

She discovered Ruby seated on the patio stringing beans from a wicker basket that rested in the empty marble basin of the fountain. As Christine approached, Ruby looked up and paused in her activities. "Well, and what have you been up to? You look scared. Did you, by any chance, bump into Aphrodite as you passed her temple?"

"No, not Aphrodite." Christine smiled as she seated herself on a huge slab of sun-warmed marble that was evidently used as a garden seat. "But I did come across someone not nearly as beautiful—in fact he had a face like a walnut and longish black hair topped by a cap."

She thought she detected a slight sharpening of Ruby's heavily made-up eyes, but an instant later the little woman was once again thoughtfully stringing the beans.

"Hmm, so you've met Stavros, have you! Well, take my advice and stay clear of that young man. He's generally avoided, even by the villagers."

"I fully intend to keep out of his way," Christine told her dryly. "But I can't imagine why he should throw stones at me."

Ruby showed no signs of surprise at this piece of information. "All the Tracos family are notoriously bad-tempered. There was another brother who had to leave home. He injured another man badly in a fight and discreetly decided to keep out of sight for a few years."

"But why pick on me?" Christine protested, a little disgruntled by Ruby's casual reception of her news.

Ruby glanced at her doubtfully, as though considering the wisdom of answering her question. Then, as though coming to a decision, she shrugged and promptly changed the subject.

"What news have you of Mariga? Did she give any explanation for not turning up? This should have been her job, you know, for if there's one thing I detest more than any other, it's stringing beans. But Mariga seems to enjoy it. I expect it's because it gives her time to brood. All the Tracos family are great brooders. I think perhaps that's what helps to make them so unpopular."

"I'm afraid you'll have to do your own stringing today," Christine told her a little tartly. "When I passed the Tracos place Mariga was on the point of departing for Athens. I'd say she was bent on a shopping spree."

Ruby sighed. "I shouldn't be at all surprised. And it's really all my own fault. I shouldn't have given her an advance on her wages when she asked me—I ought to have known what she'd do with it. The girl's crazy about clothes and I really believe the only thing she reads is fashion magazines. Sometimes I wonder where she puts all the things she's collected over the years. She never wears anything for long before her eye lights on something else and it's off with the old and on with the new. The house and outbuildings must be stuffed with her discarded garments."

"All I know is that one of the outhouses held Stavros today," Christine told her dryly. "He saw me set off for Nick's place and evidently took up a good position overlooking the track and waited for my return. I expect if I hadn't retraced my steps and faced him, he'd have bombarded me with stones."

Once again Christine got the distinct impression that Ruby knew the answer to Stavros's weird behavior. But, as before, and again with a distinct lack of subtlety, she promptly changed the subject.

"And how was Nick?" she asked brightly.

"Nick Martinos was his usual insufferable self," Christine replied snappishly, and to her annoyance she saw Ruby's heavily lipsticked mouth tighten into a sly smile.

"Do you think him attractive?" she asked, with an air of disarming innocence that didn't for a moment deceive Christine.

"It depends on what you mean by attractive," she temporized. "Here, let me do these!" She leaned forward and lifted the wicker basket from the empty basin of the fountain and began to string the beans.

With a sigh of relief Ruby leaned back in her canvas chair. "Now I can relax. Beans are such finicky little things. I'd much sooner set to and clean an entire room than string a basketful of beans. But by any chance was your kind offer made in order to divert the conversation from Nick Martinos?"

"You're a nice one to talk of diverting the conversation!" Christine retorted.

Ruby chuckled as though well pleased that Christine had been sharp enough to detect her strategy. "All the same, I'd be interested to get your opinion of him—as an outsider, as it were. In these parts he's considered handsome and eligible to boot. He's a prosperous farmer and the place is twice as productive as it was when his father worked it. That's the sort of thing that cuts a lot of ice hereabouts, where the people's main interest is the land."

"It must be difficult for a man to run a farm like that on his own. I'm surprised he isn't already married," Christine remarked casually.

Ruby directed one of her sharp glances in Christine's direction but she, with bent head, was apparently concentrating on bean stringing.

"You're not, by any chance, falling for him?" she asked bluntly.

Christine gave what she hoped was a disarming laugh. "Now, how on earth could I? I met him only yesterday."

"Love can grow over a long period, or it can strike like summer lightning," Ruby said with an unexpected somberness that made Christine look across at her in surprise.

Was the little woman referring to Clive Harvey, Christine wondered. Had she really fallen in love with the professor, or was this one of Nick Martino's impish exaggerations?

"I can assure you no summer lightning has struck me," Christine returned. "He's just not my type; he's too assured of his power as a lady-killer, and I for one am going to show him that in my case his charm simply doesn't operate."

"But what about him? It doesn't seem to have occurred to you that he may find you attractive."

Again Christine concentrated on the basket of beans, hoping that Ruby hadn't detected the pinkness that touched her cheeks. "Why on earth should he?"

Ruby squinted at the bright, sun-drenched sky. "For one thing, Nick simply isn't the type to rescue forlorn maidens in distress. On the whole he's much too cynical. He'd assume that if a girl patronizes a café of doubtful reputation she'd be well able to take care of herself and should she be robbed—well, it was a pity, but probably no more than she deserved. But in your case I expect he saw beneath the surface. He guessed you were a fish out of water in those surroundings, unable to cope, so he came to your rescue."

"It was very gallant of him, I'm sure," Christine said sarcastically.

"Yes, considering what I know of Nick's character, it was," Ruby replied coolly. "That's what makes me think he's attracted to you."

"But that's nonsense. Why on earth should he care for me particularly? He must have met hundreds of girls in his travels, and I'm under no illusions about myself; I'm not clever or particularly pretty, just fairly average. He must have met masses of fascinating women in France and Italy."

"So he has been giving you the story of his life!" Ruby crowed. "There, I told you the man was smitten!"

"Not the story of his life," Christine contradicted hastily. "Just that after his parents died, he went to sea for a while."

Ruby looked thoughtful. "I think in his case it was really a voyage of discovery. He had all sorts of problems to sort out, and that was the best way of going about it."

"You mean, when his parents died," Christine groped.

"Yes, it must have been pretty lonely for him, especially when they seem to have died so soon after each other."

"Yes, I think that was what made him realize that if he wasn't careful he might make the same mistake as his parents."

Christine wrinkled her brows. "I don't understand. Weren't they in love?"

"Yes, very much so! That's why they were determined to marry in spite of all opposition, for his mother's people were against the match. And, for that matter, the Martinos family, too. They thought it just wouldn't work out."

"But why?"

"Well, first of all, Nick's mother came from a distinguished and at one time very wealthy English family. Alice had been brought up accustomed to every luxury. Then, suddenly, it was all over. The family lost their money—owing, I believe, to some unwise speculation on the father's part—and of course the children had to find jobs. They hadn't been trained to earn their own living, so the best Alice could do was to take a job as governess. When she married Nick's father she had no idea how hard life could be on a Greek farm, even a prosperous one like the Martinos place. I imagine she thought life would be all wine and roses, once she was married. But of course it didn't work out like that and she wasn't fit for the monotonous grind of farm life, where the woman has to do a great deal of both indoor and outdoor work. And another thing, she had never been strong and the frightfully hot summers here didn't agree with her. Gradually she began to lose strength, and when she died Nick's father was heartbroken. He didn't survive her long and I expect he blamed himself for not realizing how unfitted Alice had been to be the wife of a farmer. I think it was then that Nick began to review his parents' lives and to think that it had been a mistake for his parents, so unlike in national-ity and upbringing, to marry and that a man should choose a wife who would know what she was getting into and would be able to adapt herself to the life."

"Oh, I see!" Christine said flatly, feeling curiously deflated. "But then he doesn't really need a wife, does he, as long as Mariga keeps house for him?"

Ruby shot her a keen glance. "So you know Mariga's in love with him? Well, it's natural she should be! After all, both of them have been brought up with that in mind!"

For a moment surprise and shock left Christine bereft of words.

"You mean," she said at length, "one of those ar-ranged marriages one hears about?"

Somehow it was hard to equate the sophisticated Nick with such a primitive situation.

Ruby nodded. "The Martinoses and the Tracoses have been neighbors ever since Nick was a boy. I think Nick's father, when he realized what a mistake he himself had made, thought that a girl from a farming family would be the right sort of bride for his son. At that time, of course, the Tracoses were well-off—even more prosperous than the Martinos family. But when their father died, the two boys, instead of taking over, preferred to spend their time drinking retsina and playing backgammon in the local café. Apart from that they seem to have inherited from their mother's side of the family a lawlesss, violent streak, which makes them unpopular with the local people. Anyway, as you can see, the farm is now run-down and Mariga is in the position where she must work for other people. However, the fact that they're practically destitute doesn't make the Tracos family any the less determined that the marriage should take place and I'd say they'd give short shrift to any girl who had the presumption to think that she could secure Nicholas Martinos."

"So that explains Stavros's stone-throwing!" Christine exclaimed.

"Yes, I expect he intended to frighten you off."

"Well, he needn't trouble himself!" Christine said acidly. "I have no designs on Nick Martinos."

"But how are the Tracoses to know that?" Ruby asked with an air of bland innocence. "A pretty girl and a handsome man! To Mariga, at least, the situation would be explosive."

"But what about Nick?" Christine asked slowly. "Mariga may be in love with him, but does he care for her?"

Ruby shrugged. "Not even the Oracle could answer that one! You see, Nick, although very articulate and seemingly outgoing, has a very enigmatic side to his character. He leads his own life and goes his own way and I think that, to a certain extent, is what particularly infuriates Mariga. It seems to me that she's determined to have him formally recognize the situation between them. At any rate, Mariga is very possessive and very beautiful. Nick would be less than human if he could resist her."

CHAPTER FIVE

CHRISTINE'S THOUGHTS were brought to an abrupt termination when she noticed that Ruby was staring fixedly past her. Her green eyes held a startled and shocked expression and her mouth fell open. Following the direction of her gaze, Christine saw that a taxi had drawn up on the white dusty road; a tall figure alighted and, when he had paid the driver and collected a suitcase, advanced toward the patio with the brisk, confident steps of a man who knew his way about the Villa Helena.

It was at this point that Ruby recovered from her trance.

"Why, it's Clive Harvey!" she exclaimed shrilly. As she was speaking she was ineffectually trying to hide the dish of string beans behind a tub containing a flowering orange tree. "Oh, why didn't he tell me he was coming! Just look at me—I'm a perfect mess! I'd have put on some decent clothes and titivated myself a bit."

At Ruby's wail of distress, Christine withdrew her gaze from the advancing figure and gave her a swift glance of appraisal. Ruby did indeed look a mess! Her makeup had been applied with a particularly haphazard hand, and her red hair was a frizzy pom-pom. Her bare legs terminated in a shabby pair of espadrilles that had seen better days. If anything, Ruby looked more freakish and eccentric than usual.

But Christine was spared the effort of thinking up an innocuous reply, for Professor Harvey was already crossing the paved patio. Christine noted with pleased surprise that he was completely unlike the picture she had mentally conjured up of him. When Ruby had mentioned his name, as she so often did, Christine had vaguely imagined him to be a short, plumpish figure with an abstracted air and a scholarly stoop. Instead, the middle-aged man who approached them wore a perfectly tailored white suit and linen hat, and had a faintly old-world air of elegance. And as he came nearer Christine could detect in the light blue eyes that crinkled at the corners a faintly quizzical expression. Did he guess the source of Ruby's discomfort and was he amused by her reaction, Christine wondered.

"Well, you've a nerve, Clive Harvey!" Ruby greeted him shrilly as he joined them. "Arriving out of the blue! Why didn't you let me know you were coming? For all you knew I might have been booked up!"

But Christine realized that the tartness of her tones was simply a ruse to disguise her pleasure and agitation at his unexpected arrival. For there was no disguising the sudden pinkness that tinted Ruby's weatherbeaten cheeks, and she unconsciously put her hands up to her bushy hair and ineffectually tried to smooth it.

Clive's eyes crinkled as he sank into a canvas chair. "It so happened I was free sooner than expected, and you know perfectly well, Ruby, that you'd find a place to tuck me in, even if it were only the cellar."

"I know nothing of the sort!" grumbled Ruby. "I can just imagine your reaction if I tried to tuck you in the cellar. You'd be furious and get into one of your stuffy, pompous moods."

"Me, stuffy and pompous? Shame on you, Ruby! Why, I'm one of the most easygoing people imaginable! Otherwise why would I have put up with your slapdash methods all these years? Anyway, why are you maligning me in front of this young lady? Do you realize that she'll start off with an extremely bad impression of me?"

Christine was suddenly aware that she was being observed by those light blue eyes that seemed to have the disconcerting ability to see into one's most secret thoughts. No wonder Ruby had fallen under his spell, she thought, for there was no denying that, in his own way, Clive Harvey was an extremely attractive man. He had a youthful air that was only contradicted by the wings of white hair at his temples, which merely seemed to add to the distinction of his appearance.

"Aren't you going to introduce us?" Clive asked Ruby, and when Ruby—a little grudgingly—had done so she added, to Christine's embarrassment, a résumé of the circumstances in which the girl had arrived at the Villa Helena; Christine found herself growing hot at Ruby's bald recounting of the facts. Somehow it made her seem stupid and even a little cheap, especially when she came to the part where Christine had driven up with Nick and had asked for a job.

"So Nick Martinos is still on the farm!" Clive said, with an air of surprise. "Somehow I thought that young man was going places."

"Going what places?" Ruby snorted. "He has a splendid farm and is a good worker. Why on earth should he think of leaving? If you ask me, he has too much sense to go gallivanting off in search of better things. If he did and the farm became run down he'd probably land up in the caves like the hippies."

"Well, he's hardly likely to make a change, now that he's got a pretty girl in the vicinity," Clive said, looking pointedly in Christine's direction.

Then, as though suddenly aware that they were causing her embarrassment, he said casually, "Has it not occurred to you, Ruby, as the perfect hostess, that you should be offering me refreshment?" He fanned himself with his white linen hat with an air of exhaustion.

"Christine, be a dear and fetch some iced tea for the professor," Ruby said hastily.

Christine got to her feet with relief and crossing the

patio, reached the kitchen by a back door. It had not escaped her that Ruby had made a point of formally referring to Clive Harvey as "the professor." She felt a faint hurt. Did Ruby really believe that she would take liberties with her beloved professor, simply because Ruby had employed her?

She opened the huge refrigerator and took out a jug of ice-cold tea, then set a dainty tray with glasses on a lace cloth and added thin slices of lemon. She carried it out to the patio and as she approached she saw that Ruby and Clive had their heads close together and were evidently sharing a joke, for Ruby was laughing raucously and Clive's eyes were twinkling quizzically.

Ruby turned to her impulsively as she laid the tray down on the garden table. "We're just remembering something that happened at one of the digs!"

Clive nodded. "Yes, it's amazing how precious memories become as time rolls by. The things that at the time we thought mildly humorous become hilarious as the years pass by."

"Must you be so dismal and depressing, Clive?" Ruby said crossly, as she handed him a glass of tea. "You would think we were both a hundred, to hear you talk!"

"Well, let's admit it, Ruby, we're not as young as we used to be!" Clive said wryly. "In fact, to Christine here, I expect we're a pair of old fogies."

"Nonsense!" Ruby said sharply. "Christine thinks nothing of the kind! I certainly don't feel ancient. I expect, Clive, it's too much excavating and living in the remains of the past that's given you such a gloomy outlook. I for one am glad I gave it up. I can assure you it's much more cheerful catering for guests, even as difficult as you are, than digging up the graves of long-defunct mortals!"

Clive leaned back in his chair and regarded her fondly. "Do you know, Ruby, you haven't changed a bit, and that's a very comforting thing in this changeable old world of ours."

"Now don't try to come around me, Clive Harvey," Ruby returned with pretended exasperation. "You can have the same room that you had last year, but you'll get no more privileges than any of my other guests."

"Now don't deny it, you have a soft spot in your heart for me and can't bear to think of me returning to Athens to spend the evening alone listening to melancholy bouzouki music in some taverna."

"Well, that's what you richly deserve," Ruby told him. "Christine," she continued immediately, "run up and see that the professor has plenty of clean towels, and see if I've put out soap, and...."

Professor Harvey got to his feet. "I may as well take my things up now," he interrupted. "Christine and I can inspect my domain together."

Ruby looked a little taken aback. It was evident that she had intended to have a cozy conversation with Clive Harvey, while Christine was seeing that his room was in order. But Clive, evidently unaware of his hostess's disappointment, picked up his case and accompanied Christine into the house.

When they reached his room, he dumped his case in a corner. "I feel rather ashamed of myself, turning up like this, but I simply couldn't resist the chance of getting away early. On the other hand, I think I'm rather inclined to take advantage of Ruby's good nature."

"Oh, I'm sure she doesn't mind," Christine assured him, feeling that this was certainly an understatement because it was clear to her that, far from being annoyed by his unexpected early arrival, Ruby was highly delighted.

When she returned from the hall cupboard with a pile of Ruby's best thick, soft white towels over her arm, she found the professor standing at one of the windows of the room, gazing up the slope toward the pillars of the temple of Aphrodite outlined against the cerulean blue sky.

"Somehow you forget the magic of Greece when

you've been away for a while," he said softly, as he turned toward her. "Each time it strikes you anew. Have you fallen under its spell yet? But then you must have or you wouldn't have thought of coming to Greece in the first place. But perhaps you've got a bad impression of the country with that first unhappy experience?"

"Oh, no," Christine told him quickly. "It could have happened to me anywhere. I should have been much more careful."

"You must have felt dreadful when you realized you had been robbed of all your possessions . . and in a strange country, too."

"Yes, it was pretty horrible," Christine had to agree. "But then. . . ." She stopped. Somehow she felt she could not recount to Clive Harvey how she had gone into the taverna where she had discovered her loss and how quickly she had responded to Nick's offer of help. Perhaps it had been Ruby's bald recounting of her adventure that now made the whole incident seem undignified. After all, it was an admission that she had allowed herself to be taken in by a total stranger. It was inexcusable, in spite of the predicament in which she had found herself.

She felt grateful when Clive, as though noting her sudden embarrassment, continued smoothly, "And how brave of you to think of taking a job in a foreign country! It mustn't have been an easy decision for you. Ruby, of course, is a splendid person, but extremely unpredictable in many ways. Her tongue—as you probably have already experienced—can be rather sharp at times. But apparently she seems to have taken to you, and you'll get on well enough with her as long as you remember to be tactful. It's not everyone who can hit it off with Ruby. I can, myself, but then I've known her for a very long time and I think I understand her pretty well."

What a sensitive, understanding sort of person Clive Harvey was, Christine thought. His very presence was reassuring and comforting, and she felt happy and at ease in his company. About him there was an aura of an older and more sophisticated way of life, and instead of being fusty and old-fashioned his manner, on the contrary, had a strange charm. It was characteristic of him that he immediately turned the conversation away from Ruby as though discussing her were in a way a slight betrayal.

"And to think that you were robbed coming down from the Acropolis," he continued. "Somehow that seems to compound the offense, especially as you went to see the Parthenon almost as soon as you arrived."

Christine found herself guiltily avoiding his eye. How could she tell him that she had gone early in her stay, not out of enthusiasm, but in order to get it over, so that she would not have to return to Valerie and admit that she had skipped seeing it? She had the feeling that to a man who loved Greece as much as Clive Harvey obviously did, this would be a very shocking admission, and for some reason that she couldn't define she wished for his good opinion.

At first she listened with polite attention as he began to discuss the Acropolis, and then found herself becoming engrossed as he described the daily life-style of the ancient Greeks. He had the ability to paint in the most glowing colors the mundane affairs of people who had existed thousands of years ago, and she no longer heard of Greece as the land of ruined temples and crumbling marble. He brought to vivid life a subject that she had always considered arid and dull. She was listening enthralled, oblivious of the passage of time, when a figure appeared in the doorway and Ruby's voice exclaimed, "I was under the impression that I'd left everything in pretty good order, but apparently there was a lot more to be done, judging by the time it's taken you, Christine."

Ruby's attitude was so challenging that Christine felt guilty.

"Professor Harvey was telling me about ancient Greece," she defended herself, "and I was so interested I didn't realize how quickly the time was passing."

"Ancient Greece, my foot!" Ruby exclaimed with a snort. "And what interest would you take in ancient Greece, may I ask?"

"Well, I will admit that at one time I wasn't very interested," Christine admitted. "But somehow Professor Harvey made it so vivid and alive that I—"

"Don't flatter him," Ruby flashed. "He has a big enough opinion of himself as it is. Well, anyway, while you two have been nattering about ancient Greece I've been struggling to produce a modern lunch."

"Oh, I'm sorry," Christine said apologetically. "I'll come down right away."

But Ruby, once her ire was aroused, was not to be so easily appeased.

"I hope, Clive," she said, "that Christine has not been fooling you with the idea that she's interested in antiquities. Well, in my opinion she's no different from any other young girl. She's only interested in the present and how to catch a man."

"Well, and what's so reprehensible about that?" Clive's mellow-toned voice broke in. "We were all young once, weren't we, Ruby? And romance and youth go together."

Ruby's face was a study as she digested this. It was obvious that to her it was an extremely unacceptable remark. "In other words, I'm such an old fogy that I'm completely out of sympathy with a young girl's dreams, romance under the stars and kissing in the Acropolis."

But it was clear that Clive was unaware that his blunt words had not been acceptable to his touchy hostess.

"Let's face it, Ruby, it's nice to see a young face around this place. One grows pretty tired of the sight of old archaeologists and our female accomplices who come out on these digs. They're usually leather-faced old hags, and the less said about them the better."

Christine was uncomfortably aware that Ruby's face had flushed crimson with annoyance, and it was equally clear that Clive, for once uncharacteristically tactless, had not the slightest realization that Ruby was in love with him, and that his blunt words would, to her, have appeared extremely wounding. She was relieved when Ruby broke the silence by saying tartly, "Well, if I may, I shall borrow this pretty young face and take it downstairs with me to assist in preparing lunch."

In the kitchen Christine found herself involved in a whirlwind of activity as Ruby feverishly stirred, tasted and whisked, giving orders over her shoulder to Christine, who tried as best she could to keep up with the hectic pace.

Later on, as she inexpertly waited at table, she was aware that it was entirely Clive's presence and Ruby's obvious effort to appear affable and pleasant that protected her from being the object of some of Ruby's more pithy comments. Although she was repeatedly urged to join them, Christine spent most of lunch moving between the kitchen and the table on the patio. She had just joined them for coffee and was sinking back, cup in hand, into a comfortable wickerwork chair, when there was the sound of wheels on the white dusty road outside, and turning her head she saw Nick in an elegantly tailored suit step from behind the wheel of a dark red car. She felt a surge of resentment. Here was Nick, looking coolly self-confident, arriving to pick her up and take her to Athens for the afternoon—a man who was as good as engaged to another girl. No doubt, she thought angrily, he considered her as simply another silly English girl intent on a holiday romance. It had been tacitly understood by both of them that it would be only a very temporary affair. She had heard of men like him, and in fact Valerie had been involved in a very similar situation only to discover that her hero looked on her as a playtime acquaintance, and that his intentions were firmly set on marrying a girl of his own country. Well, she would soon show him that she wasn't the least bit interested in pursuing the friendship.

Ruby looked up. "And what is Nick doing here at this time in the afternoon, all dressed up in his Sunday best, too?" she exclaimed.

"I think he's come for me," Christine said flatly.

Ruby snorted. "Then he'd better buzz off again. You can't be spared today, so tell him so."

Yes, she would tell him, Christine decided, as she got to her feet. She would let him know in no uncertain manner that as far as she was concerned the proposed trip into Athens was definitely off.

Before he had time to cross the patio she hurried out to the car. He eyed her in surprise.

"What! Are you not ready yet?"

"No," she replied shortly.

"I was looking forward to seeing you all dolled up in that pink and blue dress you were to wear. Rush off, like a good girl, and change into it and let's be off."

"I'm not your good girl, and I'm not going," Christine told him.

He raised his brows in surprise.

"Not going? Why on earth not?"

"No reason. It's simply that I've just changed my mind, that's all."

"But you can't stand me up for no reason at all," he protested. "Unless you're playing hard to get, but somehow you don't strike me as that sort of a girl."

Angry words trembled on her lips. She longed to tell him that he had been mistaken in other ways as far as she was concerned and she had no intention of becoming involved with a man who was already as good as engaged to another girl. But even to say this would be to confess that she felt hurt and humiliated by his attitude toward her. Instead she said coldly, "I don't see why there should necessarily be a reason. It's simply that I've reconsidered and changed my mind."

She saw gathering anger darken his face. "So you've changed your mind," he exclaimed. "And what about me? What am I supposed to do?"

For a moment she was troubled with compunction. After all, Nick Martinos was a working farmer; for her sake he had taken the afternoon off and obviously gone to trouble to make himself as presentable as possible. It was an afternoon that, as a farmer, he probably could ill afford to lose. No doubt her unexpected refusal would strike him as inane, or worse still, perhaps even as a flirtatious ploy to increase his interest in her. But she decided not to weaken in her resolve.

"What you do with the afternoon is none of my business," she informed him coldly. "I've told you I am not coming and that's all I have to say."

For a moment he regarded her in silence, his brows a dark line across his broad, tanned forehead, and she could see with alarm that rage had for the time being left him bereft of speech; and then suddenly she found herself the recipient of a spate of words that, although she was unable to understand, left her in no doubt that Nick Martinos was being extremely uncomplimentary to her in his native language.

Shaken by the fury of the onslaught, she said a little unsteadily, "I don't know what you're saying."

"Perhaps that's just as well," he replied grimly. He had shown her the Greek side of his character, Christine realized, the one capable of sudden bursts of fiery invective, and it brought home to her with startling clarity that she had not fully realized the significance of the fact that he was only half English. Shaken by his onslaught, she said falteringly, "But... but Ruby needs me this afternoon."

But even this admission did not placate him.

"Oh, does she, indeed? Or is it Clive Harvey? Which of them is in need of you this afternoon, I wonder?"

"But that's ridiculous," she protested. "Why, I've only just met Professor Harvey. How could he possibly mean anything to me?"

"Then you're different from most women," he informed her. "I don't pretend to understand exactly how the old-world charm operates, but I do know that rich, obviously intelligent English girls who you'd imagine would know better come out here to work in the blazing sun each year and to scrabble in the earth just for the privilege of being near to the great man. It seems that under that quiet, gentlemanly manner of his, he's a whiz with the ladies. No doubt he has invited you to spend the afternoon inspecting the dig and no doubt you expressed yourself delighted to comply, and you'll listen enthralled as the professor in his dulcet tones explains his work. You'll feel, of course, that you have been rarely honored to have been singled out by such a man. You may even imagine you have fallen in love with him, like any of those goofy middle-aged intellectual women who come here every year and work like galley slaves just for the pleasure of looking into those big blue eyes of his."

"I think that's highly unlikely," Christine said sharply, "considering I'm neither intellectual nor middle-aged."

Then to her surprise this unpredictable man burst into a sudden shout of laughter.

"Perhaps that's the very reason that I happen to like you," he said at last and, in spite of herself, Christine couldn't restrain a smile as she saw Ruby and Clive gaze across at them in puzzlement at Nick's sudden burst of hilarity. Would she lose too much dignity, she wondered, if she were to agree now to abide by her original plans? How pleasant it would be to climb in beside Nick and be swept off for an evening's entertainment. But to her mortification Nick gave her no opportunity to stage a climb-down.

"Well, don't let me delay you," he said, getting behind

the wheel. "I'm sure you're just dying for another session of Clive's fascinating conversation." And before she could think of a suitable rejoinder he had swept off in a plume of white dust.

During the rest of the afternoon it seemed to Christine that she had not a solitary moment to herself, for if she was not helping Ruby with the housework, she was in the little cool whitewashed study, answering correspondence.

She was seated at the desk, busily typing, when through the half-open door she heard Ruby order Clive to take a walk while she prepared dinner. Imperiously she summoned Christine to join her in the kitchen. Her plans for dinner made her efforts for lunch sink into the shade, and cooking was well under way before Ruby was content to leave Christine in charge. Giving her strict instructions as to how exactly the meal should be served, she swept upstairs and began elaborate preparations for her appearance at dinner.

As Christine darted about the kitchen carrying out Ruby's directions, she could hear her footsteps hurrying overhead; the banging of drawers and the rush of water as she drew a bath. Then came the unmistakable waft of gardenia scent as Ruby liberally anointed herself with her favorite perfume, and Christine could not but wonder what would be the ultimate result of this prolonged ritual.

When Ruby did eventually make her appearance it was in a silver lamé pantsuit. She wore long, swinging chandelier earrings and her skinny fingers were loaded with rings. Her frizzy hair was held bunched on either side with glittering rhinestone pins. Clive Harvey was just returning from his enforced walk as Ruby descended the stairs, and for an instant a look of stunned surprise crossed his face, but he rose to the occasion nobly.

"You look perfectly marvelous, Ruby," he complimented her. "But then you always do. Every time I see you, you seem to grow years younger."

Although Ruby blossomed under this treatment she was not going to reveal herself as being naively deceived by his open flattery.

"Nonsense, Clive," she returned crisply as she led the way into the dining room and took her place at the head of the table. "Mutton dressed as lamb, that's me! You know it and I know it, so let's be frank about it. I enjoy dressing up."

When dinner was over Christine left Clive and Ruby engrossed in a chat on archaeology. She slipped away to the kitchen, aware that her absence would not even be noticed, and when she had washed and tidied up felt far too restless to go immediately to bed. It was such a beautiful evening that she thought she must slip out and get a breath of the wonderful thyme-scented air.

Slowly she climbed the slope toward her favorite spot where the temple of Aphrodite had once stood in ages past. She paused to gaze out over the sea. It was true, she thought, that the ancient poets of Greece had indeed described it correctly. Homer had spoken of the wine-dark sea, and that was how it appeared on this wonderful evening. She drew in a deep breath of the exquisitely scented air: peach, orange, lemon blossom and lilac mingled with subtle tang of the innumerable herbs that grew on the slopes. But even as she was thinking this, she detected an alien scent. For a minute this puzzled her, then with a little gasp of surprise she recognized that it was the unmistakable smell of tobacco smoke. She whirled around to find Nick seated on one of the fallen pillars, pipe in hand, smoking tranquilly and regarding her with quizzical interest.

"Nick! What are you doing here?" she gasped.

He stood up and moved toward her and she could see that he was smiling. When he reached her he leaned against one of the white marble pillars and for a while did not reply, and together they stood gazing out over the scene of shadowed beauty before them. She was amazed when he eventually said, "The reason I'm here is that I was waiting for a particular star to appear."

"A particular star?" she echoed, at a loss. "You're interested in stars? You care for astronomy, perhaps?"

"No, I'm not particularly interested in astronomy. In fact I'm not interested in the stars in the general sense—that is, only in óne particular star."

"And which one is that?" she asked, intrigued.

"I mean that golden glow that appears in a certain window in the Villa Helena each evening. It is a new star in my life, and naturally I'm interested."

Christine glanced at him suspiciously. This was a very different Nick from the one she had become accustomed to, and she was wondering if he were quietly deriding her. So she was a new star in his firmament! What star had shone there previously, she asked herself, resolutely closing her ear to the tenderness in his voice.

"A new star?" she queried pointedly. "Were the old ones not good enough?"

"This new one is different from all the previous ones," he assured her. "This is a star I should very much like to know more about. At night when I see that radiance in the window of your room I wonder what you are doing, what you are thinking about. And when it disappears eventually I know you will be asleep soon and I tell myself that you are dreaming of me."

His voice was low and intimate, and Christine felt her heart suddenly beat faster. But the knowledge that it was doing so only made her more determined to resist his blandishments. Her feelings probably had something to do with the insidious sweetness of the Greek night air, she told herself sternly. No doubt this was the speech that Nick Martinos had made to many another girl.

"I wish Valerie were here to see this. I know how much she would love it here."

She knew that she sounded impossibly prim, but she was determined not to let the conversation proceed along the lines that Nick Martinos apparently had in mind.

"With all respect to your friend," Nick's voice said dryly, "I'm glad she isn't with us tonight."

"But why?" Christine inquired in simulated innocence.

"Why? You know perfectly well why! Well, I'll spell it out for you. I'm glad your friend Valerie is not with us because if she were then you and I would not be alone together. This is a night meant for magic, not for three people making polite conversation about the scenery."

His manner was abrupt, almost rough, Christine thought, and wondered was it his particular reaction to her pretense of naiveté, or did he really think that she was the type of girl prepared to fling herself into a violent romance with a man about whom she knew so little? Almost desperately she racked her mind to think of something innocuous to say, yet at the same time she realized that a too blatant effort to change the conversation would arouse his wrath. She heard herself say inanely, "Do you come here often to the temple?"

"Do you come here often to the temple?" he mimicked. "You sound like a silly girl at her first dance. In a moment you'll be asking me what I think of the floor and telling me that there's a good crowd here tonight."

His voice held a cruel mockery that silenced her, and she felt a certain sickening sense of failure. Who knew what magic might have started if she had less openly shown her mistrust and suspicion. She already knew that now, suddenly, the subtle rapport between them had evaporated. The night was still as beautiful as ever, but it had lost its enchantment. She gave an involuntary little gulp of misery and then felt his arms steal about her shoulders and draw her close. With a little sigh of relief she laid her head against his sleeve. How safe and sheltered she felt, enfolded in the firm grasp of his arm, she thought dreamily.

"So you want to know do I often come to the temple," he said softly.

Christine turned her head and looked up into his face. "Only if you want to tell me, Nick."

He paused and said, "All right, I'll tell you, and whether you believe it or not, I've never told this to another girl. I come up here to the temple of Aphrodite because sometimes when I've finished work and night falls I get lonely. It's just a coincidence that Aphrodite is the goddess of love. But in a way I suppose it's appropriate in my case."

"You, lonely?" she exclaimed in surprise. "You're so independent and self-sufficient and—"

"Listen, Christine," he interrupted harshly. "Even the strongest and most self-sufficient person can be lonely at times, with nothing but an empty house to share their thoughts with."

"But . . . ." She stopped. She had been on the point of saying that it was only too clear that Mariga would be eager enough to share his life. "You could always get married, I suppose," she hazarded.

He nodded. "Oh, yes, that's a fairly obvious solution, and I've often been tempted to take it as the easiest way out. But you see, it so happens I am one of those men who are hard to please, and in my estimation loneliness would be far easier to endure than a loveless marriage to someone I didn't really care about. I suppose it's the English part of me rebelling against the arranged matches we have here in Greece—although they usually turn out happily enough. Or perhaps it's because I'm looking for something much more rare than mere contentment when I marry that makes me hesitate—even in my gloomiest mood—about taking the plunge."

Silence lay between them for a long moment, but it was a happy, companionable silence. It would not be easy for a man of Nick Martinos's nature to confide in anyone,

Christine thought sagely, yet he had done so in her. She felt a sudden impulse to placate him, to show him that she was not the stiff, overcautious person he must imagine her to be.

"I'm sorry it I spoiled your evening," she said with a rush. "I should have stuck to our arrangement. It wasn't fair of me to back out at the last minute."

To her chagrin he returned equably, "Yes, it was rather selfish of you, but to be quite frank I prefer the selfish type."

Christine drew back from him as if she had been stung.

"You don't really mean that," she said, aghast. He nodded, and she thought she detected a glint of amusement in his eyes at this outrageous statement.

"Yes, I certainly prefer them to a martyr at any rate. A selfish woman knows her own mind and insists on having her own way; a martyr does what you want and complains all the time. So you see I freely forgive you."

"That's very kind of you indeed," Christine said through tight lips. Did he already regret that momentary weakness when he had given her his confidence and revealed his thoughts so freely, she wondered. Or was it simply the Greek side of his character that refused to remain serious for any length of time? She found it impossible to tell. But she was at any rate determined to try to retrieve the situation as far as she was concerned, and not reveal how deeply his careless words had wounded her.

"I can't say it bothers me particularly whether you forgive me or not," she said, with what she hoped was a good imitation of airy indifference. "I'll remember in future to be as selfish and ill-natured and inconsiderate as possible, and no doubt I'll meet with your approval."

"Good girl," he said with a grin. "And to show there's no hard feelings, I've brought you a little present from Athens. In fact, I spent a considerable part of the afternoon choosing a suitable little gift for you."

Christine forgot her resolve to be coolly detached and unruffled.

"You bought a gift for me!" she exclaimed frostily. "Well, let me tell you, you've been wasting your time. No doubt you have mistaken me for one of those idiotic girls who go abroad on package holidays looking for romance. Well, may I inform you that I came to Greece to see the country, its beauty and its . . . its ancient monuments, not to become involved with a Greek Lothario like yourself!" she ended in a rush.

It wasn't a very dignified speech, she realized when she had finished, and not at all in keeping with the image of cool sophistication she would dearly have liked to project. She was brought down to earth by a snort of amusement from Nick.

"All right, you've had your say! Now may a Greek Lothario bestow on such an ineffably exotic creature as yourself a humble token?" And before Christine had time to draw breath he took her hand in his and pressed into her palm a little silver brooch in the form of a dove. It was exquisitely wrought and had obviously been made by a skilled craftsman, and for a moment she looked at it with pleasure. Then with an effort she tried to hand it back.

"Thanks, but I simply can't take it," she said.

"But this is the dove of Aphrodite, which means peace," he cajoled. "Surely, Christine, you'll not refuse a peace offering. Look, it's even got your initials engraved in the back for good measure."

Christine, whose resolve was already beginning to waver, made a last effort to resist.

"How do I know it hasn't been offered to a former star on your horizon with the same initials?"

His face assumed a look of mock solemnity. "Now that you mention it, in my character as a Greek Lothario, just which of my former fair ladies rejoiced in the initials C.H.? Could it have been Clarissa Hockenheimer? Or

Clementine Hamburger? Cynthia Halfpenny? Or Celandine Haddock? Or, for that matter, Chloe Higginbotham?"

In spite of herself Christine could not help laughing.

"That's better," he told her. "That's more like you. You weren't intended to be a suspicious and off-putting sort of person."

As he spoke he pinned the little brooch on her dress. She looked down at his gift and outlined it with her fingertips.

"Thanks, Nick, it's really beautiful. I shall treasure it always," she told him softly. "But I must go now. I'll have to be up early in the morning or Ruby will be reading the riot act."

"Don't let her work you too hard. I know she can be a slave driver at times and it's up to you to see that she keeps to reasonable demands," he said quietly. He sounded so soberly protective and so unlike his old quizzical self that Christine couldn't restrain a giggle.

"Well, what's so funny?" he asked her with a puzzled grin.

"It's just that you sound so concerned for my welfare, just as I imagine a big brother would feel—if I had one."

"Indeed! So that's how I seem to you. Well, let me inform you I don't at all feel like a brother—big or otherwise. In fact as far as you are concerned I feel anything but brotherly—quite the contrary, in fact."

He took her arm and tucked it firmly into his and drew her close, then together they walked in the scented moonlight toward the villa. Ruby had been wrong as far as Nick was concerned, Christine thought happily. Perhaps her own frustrated love for Clive Harvey had given her a jaundiced attitude toward all men, but as far as Nick was concerned she had made an abysmal mistake. He was the kind of man who, when he fell in love, would do so deeply and irrevocably. Christine felt convinced of that, and resolutely she closed her ears to the little voice that told her she was in love and that her eyes might be blinded by stardust.

CHAPTER SIX

ON THE FOLLOWING MORNING Christine was down early, but not before Ruby, who had already breakfasted and was standing in the hallway, dressed in an extremely becoming pantsuit.

"The professor and I are spending the day at the dig," she informed Christine. "I've had Mariga prepare a lunch basket for us as I expect we shan't return until dinner time, so you can take the day off and amuse yourself as you wish."

"So Mariga has turned up?" Christine replied, rather deflated. She had been prepared for a busy day and felt rather at a loss to know how to spend this unexpected leisure.

"Yes, you're quite free to go off after you've had breakfast," Ruby told her.

"Thanks," Christine returned. "I would like the afternoon off, all right, but I'd much prefer to catch up with things in the office this morning, and get some order established. After all...."

She had been going to add, "After all, that's what you're employing me for," but desisted. It was possible that were she to say anything like this Ruby would misunderstand and no doubt infer that Christine resented the housework she had had to do on the previous day.

"Afterward," she went on quickly, "I could go into Athens on the bus and pick up the rest of my things from the hostel."

"Just as you wish!" Ruby returned.

It was clear that she was completely uninterested. She

was looking forward to her day alone in Clive Harvey's company and was totally indifferent as to how Christine chose to spend her leisure hours.

At that moment Clive came downstairs and immediately suggested that Christine should join them.

"Any chance of your coming along with us, Christine? It's true we're going to the dig, but we'll have a picnic during the day. It should be quite pleasant. It won't be a stuffy outing, I promise."

For a moment Christine hesitated. She had never seen a dig, and she was thinking that such an outing would be very interesting. And a picnic among the sweet-smelling herbs of the Greek country was an inviting prospect.

Before she could frame a reply, Ruby said sharply, "I'm afraid that's quite out of the question, Clive. It seems that Christine has some pressing work this morning and wants to get on with it. I must say I agree with her. It's best to start off as one means to go on, and not to hare off as the mood takes one."

"What a pity!" Clive exclaimed, and to Christine's pleasure he sounded genuinely disappointed. "But she does seem rather young to be so grimly dedicated to duty."

"I've already offered her the day off," Ruby said a little defensively. "But it seems her conscience is too tender to permit her to avail herself of it."

Christine bit her lip. She was only too clearly aware of the reason for Ruby's acid remark. She was bitterly jealous of Clive's showing interest in any other female.

"Will you not change your mind?" Clive urged. "We'd love to have you with us. Wouldn't we, Ruby?"

"Yes, of course!" Ruby was forced to return, although her voice held no enthusiasm. "However, there's no point in our staying here nattering if she really doesn't want to come."

She turned away, the subject closed as far as she was

concerned, and Christine, after a few further words with the professor, made her way to the office.

From the window she watched Ruby and Clive Harvey set off on their day's outing. She was struck by the pleasant, equable way he handled Ruby's rather excited tendency to make a big event of this day in his company. He was an extraordinarily even-tempered person, Christine was thinking. There was nothing moody or touchy about him, and it would have been very pleasant to have gone along. As it was, she had a curious, lost feeling of being out of things.

As she turned away from the window she noticed an envelope on her desk propped up against the typewriter, with her name on it in Ruby's almost illegible scrawl. When she opened it she found, to her surprise, that it contained a very generous advance on her wages.

How like Ruby's curious, complex character, Christine was thinking, as she turned the envelope in her hands. Ruby, who could be so sharp and cutting at times, could also do tactful, sensitive and generous things like this. She was a person with whom it would never be easy to get along, but one could not but respect and even like the astringent and at times rather absurd little character.

Christine worked away energetically, the morning flying as she established order among the chaotic condition of Ruby's correspondence and accounts, and set up a simple filing system so that things should not again slide back into such disorder.

Her fingers were flying over the keys of the ancient typewriter when the door banged open and Mariga entered with a tray, announcing that lunch was ready.

Christine stretched and said with surprise, "How the morning has flown!" She eyed with pleasure the appetizing dish Mariga was now placing before her. It seemed to be one of the tasty Greek stews of which Valerie had told her so much, and she looked forward to sampling it.

"This looks delicious," Christine exclaimed. "How good of you, Mariga!" She was thinking that Mariga must have put herself to considerable trouble to prepare this dish although there were only two of them in the house. Perhaps it was a peace offering on the girl's part. She must therefore show proper appreciation.

But Mariga showed no signs of being mollified.

"Well, are you not going to taste it before it grows cold?" she demanded impatiently, her dark eyes sullen and unfriendly.

Christine picked up her fork, but with the first mouthful she had the greatest difficulty in swallowing. She had always disliked the flavor of garlic, and the delicious-looking dish tasted so strongly of it as to be uneatable.

As she gasped and forced herself to swallow a nauseating mouthful she glanced up and surprised a look of satisfaction on the girl's face.

"You like?" Mariga demanded challengingly.

"I . . . I . . . well, perhaps there's rather too much garlic in it," Christine admitted.

"You do not like!" Mariga announced, on her face a look of feline satisfaction. Then her brow darkened and she assumed the look of mock ferocity that Christine was becoming accustomed to. "I cook, I put myself out to please, but you do not like," she said threateningly.

"It's . . . it's very nice of you, Mariga," Christine told her, "but to tell the truth, I'm not very keen on garlic."

"If you do not like Greek food then you must not eat it," Mariga told her roughly, as she reached forward, plucked the dish from before Christine and returned it to the tray.

But she did not whisk out of the room, as Christine expected. Instead, she stood in the doorway. "If you do not like garlic, then you had better not marry a Greek man."

"What?" Christine gasped.

"You know what I am saying," Mariga told her. "A

Greek man would expect his wife to cook him the dishes of Greece."

"But . . . but . . . " Christine heard herself stutter. For an instant she had an impulse to exclaim that the dish she had tasted had been so deluged with garlic as to be uneatable. But she stopped herself in time. Ruby had warned her not to quarrel with Mariga and had let her know unmistakably that she would side with the Greek girl should such a thing ever happen. She could just imagine Ruby's acid-tongued comments should it come to her ears that she had complained of Mariga's cooking. She would be utterly indifferent to the fact that Mariga had deliberately spoiled the dish to provoke her.

"I . . . I've no intention of marrying a Greek man," she told Mariga with as much dignity as she could summon.

"I must be mistaken, then," Mariga told her with a derisive laugh. "And now I will bring you coffee."

"Oh, thanks, that will be nice," Christine heard herself murmur weakly as Mariga went out, letting the door slam behind her.

She was back very quickly, to lay before Christine a cup of coffee, black, thick and sickeningly sweet. Christine took a sip and laid the cup down. She had rather prided herself on her liking for the Turkish-style coffee popular in Greece, but this was to her completely insufferable.

She was not surprised to hear Mariga demand, "You no like?"

Christine, try as she could to hold her temper in check, could feel it rising. She said as evenly as she could, "No, it's rather sweet for my taste."

"We Greeks are very sweet-toothed," Mariga told her. "But you, you do not like anything Greek. You do not like our food, or our wines, and now you do not like our coffee. What do you like? Oh, but that I know. You like our Greek men, is that not so?"

"How dare you!" Christine began. She felt she had

taken as much as she could. And she was on the point of answering Mariga in words that would be plainly understood by her, when chancing to catch the girl's eye she saw plainly the spark of triumph there. So Mariga was openly goading her into a sparring match, forcing her into saying things that would, when repeated to Ruby, sound as though she was deliberately being offensive to the girl. No doubt, Mariga hoped that Ruby would react by instantly turning her out of the Villa Helena!

To avoid the urge to tell Mariga exactly what she thought of her, Christine got to her feet. "I'm going into Athens," she announced. "I'd better hurry, or I'll miss my bus."

And resolutely avoiding Mariga's eyes, she brushed past her and ran upstairs to her room.

But there she cooled down. It would be the time of siesta in Athens and there would be no use in going in so early. Then it struck her: she would go down and pick some flowers for the office and arrange them to her satisfaction before she set off. It would help to calm her down and take her thoughts off the unpleasantness with Mariga.

Glad that there was now no sign of the Greek girl, she went into the gardens where she picked big armfuls of lilac, white and purple and delicate mauve. But when she had done so, there remained the question of where to find vases and she was forced to go along to the kitchen and apply to Mariga.

But she had wasted her time.

Mariga swung around from the stove to give her a decided negative. "I shall give you no vases," she announced flatly. "I know what will happen. You will arrange your flowers nicely and make your office pretty and then you will forget all about them. The flowers will wither and the petals will fall upon the floor, and it is I who shall have to sweep them up. My life is hard enough here without Miss Jackson blaming me for not sweeping the floor of your office. In a short while all the guests will be here and I shall be on my feet all day attending to them. I hate those archaeologists, so selfish and untidy, thinking nothing of those who work for them. Remember, English girl, I am not your servant, to wait upon you. You are here to work, just like me, not to play the lady, arranging flowers at your leisure and going off to Athens for the afternoon!"

Again Christine had to bite back the retort that rose to her lips. It would have been so easy to remind Mariga that she herself, without warning, had coolly taken the previous day off to go into Athens on a shopping expedition.

"Very well!" she said. "Don't trouble! I'll buy a vase for myself when I'm in Athens, I've no intention of giving you extra work, and I'm well aware that I'm an employee, like yourself."

But Mariga was not mollified. "Yes, remember that!" she told Christine fiercely. "And if I were you I should not waste my money buying vases. Better save it for your fare home. You will not be here long, will you? You will be going back to your own country very shortly?"

With a little exclamation of anger, Christine turned and ran from the kitchen. In her own room she dressed quickly and pinned on the little silver brooch, Nick's present, and ran downstairs.

But she forgot her anger when, once on the bus, she was whisked through the glorious Greek countryside.

Arriving in Athens she decided to buy the curtain material for the office immediately and was almost bewildered by the variety of shades and patterns that were displayed. Eventually she settled for a gaily patterned zigzag cloth in bright colors.

Choosing the vase for her flowers was another pleasure. She decided on a reproduction of the classical Greek wine bowl with delicately wrought handles on either side. She got it comparatively cheaply in one of the shops that catered for the tourist trade, so she didn't feel that she had been too extravagant by the time she had completed her purchases.

As she strolled along she stopped outside one of the famous pastry shops where a mouth-watering display of cakes was on view. She was suddenly conscious that, thanks to Mariga's extraordinary behavior, she was ravenous. Unable to resist the tempting lure, she seated herself at one of the small tables and feasted on cakes and coffee. She was conscious that this would do her waistline no good, but she couldn't resist eating cake after cake, one more delicious than the other.

Fortified but guilty, she went off to do an errand she had rather dreaded; this was reporting at the consulate the loss of her money. But things went off much better than she had hoped and she came out feeling relieved and reassured.

At the hostel she packed the remainder of her possessions in her suitcase, and after that there was nothing for her to do but to catch the bus once more and return to the villa.

It seemed a curiously stale ending to the day, she was thinking, as she stood at the bus stop, her case by her side. For everyone else in Athens the day was just beginning, while she was tamely going back to the Villa Helena to spend a flat and uninteresting evening.

In the distance she saw her bus approaching and was stooping to pick up her case when a low red sports car drew up near her and she saw Nick at the wheel, a gaily colored kerchief around his neck.

"And where are you off to, my pretty maid?" he inquired. "I'm getting the bus back to the Villa Helena," Christine informed him, as coolly as she could manage, but he had glimpsed the pleased smile that had flashed into her face as she caught sight of him.

"You don't seem very happy about the idea," he told her blandly.

"Well, actually I'm not overjoyed," she admitted. "Somehow it seems a pity to be going home when the day is just beginning."

It was only too clear from his jaunty air, she thought, that he, at least, was anticipating an exciting and interesting evening.

"And you are quite right. In Athens the day is just beginning," he told her. "Hop in, and we'll see what we can do."

In a very few moments she found herself seated beside him, her case and parcels on the back seat, and as the bus pulled away from the stop she was pleasantly conscious that she was speeding off in quite the opposite direction with Nick.

"Now tell me, when did you last have something to eat?" he was inquiring.

"I . . . well . . . " Christine paused, considering. "I had something while I was shopping," she told him.

"And what was that something?" he inquired, steering the car in what she considered was a most hair-raising manner through the evening traffic of Athens.

"I . . . I . . . well, I had coffee and cakes at a little café," she confessed

"But this I cannot allow. You come to Greece and eat only cakes and coffee, which you can get anywhere in the world. Oh, not as good, I grant you that, but you must taste and comment on some of our particular dishes, peculiar to Greece and to be found nowhere else."

He drove her to a taverna. It was very different from any she had formerly seen in Greece. The floors were in squares of cool black and white marble; the walls were frescoed. After the heat of the Athens sun, it was delightfully cool and dim inside.

Christine let Nick order for her. When he had done so, to her surprise he said, "Here am I ordering dinner for you, and I know so little about you. You know, we don't usually move as quickly as this in Greece."

"And just what do you want to know about me?" Christine returned cautiously, a little flustered by this direct approach.

"What every man needs to know about a girl he's interested in."

"And what is that?"

"I'd like to ask you a question that's been on the tip of my tongue since we first met—are you engaged?"

"Engaged?" Christine parried.

"Yes, engaged. It's a plain, straightforward question. Are you engaged to be married?"

"No, I'm not engaged."

"Then is there an understanding?"

Christine looked at him in amazement. "What do you mean by an understanding?"

"I mean, have your parents not arranged a marriage for you with the parents of some young man of whom they approve?"

Christine found herself laughing. "Why, I can't even imagine such a thing! The idea wouldn't even occur to them. Whatever made you think of such an arrangement?"

"That's the way we do it here in Greece," he told her. "And no doubt, there's a lot to be said for it from the girl's point of view."

"The girl's point of view!" Christine exclaimed. "I think the whole idea is horrible!"

"Oh, I agree that some of our customs have their drawbacks, but how else is a girl to manage if she wants to get married?"

"I hope you're not under the impression that I want to get married," Christine said severely.

"But why shouldn't you? Every girl wants to get married sooner or later. It's human nature, after all."

"Well, I'm in no hurry," Christine said sharply. "And I must say I've no sympathy with the Greek ideas of romance. They're far too much tied up with the idea of dowries and the value of the man's farm and horrible mercenary things like that."

Nick chose to pay no attention to this outburst, but said thoughtfully, "It seems then that I may find myself committed to a journey to England."

"You're thinking of going to England?" Christine inquired. The prospect was oddly pleasing. Perhaps if he came to England on holiday they might meet again!

But he immediately disabused her of the notion. "I might perhaps come to England—to meet your parents and see if they approved of me," he replied, his eyes dancing with merriment.

"Oh!" Christine found herself blushing hotly with embarrassment. So he had been leading her on to make just such a remark.

Remembering the belief in the district that there was just such an arrangement between the Martinos and the Tracos families concerning him and Mariga, Christine let her temper flash as she asked ironically, "You would travel to England—to ask my father for my hand in marriage, no doubt? Is that what I'm supposed to think?"

"You forget that I too am not altogether in sympathy with the Greek way of doing things," he told her blandly. "I might come to England to learn the English custom."

Suddenly Christine found herself giggling. "One thing you won't find in England is my parents arranging a marriage for me," she told him.

He smiled across at her. "You're laughing. But you do want to get married someday, don't you?"

"I suppose so!" she returned. "But only if I find a man I can truly love."

"Then you haven't met him yet?"

"No, I certainly have *not*," she replied.

Hearing the overemphasis in her own voice, she wondered for an instant if she were really speaking the truth. Was it not true that she was falling in love with Nick?

But she dismissed the idea immediately. She had known him too short a time for there to be anything very serious in her feeling for him. Besides, he was so very different from the sort of man she had visualized herself falling for. No, most certainly she didn't love this man who sat across from her, his deep blue eyes searching her face as if he could read her thoughts.

She felt relief as the waiter came up with the meal.

"What is this called?" she asked, eyeing the dish that had been set before them.

"The name is *dolmades*," Nick told her. "And don't eye them so suspiciously. It's minced mutton cooked with spices and rice, and herbs and wrapped, as you can see, in vine leaves. The taste is even better than the appearance. I've never known a visitor to Greece who didn't fall for *dolmades*."

Christine tasted and found that he spoke no more than the truth. The *dolmades* were indeed delicious.

When she told him this, he said, "You see, you could get used to our Greek ways, if only you gave yourself time. But to return to your English way of life. Tell me, if a girl must in no circumstances permit her parents to arrange a marriage for her, how do the majority of English girls get married?"

Christine smiled, her former annoyance quite disappeared. "A girl meets plenty of young men at parties or dances," she told him gravely. "Or they might be her brother's friends, or through her work, or when she's playing tennis, or . . . ."

He held up his hand. "I've got the message. But I must say you give the impression of being an extremely dull bunch. We Greeks do everything very differently."

"You're not by any chance under the impression that you're conducting a romance with me?" Christine demanded.

He regarded her thoughtfully. "No. It's fairly obvious

you're not the kind of girl who indulges in indiscriminate holiday flirtations. At the same time I can't help hoping that as we get to know one another better we might find we have a lot in common. I take it you've no rooted objection to the state of matrimony."

"No, of course not," Christine informed him primly. "But, as I said, it would have to be with a man I truly loved."

"And you haven't met him yet? I think that was what you said," he said softly.

Christine regarded him suspiciously. Was he trying to lead her into a remark that she might regret? For an instant she remembered the type of man she had always thought she would come to love. In her imagination he had been gently whimsical, sensitive to her moods, softly spoken—perhaps even a little introspective and withdrawn. Nick with his dark, strong features and brash, aggressive approach to life did not even remotely resemble the man of her dreams. Yet she knew she enjoyed his company more than that of any man she had ever known.

"So you haven't met him yet!" Nick was shaking his head slowly.

"You've been having fun at my expense," she flashed.

"Perhaps," he admitted. "But you sounded so endearingly solemn that I couldn't help leading you on a little."

Well, she would give him no further opportunity to indulge in quiet mockery, she resolved. "I think it's time I was going back," she began. "Ruby will be wondering what's become of me."

"No, she won't," he told her. "She'll be too wrapped up in Clive Harvey to give you a thought."

Christine was diverted from her intention of putting Nick firmly in his place. "She has been in love with him for a long time, hasn't she?"

"Yes, for years, and I'd say the professor is pretty fond of her, in his own cool way."

"Then why haven't they got married?"

"Ruby would get married like a shot, but Clive Harvey values his freedom too much to let himself be trapped without a struggle."

"So that's how you think of marriage—as an end to freedom," she challenged.

"I should say not," he returned indignantly. "I'm all for the married state—especially with the right girl."

He was looking at her directly, and there was something in his blue eyes that made her turn away her head in confusion.

CHAPTER SEVEN

CHRISTINE PUSHED HER CHAIR BACK. "I'd better be going," she told Nick.

"All right, if you insist! But I had planned a very different ending to the evening."

"Such as?" Christine inquired as they went out into the street.

"Such as our watching together from the Acropolis the famous violet light that descends over Athens in the evenings."

She hesitated. It would be wonderful to see it in Nick's company, something to recount afterward when other girls were excitedly discussing their holidays.

"Do I detect a look of indecision?" he asked. "Can it be that your Spartan resolution is wavering?"

She smiled a little shamefacedly. "Well, perhaps! I don't want to miss out on anything while I'm in Greece."

Afterward as she saw with a thrill of pleasure the strange light that washed the city beneath her in a lavender glow, she realized how foolish she would have been to forgo such a sight.

"Well, what do you think of it?" Nick asked, his voice low. All trace of mockery had gone from his manner, as if he, too, at that moment were filled with reverent awe.

"It's beautiful beyond words," Christine whispered. "How strange to think that more than two thousand years ago people stood on this spot and saw the very same sight as they looked down on Athens."

"Not quite!" He laughed wryly. "There were none of those ghastly cement office blocks. I doubt if any of the thousands who used to come here to the Acropolis in procession would know it, could they come back now. For one thing, there was an enormous statue of Athena, goddess of Athens, here, showing her dressed in full armor. It was so huge that ships at sea could see the sun glitter on the tip of her gilded lance."

"What happened to it?" Christine asked curiously.

"Only the base of the stand on which it was erected remains. It was taken to Constantinople and was destroyed in a fire."

As he fell silent, looking out over the city, Christine was very conscious of the man by her side. This was not the Nick Martinos whom she knew, but a grave, mature man, who felt deeply the past history of his country.

She felt a new emotion engulf her. Could he tell how rapidly her heart was thudding, she wondered. Had he deliberately taken her up here with the knowledge that the beauty of the scene would weaken her defenses?

She searched in her mind for an innocuous question to ask him. She longed to appear cool and untouched. "I've heard that not one column in the colonnade in the Parthenon is the same height as another," she remarked. She was aware that her voice was high and artificial.

Nick turned to her, "Have you, indeed?" he murmured.

But she was aware that he was not in the slightest interested in her remark. His eyes had turned an even deeper blue and seemed to read only too plainly the thoughts in her heart that were making her feel confused and lightheaded. It was as though, she thought wonderingly, she were floating blissfully on that misty, grape-blue light that now shadowed the city.

Then he drew her toward him and his lips were pressing on hers.

Stunned by the suddenness of his action, and halfaware that a part of her had longed for this moment,

Christine let him hold her close. Then, tearing herself away, she raised her hand and gave him a violent slap across his cheekbone.

At the look of amazement that flashed into his face, she turned and ran down the slope toward the car.

So he considered her reaction dramatic and silly, she thought furiously, the sort of thing an inexperienced girl would do, after having allowed herself to be inveigled into such a situation. She remembered Ruby's caustic remark about "kissing on the Acropolis," and felt that Nick had gauged only too accurately her reactions to her surroundings and had planned the little adventure. Well, she'd show him, she thought as, white with anger, she got into the car and waited in silence while he got behind the wheel.

"Why all the drama?" he asked with an air of maddening reasonableness. "After all, it was only a kiss, and the scene seemed to call for it."

Christine tried to keep her voice steady as she replied, "You made the mistake of thinking I was only another silly girl in search of adventure."

"Yes, I did," he said coolly, starting the engine.

"What?"

The unexpectedness of his reply stunned her; she stared at him blankly.

"I think you are romantic, although you won't allow yourself to acknowledge it. For some reason or other, you think it's a weakness. Well, it isn't, you know."

She swung around and stared stonily ahead. "Will you drive me home, please?" she requested icily. "I'm not interested in an analysis of my character."

"All the same, you're going to get it," he told her as he swung the car onto the road toward the villa. "It seems to me that you've a very high opinion of yourself and despise any girl who is foolish enough to let her heart rule her head. Well, it's people like you who are too cautious and eventually miss out on the one thing that counts."

Christine sat in tight-lipped silence during the rest of the journey, and a little to her annoyance, Nick, too, seemed to be in no humor to make peace overtures, but drove her to the Villa Helena wrapped in his own thoughts.

ABOUT A WEEK LATER, Christine stood in her little office one day and surveyed her curtains thoughtfully. Yes, she decided, they looked effective. The brilliant lime-green and pink zigzag pattern looked dramatic against the white walls, while the brilliant sun slanted through the barred windows, making the room seem full of color. On a corner of her desk stood her vase filled with deep golden roses. At last, she thought, she had managed to achieve the effect she had wanted.

It had taken her a week to sew the curtains because Ruby had kept her so busy that she had had little time in which to ply her needle. Now that Clive Harvey was staying at the villa, Ruby had wanted the house kept spick-and-span and had demanded every moment of her time. She herself had been busy cooking the English foods he loved and accompanying him to the dig whenever she could.

Ruby, who found the organization of the Villa Helena such a difficulty, spent hours with Clive discussing future work on the dig, when eventually he would be joined by young workers from schools and universities who loved to come along for the honor of assisting in something important and interesting in the world of archaeology.

Christine found herself envying Ruby her contentment, for she herself felt wretchedly unhappy.

Nick had made no effort to get in touch with her again. Resentfully she asked herself if it was because he had expected her to be a willing partner in a holiday romance, and that, finding her uncooperative, he had turned his interests to pastures new. The thought was painful. But if

Nick had indeed disappeared from her life she was not going to let it cast a blight on her holiday, she told herself firmly.

Yet as she sat down behind her ancient typewriter, she knew dismally that her heart felt a leaden weight.

It was at this point that the door opened and Ruby came into the room, her arm through Clive's. Her face had the look, happy and serene, of a woman contented in the company of the man she loved.

It was harder to assess Clive's mood, because he was a person, Christine had found, who masked his feelings. If Ruby's rather obvious partiality was not altogether agreeable to him, he was too civilized, too much a gentleman, to permit himself to show it.

"So this is what you have been sewing the past few evenings," he remarked, glancing around the room appreciatively.

"Yes, nothing would do the silly girl but she'd buy curtain material for the office—and out of her own money, too!" Ruby exclaimed, her tone critical but her expression pleased. It was clear that she approved of Christine's efforts, but it was not in her character to give unstinted praise.

"And I see you've bought a genuine antique," he joked, nodding across at the wine bowl that was filled with golden roses.

"I dug it up in a shop in Athens that specializes in making replicas of ancient Greek vases and urns," Christine told him.

"I'm all in favor of that, as long as people are not deceived, and know they're taking home with them only a copy," he remarked.

"You mustn't talk of Christine's going home," Ruby put in. "I only wish she could stay with me for the complete season. Guests can be so troublesome. They're not all like you, Clive."

She looked up into his face with an expression of fatuous worship that was unmistakable. Christine felt a momentary embarrassment, Ruby's expression was so revealing.

Clive smoked his pipe and fingered the wine bowl critically, without answering.

He was a kind man, Christine thought, and whatever his feelings toward Ruby, he was quietly pleased that she was happy. In a way they were matched, she thought, as she looked at them, though physically they made an ill-assorted pair, Ruby wizened and considerably older than he was. But still she had a keen and inspiring mind and an astringent quality that Christine was aware appealed to Clive. Ruby would never permit him to treat her as a nonentity; her personality presented a challenge that overcame all her eccentricities, and gave her a curious sort of dignity. On the other hand her tongue had a sharpness that she was incapable of restraining. When she was displeased she lashed out with scarifying remarks that wounded and seared, yet she was vulnerable and easily hurt.

Now in one of her sudden bursts of generosity Ruby was saying, "You may as well take the rest of the day off. Christine. You've certainly earned it."

"I've a better idea," Clive put in. "Why shouldn't Christine come with us to see *Medea* at Epidaurus tomorrow evening?"

Aware that this would turn the outing into a threesome, Christine was framing words for a polite refusal when, to her surprise, Ruby said affably, "Yes, why not? After all, you'll be going home soon, Christine. We can't let you return without seeing a Greek play. Although I hope you won't be bored—these Greek plays are inclined to go on and on and on. If it weren't for the drive and the picnic we usually have on the way, I think even I would find it rather hard going."

Christine could feel her heart sink. If Ruby, with her knowledge of the language, could find the lengthy Greek plays boring, what would it be like for her?

"I'd simply love to come," she replied with false enthusiasm, "but there are a few letters to be answered yet. Besides, there should be someone here to answer the phone now that bookings are beginning to come in, and—"

But Ruby had decided to be firm. "Nonsense! Leave the phone to answer itself. It got on perfectly well before and it can surely go unanswered for one evening. And as for things not being in order, never since I took over the villa have things been so well straightened out. It's a girl like you I need to see to things for me."

"It looks as if you won't be able to do without Christine," Clive agreed. "You're the most harum-scarum person in the world, Ruby, and you definitely need someone to take care of you."

"Yes, I think I do need someone to take care of me," Ruby returned in a voice so soft and insinuating that Christine for a moment could hardly believe what she had heard, and she thought that Clive looked faintly uncomfortable before Ruby said loudly and with an added sharpness to cover her momentary lapse, "Well, we'd better let Christine get on with those letters of hers if she's going to accompany us tomorrow."

Arm in arm, Ruby and Clive went out together.

When they had gone Christine applied herself to the complicated matter of Ruby's accounts. Time flew by, and as she eventually put away the papers for the evening, she decided suddenly that after dinner she would take a stroll up the slope behind the house to the ruined temple. The air, she knew, would be honey-sweet and filled with the scents of thyme and myrtle.

Later that evening, when she was climbing the slope, she asked herself if she was being honest with herself in regard to her motives. It was a week since she had been in this spot; was it not now that she secretly hoped to find Nick there, seated upon one of the fallen columns? What should be her attitude should she come across him, smoking his pipe in the moonlight?

But of course he wouldn't be there, she told herself, with a wrench at her heart. Probably he had already forgotten her. To him, no doubt, she was only an uncooperative English girl on whom he had already wasted too much of his time.

When she arrived she found the situation taken out of her hands. Nick was there, just as she had visualized him. But his first words were, "So you couldn't keep away, after all!"

"You . . . you don't think I came up here to see *you*?" she spluttered. "I . . . I came up for a breath of air. And I wanted to be alone for a while, and—"

"If you think you'd enjoy the air better if I were gone," he began, getting slowly to his feet and tapping out his pipe against a column.

"Oh, I didn't mean that," she hastened to assure him, feeling that she had perhaps been rather too outspoken.

"So you want me to stay!"

"Really, you seem to think you're a sort of Greek Casanova!" she told him exasperatedly.

"Now, now," he admonished, raising a finger. "There you are, wearing my little dove, which, as you know, symbolizes peace, and you start off by making war."

"I didn't mean to quarrel with you," Christine told him, "or . . . or to be rude."

"No, I don't believe you did." His voice sounded amused and she could see the white flash of his teeth in the starlight. "What you intended to say was that you are wearing the dove of peace this evening as a sign that you are prepared to forgive me if I apologize first of all."

"Well . . . " she began, undecided whether to let this pass, or to give instant battle. Really, Nick could be the most infuriating person when he chose to be, she was thinking.

She was mollified when he went on, "Do you know, I've been sitting alone here for seven long evenings, and it's given me plenty of time to think things over and to come around to seeing your point of view."

Did he really mean that he had come to the temple each evening in the hope that she would come up from the villa to join him?

"Yes, on consideration, I've come to the conclusion that you did right when you suspected that dove." His voice came to her slow and deep from the shadows of the pillars. "I've remembered that I did once know a girl with the same initials as yours—her name, by the way, was Chloe Hobbs."

"Really, Nick, you are the most annoying person!" she burst out, only to be rewarded by his soft deep laugh.

"The truth is we're both impossible people," he told her, "and for that reason we should get along very well together. For instance, we should have a very nice day together tomorrow, fighting it out, as we usually do."

"Just a minute, what on earth are you talking about?" she demanded.

"I'm talking about tomorrow," he told her. "You're coming with me to the island of Koula."

"Tomorrow I'm going with Clive and Ruby to Epidaurus," she informed him with satisfaction. "And I think you've a cheek to arrange an outing for me without discussing it with me first."

Her words were drowned in his burst of derisive laughter. "Epidaurus! That's a good one! Why, the thought of your sitting through hour after hour of Euripides would make a cat laugh."

"What do you mean?" she demanded.

"I mean you don't as much as know the Greek for 'boy meets girl,' never mind the Greek of—what's the play to be?"

"Medea," she told him. "And what has my not know-ing Greek got to do with it? Lots of people who know no Greek—or at least only a little—come each year to see the plays."

"But not you, Christine," he said decisively.

"And what's different about me?"

"Because you may have your faults, but you're no scholar, and you're too honest to pretend for one moment that you're a highbrow."

There could be no answer to this and she was silent for a long moment. Eventually she said loftily, "Whether I'm a highbrow or not is beside the question. What matters is that I've been invited. Ruby and Clive would think it rude and stupid of me to refuse. Besides, it's cultural, and I'd like to see it while I'm in Greece."

"It's clear to me you've no idea what seeing a play at Epidaurus involves," he remarked.

"And what does it involve?" she queried.

"For one thing, the seats are made of stone. Row upon row of hard stone benches rising up in tiers. Why, the very front row seats there have no padding, or springs, no velvet coverings. They're just like the rest, with the addi-tional luxury of stone armrests."

"And who would sit in them?" Christine inquired fee-bly.

"The notables in ancient Greece would be conducted to these places of honor. Even today outstanding visitors to Greece find themselves seated in them."

Christine, determined to show no dismay, secretly won-dered why Clive hadn't given her any idea of what she was in for. But then the seating arrangements at Epidau-rus would be of little interest to a man like him whose mind was wrapped up in the beauties of Greek culture.

"Nevertheless I intend to go," she insisted. "I'd be ashamed to go home without seeing it, and after all, I shan't be here much longer."

"I shouldn't be too sure of that, if I were you," he commented. "I believe that Greece will lure you. You'll become mesmerized by its siren song and forget to go back to your own people. I suggest you make some suitable excuse in connection with the Epidaurus trip and instead come with me to the island. It's the Greece of today you should be seeing, not the Greece of the past."

"I think you'd a nerve to make such an arrangement without consulting me!" she harked back to her grievance.

"You won't regret it," Nick told her, with what she felt was insufferable assurance. "I'll take you to see an old aunt of mine who still lives on the island. She does the most beautiful weaving."

How she would have loved such a trip, Christine was thinking. It sounded so much more interesting than the Epidaurus venture. There would be the fact, too, that she would be in Nick's company. But what she said was, "You know I couldn't possibly do such a thing," disappointment adding sharpness to her voice.

"You don't mean you're going to let me down when I've everything arranged?" he demanded with well-simulated indignation.

"Let you down?" Christine retorted. "You know perfectly well I can't get out of my arrangement with Ruby and Clive."

"Get out of it!" Triumphantly he echoed her words. "So you'd like to get out of it if you could."

"You've far too high an opinion of yourself, Nick Martinos," she cried in exasperation. "You think you've only to arrange things and people will give up their plans and fall in with whatever you want, and—"

"And that is exactly what will happen," he told her. "Just you wait and see."

"What do you mean?" she demanded.

"Just wait and see," he repeated. "You'll find that the

Epidaurus trip will fall through and that you and I shall be sailing across the blue Aegean Sea together to the magic island of Koula."

"Once and for all, I've no intention of letting Ruby and Clive down," she told him. "So don't dare interfere with our plans. You can do whatever you like, but it won't make any difference to me."

"Oh, won't it! Just wait and see!"

And Nick's laugh followed her as she walked off down the slope.

WHEN CHRISTINE ENTERED the kitchen on the following morning she was surprised to find that Mariga was in an extremely good humor.

Affably she greeted Christine, "You are down early." And Christine, as she collected dishes in preparation for setting the table on the patio, was amazed to see how animation changed Mariga's expression. Her usually sullen regard was changed to a look of animation, her dark eyes glowed, and her expression was one of radiant happiness.

"I'll . . . I'll set the table in the patio," Christine faltered, taken aback by the change in Mariga.

"Yes, you may do so if you wish," Mariga agreed graciously. "But there is no need for you to do so. After all, this is your holiday and you may not see Greece again, so you should enjoy yourself while you have the chance."

A pile of dishes in her hand, Christine stared at her unbelievingly. "Oh, but I think I'd better do it. After all, Miss Jackson would expect it."

"Whatever you wish," Mariga agreed, "but be careful not to trip over anything."

"Trip over anything? What do you mean?"

"You will see when you go out," Mariga returned, with a radiant, almost mischievous smile.

Bewildered, Christine walked along the whitewashed passage to the patio. Once arrived there she was left in no doubt about what Mariga had meant: she also saw the reason for the girl's extraordinary good humor, for the patio, with the exception of a small area around the iron table on which they usually breakfasted, was a scene of disorder. The paving slabs had been uprooted, and near the fountain Nick stood in earnest conversation with Stavros Tracos.

So at last Nick had arrived with Stavros to set the fountain in working order!

"Ah, good morning," Nick greeted her. "You're up early, but Stavros and I are up even earlier."

"You're going to mend the fountain?" Christine queried.

"Yes, I've got around to it at last! But Nick Martinos's word is as good as his bond. How unfortunate that the only free day I could find is the one on which you had arranged to go to Epidaurus." His tone was regretful and his eyes had a look of bland innocence.

Christine planked the dishes upon the table. "I don't see what possible connection there can be between your repairing the fountain and my going to the play," she told him repressively.

"We'd better have this slab up here," Nick called briskly to Stavros, indicating a marble paving slab that even further lessened the space around the table.

As Stavros began to ease up the edge with his pick, Nick turned his attention to Christine "I think you can make up your mind that the trip to Epidaurus is definitely not on the program," he informed her.

She gazed at him blankly. "What on earth are you talking about?"

"I think you will recall that last night I warned you that I would scotch your jolly little plans to soak up culture at Epidaurus."

"Yes, I remember distinctly," she replied coolly. "And I also recollect telling you that I hadn't the smallest intention of falling in with your plans."

"You mean you don't *want* to see Koula?"

"I didn't say that," Christine replied hastily. She was somehow being put in the wrong and realized that Nick was trying to ease her into a morass of confusion. She would show him she had seen through his little game.

She drew herself up and said firmly, "I am accompanying Ruby and Clive to Epidaurus today and nothing is going to stop me."

"But I have already stopped you, my dear girl," he replied blandly. "Pray observe the patio. I think you will agree it is a lamentable spectacle."

"I do indeed," she agreed, "but I don't see what possible connection it can have with my outing with Ruby and Clive."

"Then it's plain you know very little about Ruby's character," he told her. "Do you really think she's going to allow me to organize this piece of work according to my ideas? No, Ruby will insist on supervising everything herself."

"So that's it!" Christine exclaimed. "You had it all planned!"

She was under no illusion that if Ruby was determined to supervise the work herself the trip to Epidaurus would still take place.

"Yes, that's it," Nick echoed. "My insight tells me that your cultural trip is definitely off. However, as Stavros here will no doubt do most of the work, there's no reason why you and I should not have an equally cultural conversation here on the patio."

"Do you really think I'd spend the time with you when you deliberately tried to spoil my day?" Christine asked incredulously.

"And why not? I can assure you I'll make a most interesting and amusing companion," he replied coolly. "If you realized how bored you'd be by the play, you'd be extremely grateful to me for saving you from such a fate."

"Grateful to you!" she repeated furiously. "How dare you interfere in my life!"

Before she could expand on this, Ruby put in an appearance. "Are you two quarreling?" she asked amiably. Then, as her green eyes gazed incredulously at the devastated patio, her voice rose shrilly. "What on earth's going on here?" she demanded. "Stavros, lay down that pick at once! Have you taken leave of your senses?"

With a scowl, Stavros flung his pick to one side and lounged against the wall.

"But, Ruby, I thought you wanted the fountain fixed! You're forever nagging me about it," Nick said reasonably. "And now when I find time to have a go at it, you complain."

"I asked you to have it repaired, not to devastate the entire patio," Ruby bellowed. "And you've chosen the worst possible day. We've arranged to see *Medea* at Epidaurus."

"I can't see what possible difference that makes! You go right ahead and enjoy yourself. Stavros and I shall manage perfectly well on our own. Won't we, Stavros?"

Stavros nodded without enthusiasm.

"There, you see—Stavros agrees!" Nick said suavely. "Oh, I know it all looks pretty bad, Ruby, but it seems to me to be a bigger job than I thought at first. I'm afraid the rest of the patio will have to come up. It means we won't be able to get everything back into place by this evening. But don't worry! We'll definitely be along next week. And after that, another day's work—say, roughly, in a fortnight's time—should have you shipshape again."

Ruby drew a deep breath. "You'll have the patio back in perfect order by this evening," she told him.

As she spoke, Mariga advanced toward them from the kitchen with a laden tray. She put it on the table, her face wreathed in smiles.

Ruby's outraged glance took in the lavish display of specially cooked delicacies.

"I get the picture only too clearly," she announced. "So that's how it's going to be! You and Stavros stopping off at frequent intervals for a glass of retsina, and Mariga cooking up kebabs to tempt your appetites! Well, not one step am I taking out of this place until everything is in apple-pie order once more!"

Nick looked pained although, to Christine's fury, he had difficulty in controlling a smile of satisfaction.

"But, Ruby, don't let it spoil your day. Mariga will take good care of us, and see that Stavros and I get nourishment at frequent intervals, when our energy flags."

Mariga turned a flushed and radiant face in Nick's direction, and Nick, managing to look hurt, went on, "Really, Ruby, how could you be so inhospitable! You know perfectly well that a good workman needs nourishment from time to time, if he's to do his best."

"I'll see that you do your best!" Ruby assured him. "For I intend to stand over you until the job is finished."

"Perhaps you're right!" Nick contrived to look contrite. "With you on the spot, Stavros and I shall work like furies to get the whole business over as quickly as possible."

"Then that's settled!" Ruby said decisively. "I'm sorry, Christine. I know you'll be disappointed to miss the play, but Nick's right! Greek men need an admiring female audience. And you and I can provide that," she added with a dry chuckle.

Furiously, once more Christine saw the satisfied expression that flitted across Nick's face. So his scheme appeared to have worked to plan! She must thwart him, she decided. But how?

At that moment there was a low whistle from Clive who had come out on to the patio and, like Ruby, was now staring in disbelief.

"I'm sorry, Clive, but we'll have to put off the trip to Epidaurus today," Ruby greeted him. "Nick's been promising to have this fountain of mine fixed for ages and now that he's turned up at last I daren't let the opportunity go by. If I don't seize this chance I probably won't see him again this side of the harvest. He seems to be the only man in the district who understands anything about fountains. Stavros wouldn't have a notion of what to do on his own."

There was a short pause and then Clive said, "But why should this mean that the trip is off? After all, you can see *Medea* any time, Ruby, but this would be a bitter disappointment to Christine. Wouldn't it, Christine?"

"Yes, it would be a pity to go home without seeing it," Christine answered.

With satisfaction she saw Nick's face fall, and saw how his eyes flashed to Ruby's face waiting for the veto everyone expected.

Ruby hesitated for a moment, then to Christine's surprise said rather reluctantly, "I suppose you're right. It would be mean of me to expect you to give up this chance of seeing it just because this has turned up. After all, the fountain is my problem. I mustn't let it spoil the day for you. Yes, go ahead with Clive and I'll stay and supervise things here. But why, on, why, Nick Martinos, did you have to choose today of all days to turn up at last?"

She turned to Mariga who had been listening intently to this. "I'm not going, Mariga, but you can make up a picnic hamper for Christine and the professor."

Mariga, Christine noted, had lost her radiant look, and her lovely face once more bore the look of sullen resentment that was habitual with her. It was only too clear that Ruby's decision to remain had spoiled the day for her. But Ruby, animatedly discussing plans with Nick, was unaware that as far as Mariga was concerned her presence was decidedly unwelcome.

When the picnic basket had been stowed in Ruby's car, Christine stole a glance at Nick as she got in beside Clive. He was regarding the fountain, his face set in a scowl, and

Christine felt a glow of satisfaction at the thought that she had shown him that he could not plan her life for her, and that she was not Mariga, whose idea of bliss was to be in his company.

But, try as she might to hide it from herself, she could not but be aware that she would have enjoyed the day so much more had Nick been with her. Nick with his teasing smile and devil-may-care attitude toward life would have made a more enjoyable companion than Clive Harvey.

She put herself out to hide her attitude from Clive, but he was shrewd enough to know that he was not the ideal companion.

"This trip would have been more enjoyable for you in the company of a man of your own age," he remarked dryly as they picnicked in a grove of cool juniper trees beside a little stream. He leaned back against a tree, lighted his pipe and regarded her thoughtfully as she folded the picnic cloth and repacked the hamper.

"Of course not," Christine protested, feeling slightly guilty at the silence she had allowed to fall during the picnic, and a little flurried by Clive's acuteness.

"Now you're telling fibs," he admonished gently. "An old fogy like myself, whose head is buried in the past, is hardly likely to interest a young girl like yourself who, very rightly, prefers to live in the present."

"Oh, but you're wrong," she protested. "When you speak of ancient Greece, you don't make it sound dry or dusty. You make it sound alive and interesting."

"Thanks. That's one of the nicest compliments I've had for a long time." He smiled at her, looking suddenly faintly shy and boyish.

"You know, Nick rather put me off going to see *Medea*," Christine remarked. "He made it sound boring and uncomfortable and...." She stopped, fearful of what she might give away if she were to continue.

"And now you know he simply wanted to keep you to

himself," Clive remarked quietly. "In fact his sudden enthusiasm for repairing the fountain was an attempt to prevent your going to the play, isn't that so?"

Christine nodded. "He told me he'd sabotage the scheme, but I didn't altogether believe him."

Clive got to his feet and knocked out his pipe against a tree trunk. "If I were you I'd take that young man very seriously indeed. He may appear a swashbuckling, happy-go-lucky type, but underneath that is a determination to get his own way in spite of all opposition."

It was true, Christine was thinking. Clive's words had only confirmed her own suspicions. Nick was not a man who could be taken lightly. He had a quiet strength that she could sense whenever she was in his presence. She must in future be more wary of him. It would not do for her peace of mind to become too deeply involved with Nick and his affairs.

When they were about to set off again Clive had some difficulty in starting the engine, and as they slowly gathered speed there were ominous knocking sounds from the interior of the engine.

"I only hope this holds up until we reach Epidaurus," Clive said wryly, "for the theater is set on a hillside."

But the old car rattled on valiantly and Christine gazed about, fascinated by the beauty of the Greek countryside. As they drew near to their destination they were joined by a colorful procession: groups of peasants on foot, or driving carts; an old lady dressed all in black and mounted on a donkey; cars and buses filled with eager tourists, all obviously in the highest spirits. She felt happy and excited and was looking forward to the evening when suddenly as they were halfway up the hill leading to the theater, the engine gave a wheeze and a rattle and died completely.

Clive frowned. "I might have expected this. Well, we'd better climb out and do the rest of the journey on Shanks's mare."

"There's a tourist bus behind us," Christine warned him, as the driver of the bus, a huge man with jet-black hair and beard, blared his horn belligerently.

"Oh, shut up!" Clive muttered in the direction of the blaring horn as he got out and put his shoulder against the car and, puffing and panting, his elegant white clothes wrinkled and oil-stained, pushed the car to one side of the road. Then, taking out a snow-white handkerchief that Ruby had had carefully laundered for him, he mopped his brow, then signaled the bus to pass.

To Christine's surprise the swarthy-faced driver, who had appeared to be in a towering rage, now smiled benignly and waved affably as he drove on.

Although Christine could hardly restrain a smile at Clive's highly unacademic appearance, she was wondering how they were to return that evening, as Clive was apparently making no attempt to get the car to a garage.

She put it to him as they joined the throng now moving up the hill.

"Oh, don't worry about getting back," he remarked airily. "There's a service of boats going back across the bay during the night. We'll arrive in one piece, I can assure you, however late it is."

This was reassuring, but immediately Christine's mind sprang to the consideration of how Ruby would receive them should they return very late.

However, Clive's mind was already upon the play. "Epidaurus has the most wonderful acoustics," he told her. "You can hear a whisper from the stage on the very last of the tiers of seats."

It was not until they entered the theater and she saw the size of it that Christine realized the significance of this remark, for the theater was huge.

Clive put his coat on one of the stone seats and invited Christine to sit on it. "It will help to cushion the shock," he smiled.

Christine grimaced, "I expect after the first hour one gets used to it."

"I expect if you could understand the Greek you wouldn't find the seating so uncomfortable," he remarked. "I suppose you don't know the story of Medea."

She shook her head ruefully. "Nick told me I wasn't the intellectual type," she told him. "I'm afraid he's right."

"Let's forget Nick for a little," he said rather wryly. "Although I must admit the plays of Euripides are rather complicated. *Medea* deals with murder, jealousy and sorcery. I'll try to explain the more dramatic parts as they occur."

Christine nodded gratefully, her eyes on the multicolored throng. It was strange to think that people had sat in these seats looking at this same play four hundred years before the birth of Christ.

True to his promise, as the play proceeded, Clive explained the more obscure moments, and Christine felt she would have enjoyed this outing more than she had anticipated, had she not had in the back of her mind the knowledge that when they arrived back at the Villa in the early hours of the morning she would be met by Ruby with anything but a welcome. Ruby would be prowling the villa like an angry tigress awaiting their return.

Yet, later on, when the interminable play had finally ended and Clive and herself were part of the returning crowd who filled the decks of the little steamer, it was impossible not to respond to the air of happiness and gaiety about her. Young people played the guitar while the steamer cut through the glassy water. Greek songs echoed wild and melancholy to the star-studded skies. As the lights of Piraeus drew near, Christine again experienced a feeling of apprehension. It had not been her fault the car had broken down, yet, in some inexplicable way, she had a feeling of guilt.

They took a taxi to the villa and during the journey

Clive, too, fell into a meditative silence. Was he as cool and detached as he appeared to be, or was he at last beginning to realize that their arrival could hardly go unchallenged by the unpredictable Ruby?

Moonlight bathed the patio in a silver light, making it clear as day. The orange tubs were back in their place and the little cupid pointed his arrow gaily, his plump face wreathed in a mischievous smile. Order and serenity had been restored and the tinkle of water gurgled in the marble basin.

As they approached the house the door flew open and Ruby appeared. She had not removed her makeup and in the moonlight she appeared a fearsome apparition, her red hair standing out like an orange halo, her skinny figure wrapped in a flowing mauve dressing gown.

"Well," she demanded fiercely, "and where exactly have you been?"

Clive looked somewhat taken aback by this reception. "The car broke down and we had to take the steamer across the bay."

"I suppose you couldn't have phoned and let me know what delayed you?" Ruby snorted. "Oh, no, I suppose that would have been too much trouble. No doubt your mind was on other things—and not necessarily *Medea!*"

Clive frowned. He appeared puzzled by Ruby's virulence, though Christine was not in the least doubt of what the little woman was hinting at.

"I really can't see why you should get so worked up, Ruby," he said impatiently. "After all, we're two adults and able, I imagine, to conduct our own affairs without your supervision."

Immediately Ruby realized she had gone too far. With an effort, she said conciliatingly, "You're an adult, Clive, but after all, Christine is only a young girl and I feel responsible for her. She's in a strange country and doesn't know the customs or the language. It's natural I should be concerned about her welfare."

"My dear Ruby, Christine was with me. She was perfectly safe. And now that we've made our explanations and excuses, may we come in?"

Flustered by Clive's unusual asperity, Ruby led the way into the kitchen, put the coffeepot on the stove and prepared sandwiches. But Christine was uncomfortably aware that Ruby was quietly ignoring her—not so obviously that Clive would notice, but to Christine her attitude was unmistakable.

"I should have imagined the play was rather beyond Christine," she remarked as she poured hot black coffee.

Clive smiled at Christine. "Oh, I think she enjoyed the dramatic bits. I translated the key speeches for her and that helped her to keep in touch."

Ruby burst into one of her sharp shrill laughs. "I can just imagine how impatient you would be, Clive, if you had to do that for someone who wasn't as young and pretty as Christine."

Clive smiled good-naturedly, and Christine marveled that he seemed so totally unaware of how bitterly jealous and resentful Ruby felt at what she took to be his defection.

Later when they went upstairs together and Clive had disappeared into his room, Ruby delayed Christine outside her bedroom door.

"By the way," she began, "I've just had time to take a really good look at those curtains you hung in the office, and I've realized what awful colors you've chosen."

"Awful colors?" Christine echoed, dismayed. "But I thought you liked them! You seemed pleased when you and the professor came into the office. I imagined you approved."

"Oh, in the office they're satisfactory enough! But I got a really good look at them today from the outside when I was coming back from the village, and they clash frightfully with the red of the shutters."

"Yes, I suppose they must," Christine agreed disconsolately. The brightly colored curtains that looked so attractive against the white walls of the office would look garish against the muted tones of the rose-red shutters. There was justice in what Ruby said, yet she found it hard to conceal her disappointment as she said, "Yes, I expect you're right. I'll take them down first thing tomorrow."

"Oh, don't bother," Ruby replied ungraciously. "Now that you've spent your money you may as well have the use of them, and after all, they look quite presentable in the office, but it was a pity you didn't consult me first. I could have advised you. I know that young people think they can manage their own lives without advice from their elders, but sometimes it's wise to listen to an older head. It might prevent you making mistakes you might later regret."

Later that night, as she got ready for bed, Christine realized that Ruby was warning her that in future she must make no arrangements with Clive Harvey unless they had her complete approval. In other words, Christine thought bleakly, she was being told not to poach on Ruby's preserves.

CHAPTER EIGHT

ON THE FOLLOWING MORNING, when she went into the kitchen, Christine found Ruby already busy at the stove.

Christine had been dreading this encounter. The previous night's scene was all too vividly engraved in her mind. But there was to be no time for embarrassment!

Ruby turned around and greeted her with her usual gruff cheerfulness, "As you can see," she announced, "Mariga is not among those present."

"Oh, not again!" Christine exclaimed.

Ruby nodded, then, to Christine's surprise, looked faintly embarrassed. "I'm afraid it's really my fault. I wasn't too polite to Nick yesterday. I thought he and Stavros were deliberately slowing things up, and I made a few remarks that weren't exactly complimentary. But then I've never pretended to be a lady, and as you can see, I got results," she added with satisfaction. "The fountain's going beautifully. You'd hardly guess from the look of things that almost all the patio had been torn up."

"Yes, I was surprised to see everything in apple-pie order when we came home last night," Christine replied.

"Well, it wouldn't have been the case if I hadn't put a move on them, I can assure you," Ruby told her. "On the other hand, Mariga has gone off in a huff and threatens not to return again."

"But why? What has it got to do with her?" Christine asked, puzzled.

"My dear girl, it's fairly obvious that she's crazy about Nick. She resented some of my more pithy remarks. She's fiercely protective as far as the men in her life are concerned. Anyway, it all ended up by her letting me know exactly what she thought of me. She then gathered her bits and pieces together and departed, breathing fire and brimstone, and vowing she'd never set foot in the Villa Helena again."

"But Nick, did he mind? I mean, your being, er, rather outspoken?" Christine inquired curiously.

Ruby gave a short laugh. "Not he! I think he found the whole thing excruciatingly amusing. All the same, I think perhaps a peace offering is in order. After all, he's the only man in the district who understands anything about fountains. It was neighborly of him, and I must confess I didn't show an awful lot of gratitude. But I've been racking my brains to think of something he'd like by way of an olive branch. On the whole he abhors English cooking, but there's one thing he's really crazy about, and I'm the only woman in the district who can make it to perfection."

"And what is that?" Christine inquired.

To her surprise, Ruby returned triumphantly, "Chocolate cake—of all things!"

Christine found herself bursting into laughter and was joined by Ruby, who flung herself into a kitchen chair in screams of merriment.

"You wouldn't think a man like Nick would have such a weakness. Wine, women and song perhaps, but not chocolate cake!"

"Perhaps it's wine, women and song *and* chocolate cake," Christine remarked, a little caustically.

Ruby's mascaraed eyes narrowed speculatively, and she darted a sly glance at Christine. "Aha, and what have we got here? You sound, my girl, as if you're a little more interested in Nick Martinos than you'd like to admit."

Christine found herself reddening under Ruby's probing green eyes. "Of course not!" she refuted the charge hotly. "It's simply that I get the strong impression he thinks that every girl who comes in contact with him will lose her head immediately."

"And you're not one of that foolish tribe, I suppose!" Ruby smiled.

"Certainly not!" Christine returned stoutly.

"In that case you'll have no objection to trotting off to the farm with my little olive branch!" Ruby nodded in the direction of a table under one of the windows, where Christine saw reposing on a wire rack a delicious looking cake. Thick chocolate spilled over the sides and the top was ornamented with walnuts and red cherries.

"You mean you want me to take it to him?" Christine asked uncertainly.

"That's exactly what I mean, and I want you to make a diplomatic little speech along the lines that dear Ruby didn't mean exactly what she said, et cetera, et cetera, and to let bygones be bygones. You know the sort of thing I have in mind. I'm sure you'll do it beautifully. If I went myself I'd probably wind up by saying the most horribly tactless things and starting off another battle royal."

"I can't possibly go," Christine said flatly.

"And why not, may I ask?" Ruby demanded.

"Well, for one thing, we're not the best of friends at present, and I don't want him to get the idea that I'm...." She stopped.

"Running after him? Is that it?" Ruby interjected. "My dear girl, you sound as if you're hopelessly smitten."

"That's absolute rubbish," Christine returned. "If anything, I think he has much too good an opinion of himself."

"That's not to say you haven't fallen for him!"

"But I haven't," Christine protested.

"Then in that case, what's to prevent you going over with the cake? It seems to me you're avoiding him in case you'll fall in love. If your heart is in no danger there's no reason why you shouldn't go "

"Oh, very well, you win," Christine returned ruefully. "I suppose I'll have to, or you won't believe me."

"Frankly, I don't believe you," Ruby told her briskly, as she proceeded to wrap the cake carefully and place it in the bottom of a large basket.

After breakfast, Christine set off.

"I feel rather like Red Riding Hood," she told Ruby, as she put the basket over her arm.

"Let's hope you don't encounter the wolf," Ruby called after her, as she took the path leading up the slope behind the villa, "but if you should, and he happens to be in the shape of Nick Martinos, give him my love."

As she descended the slope beyond the ruined temple, and approached the Tracos house, Christine could see no signs of life. There was no smoke from the chimneys and not even a glimpse of Stavros in the outhouses. Probably Mariga had gone jaunting off to Athens, she surmised.

It was not until she reached Nick's farm that she realized how mistaken she had been, because as she approached the open door she was struck by the vision of Mariga sweeping the kitchen with a large fiber broom.

She flung the broom aside as she saw Christine approach, placed her hands on her hips in an aggressive and belligerent manner and asked rudely, "Well, what do you want?"

Taken aback by this reception, Christine said a little diffidently, "Ruby asked me to bring over a cake for Nick. She baked it especially for him."

"Oh, did she?" Mariga laughed shrilly. "Then why did she not bring it herself? Why send you?"

Christine hesitated. It would require considerable diplomacy, she realized, to explain why Ruby had sent an emissary.

"I think," she began, "that she felt Nick might not be too pleased to see her."

"It does not surprise me," said Mariga. "She is a horrible, wicked woman. She said dreadful things to Nick and Stavros yesterday. I shall never set foot in her house again."

"Don't you think you're taking it all a bit too seriously?" Christine ventured. "Everyone knows that Ruby says things on the spur of the moment, and is usually sorry for them afterward."

Mariga tossed her dark head. "Nonsense! She cannot speak to my man in that fashion. I shan't allow it."

"Your man?" Christine echoed feebly.

"Yes, of course!" Mariga's dark, brilliant eyes stared at her defiantly. "Do you not know I am going to marry him? It was all arranged a long time ago."

Christine stared at her, at a loss for words.

"So you think we will not marry!" Mariga sneered. "Perhaps it is because you have fallen in love with him, and cannot bear to think of him married to another woman."

"Oh, don't be ridiculous," Christine said sharply. "How on earth did you get that idea into your head? Do you think that every girl who meets Nick Martinos falls madly in love with him?"

"Perhaps not every girl," Mariga conceded, "but you have! I know. You were delighted when Ruby sent you here this morning, weren't you?"

With a dramatic gesture she beckoned Christine toward her. "Come in and see what I have done to his house."

Curiously Christine followed her into the house. The kitchen was sparklingly clean.

"All the rooms are the same," Mariga informed her. "He cannot manage without me. Nick is a farmer. He will expect his wife to work in the house, and help outdoors as well. You stand no chance with him, so don't bother coming here again. He may flirt with you because you are a stranger, and an English girl, but he will never marry you."

In sudden hot anger Christine planked the basket on the table. There was no sign of Nick and she was anxious now to make herself scarce before he put in an appearance.

"Just tell him that Ruby sent the cake," she told Mariga shortly. "If you'll give me the basket I'll go immediately."

Her attitude of cold disdain seemed to infuriate Mariga. With electrifying suddenness she went over to the basket, and scooping out the cake, drew back her arm and threw it with unerring aim through the open doorway.

Christine stood, shocked into silence, while Mariga surveyed her with a triumphant smile, evidently well pleased with the impression she had made on Christine.

"Who's tossing chocolate cakes about?" Nick had appeared on the scene. He sounded casual and unconcerned, but his eyes went from one girl to the other and it was obvious that he intended to get an answer.

Mariga flung back her head proudly. "I did it," she announced. "We do not want Ruby Jackson's chocolate cakes in this house. She thinks that if she sends you a present, you will forget her dreadful words."

"Really, Mariga, must you be so dramatic?" Nick sounded faintly irritated. "I happen to have a partiality for Ruby's chocolate cake, and there's nothing I'd like better at this moment than a good thick wedge of it."

"You mean you would take a present from that horrible woman?" Mariga inquired, outraged.

"Of course I would," he told her. "Ruby's not a bad old sort. Her bark is worse than her bite and her chocolate cakes are superlative. In future, Mariga, I'd be glad if you'd consult me before you begin tossing them about."

He turned to Christine. "Sorry about that. I suppose it will rather put you on the spot when you recount to Ruby the fate that overcame her olive branch."

"I haven't the slightest intention of telling Ruby," Christine told him coldly. "I'm just sorry that she went to the trouble of trying to placate you."

"Oh, come now! It wasn't my fault, was it?" he cajoled. "I'd have shed the last drop of my blood to defend that cake had I been on the spot."

"I don't think it's funny," Christine told him.

"Neither do I," he returned. "In fact, the more I think of it the more disappointed I feel. In future I'll keep a close eye on Mariga and see that she behaves like a little lady."

Mariga, who had been listening to this exchange with growing fury, tore off her apron and, snatching up her handbag, flounced toward the door.

"So you want a lady, do you, Nick Martinos! Well, I shall leave you with her. You can have your milk-and-water English girl!" she yelled as she whisked through the kitchen door and pulled it shut behind her with a resounding crash.

"You mustn't take any notice of Mariga," Nick told Christine easily. "She's inclined to be temperamental."

"So I've noticed," Christine returned coldly.

He grinned. "So you don't approve of us fiery Greeks, is that it?"

Christine picked up the basket. "I think it's time I was going. I'm sorry I came in the first place. I shouldn't have done so, if Ruby hadn't insisted."

"In other words you're letting me know that you're not particularly keen on my society."

"Exactly!" she returned shortly. The basket over her arm, she walked toward the door.

"Don't go yet," said Nick. "I'm anxious to know how you enjoyed your trip to Epidaurus. No doubt the professor proved more civilized in his approach."

In spite of her resolve to make an immediate dignified exit, Christine couldn't resist pausing to say, "I enjoyed it thoroughly. It was most interesting, and the professor did everything to make it clear to me."

"You mean," Nick asked in mock surprise, "that you didn't find the seats rather hard?"

"Well, perhaps," she admitted. "But the professor gave me his coat to sit upon."

Immediately she had said it, she realized what a mistake she had made, for Nick flung back his head and gave vent to gusts of laughter.

Christine could feel herself redden. "I don't see what's so amusing about it. I don't suppose it would have occurred to you to do such a thing."

"It certainly wouldn't," he assured her. "I've no intention of setting myself up as a sort of modern Sir Walter Raleigh. But you haven't told me what you thought of the play."

It was on the tip of Christine's tongue to tell him that on the whole she had found it boring, but she decided not to give him the satisfaction. "Some of it," she conceded, "I found difficult to follow, but Professor Harvey explained some of the more obscure parts to me."

"Did he indeed! The professor seems to have danced attention on you throughout. You'd better be careful or Ruby may turn into a modern Medea."

Something in the tone of his voice made her ask hesitantly, "What on earth do you mean?"

"The play you saw last night was really only a portion of the story of Jason and Medea. Previously to that Medea had helped Jason to find the Golden Fleece. Naturally she felt rather peeved when he fell in love with another woman and, as you saw, she murdered the intended bride. I'm not saying that Ruby would go to such lengths, but I'm perfectly sure she would resent the professor taking an interest in you."

"You're talking nonsense!" Christine exclaimed. "Clive Harvey hasn't the smallest interest in me. And as for Ruby—well, I suppose she's inclined to be a bit outspoken, but she's completely without malice, and although she does her best to conceal it, she has a very kind heart."

"Indeed! So that's your considered opinion."

"It certainly is," she replied stoutly, "and I think it's horrible of you to make such comparisons."

She was aware that, in spite of his casual manner, Nick was observing her closely.

"Perhaps you think that we Greeks are a bloodthirsty and revengeful lot. Our plays certainly give that impression, but I can assure you that, on the whole, we're the exact opposite—more inclined to forgive and forget than to harbor grudges."

Something in his manner made Christine hesitate before replying. Could it be that the arrogant, self-assured Nick Martinos was actually appealing to her for understanding?

Then abruptly, he said, "One of these days I want to take you to the island of Koula. When I was a boy I spent many happy days there. I'd like you to see it, too."

In spite of her resolutions, Christine found herself saying weakly, "Yes, I'd enjoy that very much."

"Then it's settled!" he said briskly. "Tomorrow I'll pop over to the Villa Helena. Ruby seems to be in a receptive mood and I'll put the proposition to her. She'll probably agree right away. She's smart enough to realize that for the first time in her life her affairs are in apple-pie order. If it hadn't been for me she would never have had the good fortune of having you to work for her, so I don't see how she can put up any opposition when I approach her about the scheme."

In spite of herself Christine couldn't restrain a smile. "You seem very sure of yourself."

"Oh, but I am," he assured her solemnly. "I'm fully determined to take you to Koula, and when a Greek makes up his mind to do a thing he usually succeeds."

"But how can you be sure Ruby will agree? After all, I haven't been here very long," she pointed out.

"True! But haven't you seen the significance of that late lamented chocolate cake? Ruby knows it's one of my weaknesses and it was by way of a peace offering. It's obvious she's in a receptive mood, and I shall take advantage of it. Anyway, I've the feeling she'll be glad to get you out of the way for a while. No doubt you've noted that she's very possessive when it comes to the professor. She's hardly likely to relish the idea of your being on the premises all the time. You and I are headed for Koula, so make up your mind for it."

As Nick had prophesied, Ruby was most affable when he called at the villa a few days later and laid his plans before her. Christine marveled at the way he concealed the fate of the chocolate cake and managed subtly to convey the impression that her offering had been consumed and thoroughly enjoyed.

"If you ask me, that young man is badly smitten," Ruby remarked when he had gone. "But if I were you, my girl, I'd watch my step. Mariga is certainly not going to take this lying down."

As though to confirm her words Mariga, when at last she was persuaded to return to work at the villa, was sullen and antagonistic to Christine. Her face darkened ominously when on the morning of the day Nick was to call for Christine, Ruby instructed her to make up a picnic basket.

"Be sure to include something Nick is especially fond of! You should know what he likes, Mariga," Ruby added dryly.

Mariga gave a short laugh. "But of course I know. If I am to be a good wife, I must know the dishes my husband likes best." She darted a venomous glance in Christine's direction as though to emphasize her point.

"Well, you're not Nick's wife yet," Ruby told her tartly. "If I were you I wouldn't count my chickens before they're hatched." As the girl looked a little puzzled at this reference, Ruby said, "What I mean is, 'There's many a slip 'twixt the cup and the lip.' " Then she added exasperatedly, as she realized she was only complicating things further, "You're not married to Nick yet. I always think it's silly for a girl to pin all her hopes on one man. In the end you can be let down. If I were you I'd wait until I was actually walking down the aisle before I'd feel he was really mine."

Mariga's eyes flashed dangerously. "I *shall* walk down the aisle, and I shall be dressed in white, with orange blossom in my hair." She turned and stalked from the room.

"What did I tell you?" Ruby laughed. "You're being warned that you don't stand a chance. All the same, Christine, I'd be careful of that girl. She comes of a wild lawless breed, and when she's all sweetness and light she can be at her most dangerous."

Christine was to learn on the following morning exactly what Ruby meant.

She had done her morning stint on the typewriter and was considering going upstairs to change when Mariga entered. A bright smile wreathed her face and her perfect teeth showed small and pearly. Mariga was admittedly lovely, Christine was thinking, but she was even more beautiful when she was in an affable mood.

Christine pulled the cover over her typewriter. It would not be long until Nick would come for her.

"Would you like me to dust the room?" Mariga inquired courteously.

Christine was a little surprised at this offer. She had herself dusted the room that morning before settling down to work. But Mariga's manner was so friendly that she felt it might appear boorish to give a flat refusal.

"Thanks!" she replied gratefully. "I was just on the point of going up to change."

"Ah, yes, you are getting ready for Nick, isn't that it? You are going to spend the day with him, but you have not told me where he is taking you."

Christine hesitated. She felt awkward and embarrassed at the line the conversation was taking. Although Mariga's manner was still affable, Christine realized that she would hardly be gratified to learn that she was to spend the day on an island with Nick.

"We're thinking of . . . of going to . . . to Koula," she said at last.

"Koula? Nick is taking you to the island?"

The brilliant dark eyes narrowed for a moment and Christine got the impression that the news both shocked and surprised the girl.

Had Mariga shown anger, Christine felt it could only have been expected, but this reaction both puzzled and intrigued her. "You know Koula?" she inquired.

"Yes, I know the island," Mariga replied shortly, then began to dust furiously. She was showing unmistakably that she had no intention of pursuing the subject and Christine, a little dissatisfied, went upstairs to dress. Why should Mariga have reacted so oddly to the news that she was going to the island, she wondered.

She sat down before her dressing table and made up carefully. She knew how damaging hot sun and wind can be to even the best of complexions. But at the same time she had no intention of emulating Ruby.

When she had finished she observed her reflection in the long mirror with satisfaction. Her cheeks had a faint apricot tint and she had applied lipstick sparingly. The lime-green shantung pantsuit had been an excellent choice, she thought with satisfaction. But although she had combed her hair softly back from her face she knew it wouldn't remain that way very long at sea: she took from a drawer a square of fine white silk and tied it peasant fashion about her hair.

Nick would arrive at any moment. She crossed to the window and felt a little thrill of pleasure as she saw the plume of fine dust that rose in the sparkling, translucent air. Nick was driving toward the villa! Soon she would see him, be seated beside him in the car, bent on a day on an island in the blue Aegean Sea!

She felt excited and expectant. It was like being a child again and waiting to see what good things the parcels contained that were piled under the Christmas tree.

She hurried from the room and ran downstairs, happy and a little light-headed. How wonderful if life could always be like this, she thought, with each day holding something to look forward to and the sun always shining in the blue sky.

She was humming to herself as she reached the last few steps, and it was just then that Mariga came out of the office, bearing in her hands the Greek vase.

No doubt Mariga thought that the water in the vase should be changed, but Christine knew that she had attended to this herself that morning and the sweet peas had not lost their pale, ethereal beauty. She was about to call out to Mariga to return the vase to its place on her desk when the other girl caught sight of her.

A strange stillness seemed to come over Mariga as she looked up at Christine standing a little above her on one of the steps. Her dark eyes scanned Christine from the top of her white head-scarf to the tips of her green sandals.

"You have made yourself look lovely," she said slowly. "I suppose you hope that Nick will find you attractive."

The quiet insolence of the question left Christine at a loss for a moment. "I'm sure you didn't mean that." she said at last.

She knew it sounded feeble and inadequate, and was aware that Mariga thought so, too, for her lips curled scornfully.

"Do you take me for a fool? I can see in your eyes that you're in love. Nick may not know. But I am a woman and I know. You would like to spend all your time with him, wouldn't you?"

Christine made a desperate effort to avert the scene she could clearly see was about to ensue. Mariga's voice was rising and Nick, when he arrived, would hear it ringing about the patio. Feverishly she searched her mind for something to say that might stave things off.

"Don't bother to change the water in the vase," she began. "I did it myself this morning."

As soon as she had said the words she realized how inane they sounded. This was hardly the sort of remark calculated to stem the tide of Mariga's growing rage.

To her surprise the stream of abuse she expected was not forthcoming. Instead, Mariga slowly opened her fingers and let the vase slip to the floor. It splintered into tiny pieces as it struck the tiles and Christine gazed down unbelievingly at the ugly jumble of broken flowers, water and fragments of pottery.

Suddenly overwhelming anger seized her. "You deliberately dropped my vase," she accused furiously. "How could you do such a rotten thing? I wanted us to be friends; instead you treat me as if I were your worst enemy!"

Mariga gave a slow smile of satisfaction: her eyes glittered spitefully. "You *are* my enemy. You're trying to take from me the man I love."

"You speak as if Nick had no right to be friendly with any girl but you," Christine cried furiously.

"It was arranged many years ago that we should marry. He has no right to look at another woman."

Christine gazed at her in exasperation. She could hear Nick impatiently sounding the horn. It was perfectly clear that it was useless to argue with Mariga and were she to delay any longer Nick would come in search of her; it would be mortifying if he were to come upon her engaged in an altercation with the Greek girl.

Mariga tossed her head. "Go to him Tell him ɪ dropped your vase deliberately. Do you think he will believe you?"

"I should imagine," Christine said dryly, "that if he were to put it to you, you would deny it."

"That is so," Mariga said coolly. "It slipped through my fingers. Such a pity! It was a pretty vase and you were fond of it, too."

"Oh, you're impossible!" Christine exclaimed exasperatedly. She hurried across the hall, feeling that she must get into the fresh air, away from the house and the oppressive brooding hatred that seemed to emanate from Mariga.

CHAPTER NINE

NICK LOOKED AT CHRISTINE searchingly as she got into the car beside him.

"What's the matter? You look worried and upset. I thought you'd be all aglow at the prospect of spending the rest of the day with me!" As he started the car he said abruptly, "I expect it's Ruby, isn't it? But it's best to take her lightly and not allow yourself to get riled. She's a bit of an eccentric and enjoys acting the part."

Christine shook her head. "It's not Ruby."

She saw him frown. "Then what is it? You look as if the sky had fallen on your head."

And that was exactly how she did feel, Christine was thinking. Yet it would be impossible to tell him how Mariga had deliberately smashed the vase. He would certainly assure her that she was mistaken or, worse still, be secretly irritated at being involved in such a typically feminine squabble between the two girls.

Then, in case he should suspect that Mariga and herself were at daggers drawn, she said quickly, "I suspect Ruby is really very lonely and tries to hide it by pretending to be tough and independent."

He glanced at her quickly. "I didn't think you were so observant."

"That's because you know absolutely nothing about me," she said decisively.

"Oh, but I do! I know, for instance, that you have freckles on your left cheek, and like iced melon."

"I shouldn't consider that a particularly good insight into my character," she smiled.

"Do you really want to know what I've discovered about you?" he asked slowly.

She glanced at his profile, sharp and incisive, as though carved by a chisel. But his eyes were on the road ahead and she could not discern his expression. "I don't suppose it's particularly flattering," she said cautiously.

"Oh, but it is! I've been observing you and I've decided that you're gentle, loyal and, what's more, have a quiet sense of humor."

"I'm not altogether sure that gentleness is particularly admired in Greece," Christine said dryly.

"Oh, I know we're given to wild yelling matches at the smallest opportunity," he agreed, "but I assure you, it all blows over fairly quickly."

"I'm not so sure," she said slowly, as she remembered Mariga's malevolence.

For a moment he maintained a thoughtful silence. "Well, if things are all right between Ruby and yourself, you surely haven't managed to quarrel with Clive Harvey. I should have imagined that would be impossible."

"You despise him, don't you?"

He glanced at her in surprise. "No, what makes you think that? Though I admit he exasperates me at times. It hasn't dawned on him yet that Ruby would love to be Mrs. Harvey."

Christine nodded. "I expect it's because he's so wrapped up in his work he doesn't realize what's going on around him. But where are we going now?" she asked quickly, anxious to change the subject.

Nick grinned at her. "Down to the jetty! My boat is anchored there."

He didn't elaborate, and when they reached their destination she found, to her surprise, a glistening white cabin cruiser, its brasses gleaming like gold in the pellucid early morning light. She saw the name *Penelope* emblazoned on its bows.

"It's beautiful!" she exclaimed, and felt a little over-whelmed. She had not expected anything so opulent.

Nick nodded with satisfaction. "Yes, I'm rather proud of the *Penelope*. She has been as faithful to me in her own way as the original Penelope was to Ulysses."

The miniature cabin delighted Christine. It was so small, yet so perfect, everything fresh and gleaming. Ice-blue curtains flapped at the open ports and there was a matching blue settee with foldaway table. The galley was miniature, but it, too, was perfectly equipped and sparkled with cleanliness.

"How do you manage to keep everything in such ship-shape order?" she inquired. "I shouldn't have imagined you as the type of man who is house-proud, or should I say boat-proud?"

"But then you really don't know very much about me, do you? Perhaps if we knock about together for a little longer you may discover all sorts of interesting facets in my character."

His voice was teasing, but she sensed an underlying seriousness. She turned away and appeared to be engrossed in the workings of the tiny pressure stove.

"All right, so you don't want to pursue the subject!" he grinned. "Well, what shall we talk about? Or shall we complete the journey to Koula in a dignified silence?"

"Oh, I think that's going a bit too far," Christine replied demurely. "But I am curious about one thing."

"All right, speak up. I'd rather like you to ask me a personal question."

"Oh, it's not personal," Christine replied. "But I'm curious to know why you called your boat *Penelope*."

"Are you?" He raised his eyebrows in mock surprise. "People call their boats all sorts of things. Sometimes there are sentimental connections. At other times the names are just plain goofy."

Christine opened the door of the tiny oven and inspected the interior narrowly. "And has the name Penelope sentimental connections for you?"

He burst into a roar of laughter so that every article in the tiny galley seemed to vibrate. "Aha, so that's it! You want to know if I called it after a girl friend."

"No, that's not what I meant," Christine protested hastily, her cheeks growing pink.

"Oh, yes, it was, so to put you straight on the matter I'll tell you the story of Penelope on the way to Koula."

Later she stood beside him as he steered the rakish little craft through the smooth turquoise blue water.

"To begin with," he told her, "Penelope was the wife of Ulysses, King of Ithaca. When he sailed off to the Trojan War he left her in charge of his kingdom. When after many years he hadn't returned, she was told he was dead. But Penelope always had the feeling that he would come back, so she steadfastly refused the suitors who were queueing up for her hand. She knew the kingdom would be taken from her unless she agreed to marry one of them, but she wanted to keep it intact for her husband when he returned. So to stave off the suitors she told them that when she had completed the web she was working on she would make up her mind which of them she would marry. But she was so certain that Ulysses would return to her that secretly each night she would unpick the work she had done during the day. So, you see, the web was never finished, and when finally Ulysses did return, his wife and his kingdom were waiting for him."

"But this doesn't explain why you particularly favored the name Penelope," Christine pointed out.

"Well, for one thing, she was faithful. I admire that quality in a woman."

"But it's only a legend," Christine insisted. "I should have imagined you would have called your boat after a living woman whom you knew."

"Like whom, for instance?"

"Well, like . . . like Mariga," she ventured.

As Nick didn't answer, she stole a glance at his profile. He was staring straight ahead, his face impassive, his eyes fixed on an island that now appeared like a gray blur on the horizon. "Mariga doesn't like the sea," he stated tersely.

She was a little disconcerted by the shortness of his reply, and said awkwardly, "Oh! I thought that to Greeks the sea is their natural element."

"Well, it's not Mariga's. She's a bad sailor. Storms can spring up quite suddenly in these parts. If it's at all rough she gets seasick, so naturally she takes no interest in boats."

Christine received this in silence. She had a suspicion that a seasick passenger would irritate Nick Martinos considerably. The sea at that moment was as smooth and unruffled as a great sheet of blue enamel. Suppose a storm were to spring up, would she, too, prove to be a bad sailor?

It was comforting to see the island draw nearer and soon she found herself too engrossed in the activity of the inhabitants to worry about the prospect any more.

The village they were approaching, she saw, was set in boxlike tiers above the harbor. Against the barren rocks the houses looked enchanting with their walls washed in varying shades of sun-bleached pink, blue and green. They looked, Christine thought, like gigantic toy blocks scattered by a benevolent giant. Fishermen's caiques were drawn up on the small stony beach and the water was as transparent as crystal.

But it was the people crowding the small wharf who intrigued her. Evidently the whole village had assembled to witness their arrival, and it was clear that they had been expected. They chattered among themselves, pointing and gesturing; the old women in unrelieved fusty black, their kerchiefs wound around their heads and the lower parts of their faces and tied behind their necks. They reminded Christine of rather bedraggled crows. The men wore knee-high boots and some had a fringed headdress that they wore at a rakish angle.

"Don't look so scared," Nick smiled. "Our arrival is quite an event here. On Koula we have no television and only the fairly affluent own a radio, so the people grasp at any opportunity of a diversion."

He tied up the *Penelope*, eagerly helped by the men. Instantly Christine found herself surrounded by a group of questioning women. She shook her head helplessly and appealed to Nick.

"They want to know if you're married and, if not, why."

"Tell them I'm not so very ancient," Christine replied in mock indignation.

"That excuse won't do," he told her. "On Koula, a girl marries very young—but of course she must have her dowry."

"Tell them I haven't any."

He exchanged a few rapid words with the eagerly listening audience and she saw the looks of incredulity that flitted from face to face.

"They say they simply don't believe it," he told her. "They say you have a gold watch and necklace, and shop-bought clothes, and anyway, you're much too pretty to remain unmarried for very long, even without a dowry."

"I believe you're making it up," Christine told him suspiciously.

"Cross my heart," he assured her solemnly. "In fact, I haven't told you *all* they said."

He stopped and eyed her blandly and Christine, although she suspected mischief, was unable to restrain her curiosity. She said with an air of casual interest, "I don't suppose it was anything so very dreadful. Why don't you tell me?"

He shook his head. "You'd probably object. We Greeks don't mince our words, you know."

"Well, you're mincing yours now," Christine said exasperatedly. "Now, will you tell me?"

"They asked me if I had brought you to Koula to present you to Aunt Eloula as my future bride. You see, marriage is always very much on the minds of women living in small Greek villages."

"Well, it certainly isn't on mine," Christine remarked crisply, regretting her unfortunate curiosity, and she saw the faint smile of amusement on Nick's face as he took her arm and led her through the chattering Greek throng.

A rough flinty white road led up the hill, on the side of which, perched on a sort of plateau, stood a tiny pink cube of a house.

"That's Aunt Eloula's domain," Nick announced. "She lives by herself up there. I've asked her time and time again to come and live with me, but she always refuses. She's a true Greek. She values her independence too much to give it up for a more comfortable way of life."

Although a slight breeze blew from the sea, it did little to counteract the fierce heat that was reflected back by the huge white rocks, and Christine drew her scarf about her cheeks and tied it under her chin. It was not surprising, she thought, that the peasants kept themselves well wrapped up in an effort to escape the burning rays of the sun.

As they climbed the steep hillside and drew nearer, Christine could see a small courtyard lying to one side of the house, paved in an intricate pattern of white and black cobbles.

As they approached, an elderly woman appeared in the doorway of the house. Her face was burned to the color of a walnut from years spent working in the sun. From an ironwork balcony above hung strings of green and red peppers, bunches of garlic and herbs. It was easy to see that Aunt Eloula kept herself well occupied in her solitude.

She greeted Nick warmly, giving little shrill cries of pleasure. Then as Nick introduced Christine, she shook hands, her eyes wary, and ushered them into the small whitewashed kitchen.

When they were comfortably seated she retired into a small back room and reappeared with a tray on which was a pot of jam covered with a bead-fringed lace cloth. Beside it stood glasses of cool spring water, in each of which was placed a spoon.

Nick watched Christine with sly amusement as she considered what she was supposed to do with this offering.

"It's a Greek symbol of hospitality," he told her. "I'll do it first, then you can follow the drill."

She watched him as he helped himself to a spoonful of jam then replaced the spoon in a glass of water.

Aunt Eloula's brown, leathery face broke into a delighted smile as he said slowly in English, "Your rose-petal jam is as delicious as ever, Aunt Eloula."

So Aunt Eloula understood English, Christine was thinking as she heard Nick say, "This offering of jam to a guest is an old Greek custom that she likes to keep up."

"Welcome," the old lady told Christine.

"But must it be rose-petal jam?" Christine inquired.

"Oh, no," he assured her. "Sometimes it's cherry, or quince, or mandarin. It can even be preserved fruits."

"I think it's a very charming custom," Christine remarked, and Aunt Eloula appeared even more delighted with this accolade than she had been with Nick's compliments.

When it came to her turn to take a spoon of jam, Christine found that she was in for a disappointment. Delicious as it sounded, rose-petal jam, she discovered, simply tasted to her like cheap rose scent. However, knowing that she was being closely observed by Nick's aunt, she managed to smile and nod as if she were thoroughly enjoying the treat.

"Your aunt understands English," she remarked to Nick

"Oh, yes, she understands it if one speaks slowly, and can even speak it well enough, although she is rusty and not very fluent. However, when she plucks up courage to speak to you I hope she'll have enough English for you to understand one another."

Just how well they were to understand each other Christine was to understand, to her discomfiture, when Nick left the two women together on the flimsy excuse that he had something to do to the boat.

"He is off to the taverna for a glass of ouzo with his friends," the old lady smiled. "You see, Greek men do not gossip much with the women. But then you are English and will find that hard to understand."

Christine got a strong impression that the words held an underlying message.

"I noticed that women take a back place in Greece," she remarked.

"And you do not mind?" Aunt Eloula asked.

'Why should I?" Christine answered lightly. "I am not Greek, and I shall be returning home soon."

The old woman rocked backward and forward on her chair, her head to one side as she eyed her visitor slyly, so that she had rather the appearance of an inquisitive blackbird. "You might stay on if a man were to offer you marriage."

The unexpectedness of this remark left Christine speechless.

"Offer me marriage?" she echoed after a moment. "I don't understand."

Aunt Eloula gave a witchlike cackle. "But I think you do. You are in love with Nick, although you may not know it. And he . . . well, he is a man, and you are a pretty girl, and a foreigner."

She stopped and shrugged.

Her attitude was only too plain and Christine felt an angry resentment. "You mean, he's simply flirting with me, because I'll soon be out of his life for good?"

Again the old woman shrugged. "Nick is a Greek. He will marry a Greek girl who will work by his side and give him many children. It is arranged," she finished with an air of finality.

"You mean Mariga Tracos?" Christine asked flatly. "You must like her very much if you feel she is the right girl for Nick."

"Like her?" Aunt Eloula's voice had risen shrilly. "Why is it that I do not go to live with my nephew although he asks me many times, do you think? I no go because I know he will marry some day soon and I will not live under the same roof with such a witch. The Tracoses have bad blood, and Stavros Tracos is a good-for-nothing. No, I will never live in the same house as one of that breed!"

"But I don't understand," Christine said, bewilderment taking the place of anger. Eloula shook her head as though impatient of Christine's obtuseness. "Do you not understand? The Tracos family have many sheep and good vineyards. With Nick in charge all will go well, and they will have much money. My brother was a good farmer, but Nick is even better, and willing to try new ways."

"But why do you wish him to marry Mariga when you feel as you do about her?" Christine asked.

"Because she is a Greek girl and understands the land and the life that lies before her as Nick's wife. She does not expect her life to be a path of roses. She will not grow into an old woman before her time, as Nick's mother did. I told my brother over and over again how it would end, but he was too much in love with her to listen. Nothing would make him give her up, he told me, and I would see that all would go well."

Eloula's withered nut of a face creased into a sneer.

"Well, it was as I foretold. She was not able for the life. She was used to the soft ways of the wealthy Panos family. She did not know what it was to be a farmer's wife—how hot it would be in the summer, how hard a woman must work when her husband's living is made off the land. After a few years I could see her turn into an old woman, although my brother saw no change in her. For him she was always beautiful and young. When she died he was filled with grief. But he was foolish to have married her in the first place," Eloula added contemptuously.

Christine contemplated the old woman in silent wonder. How hard and bitter she seemed! Yet, in spite of her cynicism, she appeared to have a deep affection for her nephew.

"It must have been hard on Nick to have lost his mother so early," she ventured.

Eloula nodded, her face softening. "Yes, but he had me to turn to! He came often to the island. He was a strange one, always dreaming romantic dreams—I expect that was the side of him that took after his mother, for only a woman full of foolish dreams would have married my brother in the first place."

"Nick romantic!" Christine exclaimed, laughing. "I find that almost impossible to believe."

"Oh, but he was," Eloula insisted. "He was always fond of boats and often I would find him working on an old caique on the beach. 'What are you doing?' I would ask him, and he would reply so seriously, 'When I have mended the boat I am going in search of a princess, and when I have found her, I shall sail back to Koula and I shall build a marble palace and we shall live on the island for always.' "

Christine blinked in disbelief. Eloula's manner was so earnest that it was impossible to doubt her veracity, yet it was equally impossible for her to visualize Nick as an eager and romantic boy

For the next half hour she was regaled with vignettes of Nick's childhood on the island of Koula. Nick returned as Eloula was concluding her reminiscences, and she looked faintly guilty when he said accusingly, "You have been telling tales. Now what on earth have you been saying about me?"

"Your aunt has been telling me how you planned to build a marble palace and marry a princess," Christine told him demurely.

To her satisfaction he looked faintly disconcerted, then changed the subject by declaring that the sail had made him ravenously hungry and asking if his aunt intended to let them starve.

Immediately Eloula got to her feet, clucking happily, and began to dish up the meal that had been simmering on the stove.

"I have made your favorite dish," she announced proudly.

Nick sniffed appreciatively. "You mean *tsadziki?*"

Eloula nodded. "And with plenty of garlic—just as you like it."

Christine felt her heart sink at the announcement. Valerie had told her, among other things, that in Greece it was considered a mortal insult to refuse hospitality, but that even the taking of one or two forkfuls of a dish would suffice to prevent her affronting her hostess. But Christine had always loathed garlic. Even the smell of it she found repugnant. She would hardly dare to take only a forkful, and the idea of having to force herself to devour a complete meal that included it filled her with revulsion.

Unconsciously her face had reflected her apprehensions.

Nick regarded her covertly, his eyes twinkling. "I think you'll enjoy *tsadziki*," he told her blandly. "It is made of fish roes, lemon and garlic. Personally, I prefer it with lots of garlic."

"I'm sure it's wonderful," Christine replied feebly. "It's just that I've never been very fond of garlic."

"Not fond of garlic?" Nick appeared outraged. "My dear girl, do you realize what you are saying? Why, a dish is completely insipid without that wonderful flavor, and I can personally recommend Aunt Eloula's *tsadziki.*"

Surprisingly, it was the old lady who came to her rescue. "Do not mind him! I know that people do not like some of our dishes, so I shall give you something different."

As she spoke the old lady whipped up a large frying pan and in a surprisingly short time placed before her a large pancake covered with meat and garnished with tomatoes, peppers and olives, and topped with creamy yogurt.

Much to Eloula's satisfaction they both did justice to her cooking and after a chat, during which Nick and his aunt exchanged gossip about their neighbors, Nick decided that it was time for the return journey.

When goodbyes had been said, Eloula managed to draw Christine aside for a moment to whisper, "Do not set your heart on Nick. I know him. He will not take for his wife a foreigner. He knows now that it can bring unhappiness."

For a moment Christine was on the verge of an angry retort, then she saw that the withered old face had a look of sad knowledge. It was not malice that prompted the words, but rather a sincere wish for her nephew's happiness

But as she walked with Nick down the steep path Christine's heart felt a dull pain. Eloula had sounded so certain, and she herself felt too confused to understand clearly her own feelings.

Halfway down the steep path Nick stopped where a small tangled track led off at a sharp angle. It was narrow and rutted and on either side grew banks of myrtle and rosemary, and straggling creepers.

"I have something to show you," he said abruptly, and taking her hand, led her eagerly through the rough growth.

Christine was hot and bewildered by the time they emerged onto a plateau high above the harbor. For a moment she stood frozen with surprise. A large white house, gracious and imposing, with elegantly carved balconies, stood in the center. Around it was raw, bulldozed earth. The windows were wide, but blank and uncurtained, and no smoke rose from the chimneys. It had obviously been newly completed and gleamed, fresh and pristine in the brilliant sunlight.

Without speaking Nick led her over the crumbly, newly turned ground and up a flight of white marble stairs that led to wide double doors. As though in a dream she entered the broad, spacious hall paved with slabs of honey-colored marble.

They made a tour of the house. The rooms were large and cool, but modern in their fittings, so that old and new were in perfect harmony.

"Well, what do you think of it?" Nick asked, his eyes bright with pride.

Christine shook her head helplessly. They were standing on a balcony that led off a large room on the second floor that was obviously intended as a bedroom. Below the land fell away in terraced flurries of oleander and bougainvillea and the *Penelope* bobbed like a tiny toy boat at the jetty far beneath. Across the stretch of turquoise blue sea there was a purple mist through which the mainland could faintly be defined. "At night you can see the lights of Piraeus," Nick told her, "so one would never be lonely or feel completely cut off here."

"Then this . . . this is all yours?" Christine asked in bewilderment.

"Of course! Did you think I was trespassing?" he laughed.

"But . . . the marble . . . ." She gulped. "It seems so—"

"I know what you're thinking—that only a millionaire could afford such a house! But my dear girl, don't you realize that this island is mostly formed of marble? In these parts it's the cheapest stone available."

"This is the marble palace for your princess," Christine said slowly.

"Oh, don't bring that up again!" he grimaced. "Aunt Eloula is always telling that ridiculous story."

"But it is your marble palace, isn't it?" she insisted.

"Yes, I suppose you could call it that. But these days I don't aspire as high as a princess. I'll settle for a bride who doesn't necessarily have royal blood—as long as she shares my dreams I'll be perfectly satisfied."

"And what are your dreams?"

He drew her close to the rails of the veranda and pointed with a sweeping gesture to the surrounding land and the terraces that fell toward the sea.

"All this goes with Elysium."

"Elysium?" she queried.

"Yes." And Nick, to her surprise, showed a slight embarrassment. "Elysium means . . . well, you might say it means heaven. I suppose you consider it a pretty silly name for a home?" He looked at her sideways, almost shyly.

She shook her head. "No, on the contrary, I think it's very suitable. If you marry the girl you want and your dreams come true, well then, Elysium would be a perfect name."

But her words were automatic. She was simply being polite, saying what was expected of her.

Nick, however, appeared to be satisfied with her response. "Some day I want to see this planted with olive groves and vineyards and tall trees. Oh, I've all sorts of plans, but it would take a lot of courage for a woman to marry me and to help me to carry out all this."

Suddenly Christine felt as if a cold and chilling breeze

had blown up from the sea. Was he telling her then what Eloula had already impressed upon her, that the girl he would marry would be a countrywoman, with an understanding and love of the land that was part of being Greek?

Without answering, she turned and walked back into the room, her feet echoing in its bare emptiness.

He walked by her side, glancing puzzled at her averted face. "You're tired," he said abruptly. "I keep forgetting that you're not used to our rough, steep paths, like a Greek girl."

"No, I'm afraid I haven't the stamina of the Greeks. They seem to be as surefooted as mountain goats," she replied, trying to sound faintly amused, as though she thought the idea humorous.

She saw his face cloud. "I've bored you, I expect. You have your own life to live. It can't be very interesting to have to listen to someone else's plans."

She didn't answer, afraid that she might burst out how she longed to share his dream and that nothing would give her greater happiness than being part of his life.

It was almost in silence that they sailed back to the mainland. Nick, at the wheel, seemed lost in his own thoughts and hardly aware of her withdrawal. It was now, she told herself, that she must acknowledge that she had fallen deeply in love with Nick Martinos. It was something that she had so firmly resolved not to do, but now that it had happened, she must take firm action. She must strive to cut him out of her heart, no matter how hard the process. Tomorrow she would begin, she told herself. Not tonight! The stars clustered in the sky. They seemed to be alone together in the expanse of midnight-blue water that separated them from the mainland and reality.

Covertly she watched him at the wheel, his strong brown face chiseled like a statue. No, tonight she would let her love take full possession of her heart. Tomorrow perhaps she might find the strength to begin anew.

CHRISTINE SAT in front of the ancient typewriter and disconsolately inserted a sheet of paper. Somehow or other all her enthusiasm for the job had evaporated. The little cool white room with its barred windows that looked out onto a blooming jacaranda was familiar and orderly, yet she felt a strange blankness. It was as though her work here were finished, although she knew that nothing could be further from the truth, for applications for accommodation were flooding in.

"You'd think it was the Hilton Hotel," Ruby had grumbled, though patently gratified by the evident popularity of the Villa Helena.

But Christine found it difficult to work up any enthusiasm. Gloom settled on her when she recollected how short her stay would be and how every moment was bringing her nearer the hour of departure. To put down even the most fragile of roots in this beautiful land would be fatal, for it offered her no future. Nick had made that only too plain, and ultimately the parting would be unendurably painful.

Since her resolve that evening when Nick had brought her back from Koula, she had managed to keep her manner toward him cool and detached. She knew her attitude puzzled him, but instead of being properly subdued by it, he seemed only to be intrigued. Did he think, she wondered, her cheeks growing hot at the idea, that she was deliberately playing hard to get by appearing remote?

She tugged at the paper in impatience, and it parted in a jagged tear. She crumpled it up and threw it in the wastepaper basket. For her it was the last straw. Tears rose to her eyes. She wished she could rush from this little room into the open, sun-drenched country and climb the sage-scented hills. Perhaps up there alone among the wild flowers, she might come to terms with herself.

The idea, of course, was impossible. A neat pile of bills and unanswered correspondence still remained to be dealt with. With a sigh she picked up a fresh sheet of paper and inserted it in the machine.

It was then that Clive Harvey chose to wander in, hands in pockets. He was dressed casually, and at the open neck of his sports shirt he had knotted a silk scarf that gave his scholarly face an almost rakish air.

He took his pipe out of his mouth and regarded Christine thoughtfully. "You're crying," he said quietly.

"No . . . no, I'm not," she sniffled, and feeling for her handkerchief, blew her nose vigorously, then blinked rapidly to disperse any lingering tears.

"Oh, yes, you are, and what's more, I want to know all about it," he stated. "Don't think I haven't noticed you've been peaking and pining lately."

He drew up a chair, straddled it in front of her desk, then, sucking his pipe thoughtfully, regarded her with troubled eyes.

Christine remained silent. She had always been a little in awe of the professor.

"It's Nick, isn't it? You don't see as much of that young man as you used to. You haven't quarreled, I hope."

Christine shook her head and twiddled at the knob at the end of the roller. "No, not exactly."

He raised his brows. "Not exactly! To my mind that sounds even more serious than a straightforward quarrel."

"It's just that I feel it's better not to get too involved," she replied. "After all, I shan't be staying here long. It's better not to allow oneself to become too attached to a place—"

"Or a person," he ended dryly.

She nodded wordlessly.

"I see." He pursed his lips thoughtfully around the stem of his pipe and gazed through the window. "Well, perhaps you're right! It's a mistake to become too attached to a country. It happened to me. I began to love

Greece more than my native land. Yet, I suppose, when my working days here are over I'll return to England for good, although a large part of my heart will remain behind in Greece."

Then, abruptly, he got to his feet. "But that's enough of that! I suggest you and I drive into Athens and do a bit of window-shopping and have dinner. It might brush away some of those dreary cobwebs."

"Oh, but I couldn't," Christine protested quickly. "I've work to do, and I'd hate to let Ruby down when she's been so good to me."

"But, my dear girl, who's suggesting that you let Ruby down? Life in Athens doesn't begin till late and the shops stay open till all hours. We needn't set off until you've finished your work."

Christine hesitated. She remembered Ruby's reaction when she had returned from Epidaurus with Clive. It would, of course, be wonderful to get away for a while and dissipate those depressing thoughts that seemed to press down upon her like a dark cloud. But she had no desire to antagonize the little woman, unreasonable though she might be.

"Don't worry," Clive said with a wry smile. "I think I know what's troubling you. But this time there should be no accident and we shall return at a perfectly respectable hour. There should be no excuse for our hostess to create an unpleasant scene."

"I'd certainly enjoy an evening in Athens," Christine said a little shyly.

"Good! Then it's settled!" Clive said briskly, getting to his feet, his thin, ascetic features bright with pleasure. "I'll push off now and let you get on with your work. It will certainly be a boost to my morale to be escorting a pretty young girl for a change. One gets so tired of earnest archaeologists, especially the female ones in stout shoes and tweed skirts."

As he left the room Christine returned to work once more, but her mood of despondency had evaporated. It would be fun spending the evening in Clive's company, for there was nothing professorish about his pleasant, faintly dry humor. In his company it would be easy to dispel thoughts of Nick.

When all the correspondence had been dealt with and was piled up neatly, waiting for Ruby's signature, Christine decided that it would be diplomatic to tell her of her plans for the evening. It might placate the fiery little woman, even though she had no grounds for complaint.

There were, however, no signs of Ruby about the villa. When she reached the kitchen Christine found Mariga slouched in a chair by the window buffering her nails. She looked up when Christine entered.

A sort of truce had been established between the two girls. They avoided each other's company as much as possible, addressing each other only when it was necessary.

"Well, what do you want?" Mariga inquired rudely.

"I'm looking for Miss Jackson," Christine told her stiffly.

"Well, you won't find her here! She has gone to the village." Mariga proceeded to study her nails critically.

It was obvious that she had no intention of expanding on the statement and, suppressing an urge to answer with equal rudeness, Christine said, with an effort, "When she comes back would you tell her that I've gone into Athens with Professor Harvey."

Mariga instantly lost interest in her nails and looked up, her black eyes snapping malevolently.

"Oh, so you're going into Athens with the professor, are you? You must feel very proud of yourself! First Nick and now the professor, even though he is second best! Perhaps it has begun to dawn on you that Nick was interested in you only because you are a foreigner, and a new face! Men are like that! But when it comes to marriage, they look for something else."

CHAPTER TEN

TONIGHT SHE WOULD LOOK her very best, Christine decided defiantly. Not only would it be a boost to her sadly shattered self-confidence, but it would show Mariga that she was not intimidated by the suggestion that she had set out to capture Clive Harvey.

She would wear the dress of champagne-colored chiffon that she had bought when she and Valerie had been planning their Greek holiday and had set off on a shopping spree, each urging the other to splurge recklessly when hearts quailed at the fantastic prices of the articles they longed for most.

It had needed much urging from Valerie to make her decide on the glamorous chiffon gown, and when she had at last succumbed she had known that she had been wildly and imprudently extravagant.

Now as she stood in front of the mirror she decided, with a glow of pleasure, that it had been well worth while.

The reflection showed a young girl, her hair softly piled on her small, neat head and secured with a golden buckle. Soft floating folds of the diaphanous material hung from her slender waist, and her faintly tanned shoulders gleamed through a transparent short cape of the same material. Excitement and expectation had flushed her cheeks to a dusky, russet pink.

As she joined Clive at the front of the house, she saw his look of almost startled admiration.

"You look very lovely, Christine," he said quietly. Then, as though fearful that his words might embarrass her, added quietly, "We'll go in Ruby's car. She lets me use it when I stay at the Villa Helena."

"Oh, but do you think we should?" Christine put in.

She was not as assured of Ruby's compliance as the professor seemed to be.

"Why not? She's spending the evening with a friend in the village. She can have no objection to our using it."

Then, as he saw she was still doubtful, he said, smiling, "I do believe you're afraid of Ruby."

"Perhaps I am," Christine agreed ruefully. "And I expect you would be, too, if you worked for her."

Clive considered this with the grave thoughtfulness that was one of his charms, then nodded. "Yes, I expect I should be. Ruby has a heart of gold, but likes to give the impression that it has become a little tarnished. Don't worry yourself on that score. I'll take full responsibility, and she can let her wrath descend on my head if she wishes."

But no wrath would descend on his head—and he knew it, Christine was thinking as she took the seat beside him. Yet, strangely enough, it apparently had not dawned on him that the reason why Ruby treated him with uncharacteristic benevolence was because she was deeply in love with him.

As they drove off, Christine caught a glimpse of Mariga at the open kitchen window. For once, her beautiful, sullen face was smiling, but there could be no mistaking the malice that glittered in her dark eyes, and Christine felt a renewal of her earlier apprehension. Had she made a dreadful mistake in allowing the professor to take her on this jaunt into Athens?

But her misgivings were dispelled as they drove swiftly through the dreamlike Greek countryside.

When they reached the city, they immediately began window-shopping and, guided by Clive, Christine enjoyed herself thoroughly. He had a deep knowledge of the handicrafts of the different islands and could identify, by their different patterns, the exact location from which the beautiful handloomed rugs originated.

One shop particularly fascinated Christine. It was festooned with colorful woven bags. They were called *tagharia* and were from Arachova, Clive told her. What particularly attracted Christine was that they were large and roomy and practical, just the sort of thing to hold all her odds and ends.

They were so attractive that it was difficult to decide which to purchase, and Christine stood pondering, unaware that Clive, observing her dilemma, was watching her with twinkling eyes.

"Which do you prefer?" he asked.

She shook her head hopelessly. "They're all so lovely I simply can't make up my mind."

"Then let me do it for you. I suggest that one." He pointed to one of a bright zigzag pattern in mauve, green and white.

She nodded. "Yes, I think that's the nicest."

And before she could guess what he was up to, he had slipped into the shop and purchased it.

"If I'd known what you were up to, I shouldn't have agreed with you," she told him severely, when he presented it to her with the sort of old-world courtesy that was habitual with him.

She slipped her bag into it and put it over her arm. "I'll use it tonight," she told him. "It will be its sort of official debut."

To her surprise she saw the look of almost boyish pleasure her simple gesture had caused him.

"And afterward, when you're far away from Athens, when you use it, will you remember me?" he asked quietly.

"But of course I'll always remember," she told him warmly. "It was you who made Greece come alive for me. How could I forget that?"

"Thank you," he said simply. "You see, I'm not trying to make love to you—as I think you know. But perhaps if

I had been twenty years younger it would have been a very different matter," he added dryly. "It's simply that sometimes I feel I'm as forgotten and useless as one of those shards I dig up. It's pleasant to know that at least someone knows I'm alive."

Then, as though regretting his words, he added quickly, "But I must show you the beautiful filigree work they do in silver, and after that I suggest a meal. Window-shopping can be exhausting."

Later, after a rather mad ride in a taxi, driven by a loquacious and excitable Greek, they drew up outside an enormous and opulent-looking hotel. Christine could see that from its windows, its clientele would have a magnificent view of the Acropolis. It was one of those luxurious hotels where the wealthy would stay while visiting Greece. Beautifully dressed women and well-tailored men moved casually about the foyer.

Thank heaven she was wearing her very best outfit, she thought with relief. Although it must have cost only a fraction of what these glamorous women must have paid for their haute couture clothes, at least she did not look as incongruous as she would have in these luxurious surroundings had she turned up in a print dress. Not that it would have mattered to Clive! She had the feeling that he would have been sublimely unaware whether she was fittingly dressed or not.

The dining room had an almost Eastern opulence and enormous menus that seemed to surround one like an enveloping screen.

She allowed the professor to order for her and sat back happily while he instructed the waiter with an air of precise concentration.

Afterward, he regarded her quizzically. "Do you know, it's most pleasant to know that one's companion is causing heads to turn."

"You're not pretending this is the first time you've asked a woman to dinner," Christine teased.

"One tends to mix with people of the same interests," he said thoughtfully, "and for some reason or other women archaeologists seem to be among the least glamorous of the species."

"Perhaps when you're with them, you let your work take first place," she said quickly. "I fancy a woman can always sense this, so perhaps they don't really make an effort to appear attractive."

"But you did," he said quietly.

Christine fingered a wineglass. Not only would it be embarrassing, but it would spoil the evening completely were Clive to become amorous.

But with his usual sensitiveness he sensed her sudden withdrawal. "You mustn't think I'm trying to flirt with you," he said quietly. "I know it's natural for a pretty girl to make herself as attractive as possible. Perhaps I'm simply jealous of people who live a more normal life. I've missed out on so many things! Take Nick Martinos, for instance. He's building a home—and a very beautiful one at that, I'm told—on the island of Koula. He's planning for the future, for the time when he takes a wife and fills that home with healthy and happy children. Whereas my interests are in the past."

"You know about Nick's house?" Christine exclaimed.

"Of course! Everyone knows about it for miles around. The house was begun years ago. He built it, bit by bit, putting only the best materials into it. When it's finished it will be a home any woman would be proud of."

"Oh, but it is finished," Christine said with animation. "And it is a wonderful place; he calls it Elysium."

"So you've seen it!" Clive smiled. "And he intends to call it the Greek word for paradise. Well, if he marries Mariga I'm afraid the name will be sadly inappropriate."

Christine laid down her fork, her appetite suddenly evaporating. She gazed at him blankly. "So you think he'll marry Mariga?"

"My dear, I know very little about Nick's affairs, but according to local gossip, there is a sort of understanding between him and the Tracos family that he should marry Mariga. Apparently his father's marriage to an English girl ended tragically and it was considered wiser for Nick to take for his wife a Greek girl. I know these traditions seem strange to most foreigners, but from my long experience of the Greeks, I think on the whole it's a very wise custom as far as they're concerned. They don't conform to our ideas of romance, but most of these marriages work out very successfully. After all, how often the most idealistically happy marriages among us end on the rocks!"

Christine made no reply. She picked up her fork and made a pretense of concentrating on the food before her.

Clive gazed at her for a long moment. "Now I've spoken like a soured old bachelor, haven't I?" he asked ruefully. "You're in love with Nick, isn't that it?"

Christine nodded.

"I see." He smiled wryly. "In that case my little speech must have struck you as singularly depressing. I'm sorry, I hope it won't spoil your evening. I expect I'm suffering from sour grapes. I only wish I had as good an excuse as you for spending the rest of my life in Greece."

"But you have—only you don't seem to realize it," Christine said impulsively.

Clive stared at her incredulously.

"I'm sorry, I . . . I shouldn't have said that," she stammered. "It's none of my business."

"But perhaps it is my business," he replied quietly. "And now, suppose you enlarge on that extraordinary statement, young lady."

She was suddenly overcome by the thought of the enormity of her indiscretion. She had no right to interfere in his affairs. Apart from that, to reveal that Ruby cared for him would be a sort of betrayal. Suppose he were to be only tolerantly amused at the idea of Ruby falling in love with him! She wished fervently now that she had exercised more control of her tongue.

"You can't stop now, you know," Clive said. "It's simply not fair."

She saw he was determined that she should explain what she meant by her enigmatic statement.

"I was thinking of Ruby," she said reluctantly. "It's so obvious she's in love with you—at least, to a woman it is."

"Ruby in love with me!" Clive's usually measured tones had risen incredulously and some of the other diners turned amused glances in their direction.

"Sorry!" he said a little sheepishly. "I didn't intend to cause a sensation. But the idea is so incredible that it simply floored me."

"But why should it seem so incredible?" Christine asked, a little irritated by his obtuseness. "I suspect she's been in love with you for years, only you didn't seem to be aware of the fact."

He raised his hands protestingly. "But why on earth should I? Ruby is just Ruby—lovable and maddening, all at the same time! She never showed me any particular favor that I can think of."

"Really, Mr. Harvey!" Christine returned in despair. "She's shown in a hundred ways that she's crazy about you."

"Why don't you call me Clive? This is the sort of conversation that calls for informality."

"All right, then, Clive!" Christine leaned forward and addressed him with a certain severity. "Over the years you've come to regard Ruby as someone who makes things comfortable for you, cooks beautiful food and sees you want for nothing. It doesn't seem to have occurred to you that she's a woman, and a lonely one at that."

"It certainly didn't occur to me that I was anything

more to her than a lodger, and a rather tiresome one at that! Ruby can be quite caustic, you know, especially if one leaves one's room untidy or scatters cigarette ash on the carpet. I always felt I was the sort of person that no woman would be interested in. It just didn't dawn on me that she could possibly care for me."

For a long moment he remained silent, oblivious of the fact that the waiter was changing courses. Then Christine saw his eyes begin to glow as if, for the first time, the full implications of her revelation had dawned on him.

"But this changes everything!" he exclaimed wonderingly. "Ruby and I could make a life here. It means I shan't have to return to England permanently when my work's finished, and stay at some dreary private hotel, getting more and more fossilized as the years pass."

"Well, I'm glad I didn't make a dreadful mistake in telling you," Christine said in relief. "I suppose I really shouldn't have done it. It wasn't fair to Ruby."

"But, my dear girl, don't you see you've done us both a wonderful favor? In some ways I know Ruby better than you think. I know that, in spite of her outgoing manner, she's proud. She would never have hinted to me of her feelings, and if you hadn't told me, we should have gone on without any chance of ever finding happiness. This will make all the difference to our lives. Why, I feel years younger already!"

But Christine was no longer listening.

She had happened to glance in one of the mirror panels that reflected a group of tables at the other end of the room and she had caught sight of a distinguished-looking man who bore an astonishing resemblance to Nick Martinos.

Then she stared in amazement. It was Nick—but very different from the man she had known. Instead of the well-worn, casual clothes he usually wore, this was a Nick elegantly groomed, his unruly hair slicked back smoothly, accentuating his almost classically perfect features. The dinner jacket he wore was expertly tailored and he had a cosmopolitan self-confidence that was unmistakable.

Immediately her eyes went to his companion, a small, swarthy little man, who gestured widely with one hand while he fingered worry beads with the other.

How long had Nick been aware of her presence, she wondered.

It was disconcerting to think that his observant eyes had been watching Clive and herself without their being aware of it.

"You look as if you'd seen a ghost," Clive observed.

"Not a ghost! Nick Martinos," she replied briefly. "He's with an excitable little man with a brown face."

Clive turned and regarded the other end of the room for an instant. "That excitable little man happens to be one of the wealthiest businessmen in Athens."

"But why on earth is Nick with him?" she asked.

"My dear, did you think Nick was a simple·farmer?"

"Well, he certainly gave me the impression he was a farmer—even though he's not particularly simple," she replied with a smile.

"Perhaps that's the impression he wants to convey," Clive remarked, "because I can assure you that he's not only a farmer, but he's an extremely astute businessman."

Christine resumed her meal. Nick had seen her with the professor, of that she felt sure; little escaped those penetrating blue eyes. Yet, in spite of the fact that she occasionally stole a glance in the mirror, not once did he seem to look in their direction. Did he imagine that she had turned her attentions to Clive Harvey, she wondered. Her appearance alone would have told him that, to her, this was a very special occasion. Perhaps he was thinking that she had made herself as attractive as possible in the hope of ensnaring Clive!

She made an effort to keep up an animated chatter and

was relieved to see that Clive was too wrapped up in happy thoughts to spot anything artificial in her manner.

When at last the meal was over and it was time for them to go, she saw that the voluble little man, gesturing excitedly, was being listened to closely by Nick. He hadn't even seemed to notice when she left, she was thinking miserably as, almost in silence, they drove back to the villa.

Clive looked happy and expectant and was, she thought a little enviously, no doubt already rehearsing his proposal to Ruby.

How strange and unpredictable life was! Only a short time previously he had been bemoaning the lonely and solitary life that lay before him. Now he was eagerly looking forward to a new and happy future. She, on the other hand, felt lonely and insecure. It looked as though Nick had decided definitely to step out of her life.

She tried to hide her sense of desolation as she thanked Clive with all the enthusiasm she could muster.

"But it's I who have a special reason for thanking you," he told her, before they parted to go to their rooms. "If you hadn't accepted my invitation I shouldn't have known how Ruby felt and I should perhaps have missed all the happiness that I feel sure is lying in store for me. In fact," he added, "I feel the urge to wake Ruby up and propose on the spot."

"Oh, no, you don't!" Christine instructed in alarm. "I feel perfectly sure she'd be furious at being disturbed."

She did not add that she rather dreaded Ruby's reactions to the fact that, once again, they had been out together.

"Don't worry," Clive whispered. "I certainly shan't jeopardize my chances by rousing Ruby's ire." Then, to Christine's relief, he disappeared into his room with exaggerated caution.

Before she switched off her bedside light Christine's

eye was caught by the brilliant zigzag design of her new bag where she had placed it on top of her dressing table. Ruby would be sure to question her about it in her usual forthright manner. And as she fell asleep, Christine was wondering uneasily how Ruby would receive the news that it was a gift from Clive.

She had not long to wait to discover Ruby's reaction.

She got up early on the following morning and breakfasted alone, then, taking the bull by the horns, she went up to her room for the *taghari*, put into it the half-knitted sweater she was working on, and took it down to the office with her. Better to get Ruby's inquisition over as soon as possible. At least then she would know where she stood!

Ruby lost no time when, a little later, she strolled into the room and saw it on a chair beside the desk.

"You brought that here," she remarked, "didn't you? It looks like a pattern from Arachova to me."

Christine tried to sound casual as she said, "Yes, it's very pretty, isn't it? Clive bought it for me in Athens yesterday evening."

Without answering, Ruby prowled about the office abstractedly fingering objects.

"Yes, I heard of your little trip," she said at last, with surprising mildness.

She stopped at the window and with her back to the room lighted a cigarette and smoked thoughtfully.

The silence was so lengthy that Christine began to hope that Ruby had dismissed the matter from her mind. She had got up from her chair and was crossing the room to a cupboard to fetch envelopes when Ruby's next words froze her in her tracks.

"I want you to go, Christine," Ruby said quietly.

"Go?" Christine echoed blankly.

"You heard what I said." Ruby's voice had sharpened. "After all, you would be leaving here anyway when your holiday was over, but I want you out of my house immediately."

Christine stared at her in dismay. "Immediately?"

"Yes. Today."

"But I can't," Christine protested. "Things aren't settled up yet at the consulate . . . I mean, about my money, and anyway—"

"Anyway, nothing!" Ruby broke in. "You're leaving here today. My mind is made up. I'll see you have enough money, and you can always forward it from England later."

"But why?" Christine could hear her own voice quiver. She felt shocked and unnerved by the suddenness of it all.

Ruby swung around, and as she saw Christine's white face and taut figure said more gently, "Look, Christine, I've nothing against you personally. And I'm sure your little trip with Clive was on the up-and-up. But the fact is that I can't afford to have a pretty girl like you around. Clive's bound to make comparisons. After all, he's only human and, I'll be frank with you, I simply can't stand the competition. I want to marry him more than anything in the world. I've wanted to for years. I don't think I stand much chance, but with you about I stand even less. Oh, I know he's not in love with you," she added impatiently as Christine was on the point of protesting. "But while you're around he's going to want your company. With no one else to distract him, he'll have to turn to me. I know I sound cold-blooded, but he's the only man I've ever cared for. I'm not getting any younger and I can't afford to wait any longer."

"I see." Christine sank into the chair behind the desk and gazed at Ruby blankly.

It would, of course, be impossible to tell her that Clive intended to propose—and even if she did, would it make any difference? She had the feeling that Ruby was long past reasoning with.

"I want you to pack immediately," Ruby continued. "I'll arrange for a taxi. As I said, I'll fix you up as far as money goes, and you won't find me ungenerous. Clive and I shall go along to the dig and spend the day there. I shan't tell him you're leaving; it will save any embarrassment that way. And when I return I want to find you gone. You understand that?"

"Yes," Christine nodded, her mouth dry. "I understand."

There could be no appeal, she knew. Fear of advancing age and loneliness had made Ruby utterly ruthless.

Now she would have to leave without seeing Nick again! And even were she to return to Greece again some day, nothing would ever be the same again.

Something of her misery must have been reflected in her face, for Ruby said, almost appealingly, "You must hate me for this, but at least it's not as if you had any ties in this country. I used to think you and Nick Martinos might hit it off, but it didn't seem to work out. Tradition dies hard in Greece. He may flirt with a foreigner, but marriage is a different cup of tea."

Then, as Christine didn't answer, she continued bracingly, "When you go home you'll meet a suitable boy somewhere or other and settle down, and after a while Greece will become nothing more than a vague memory. Believe me, that's the usual end to holiday romances."

But Christine didn't wait to hear any more. She made an effort to stifle her sobs as she rushed from the room.

She packed swiftly. She mustn't allow herself to think of Nick Martinos—not now! Her one concern must be to leave this house where she was unwanted. Later on, misery would overwhelm her, made even more acute by having to be suppressed.

When she had finished, she carried her cases downstairs. Mariga came out of the kitchen as Christine placed them by the door. Triumph made Mariga look even more beautiful. She took an envelope from her pocket and handed it to Christine. "Ruby left this for you," she stated rudely.

Christine took it. She could feel the wad of notes inside. Ruby had, true to her word, been generous. At least she wouldn't have to worry about finances.

Mariga, hands on hips, surveyed her gloatingly. "You thought you had only to lift your little finger and every man would fall at your feet, didn't you? First of all you tried to steal Nick, and then the professor. Now Ruby has flung you out, as I knew she would. As for Nick, he is mine and always will be!"

To her relief Christine could hear a car draw up on the road outside. So the taxi had arrived! At last she could go and put Mariga and her hateful jeering voice behind her for good!

Christine bent down to pick up one of her cases, but Mariga was not going to allow her to depart without indulging in one of her dramatic gestures. She hissed an imprecation in Greek and snatching the suitcase from Christine's grasp flung it with all her strength through the open door.

As it struck one of the paving slabs, the case burst open, spilling its contents over the patio. The girl gave peal after peal of frenzied laughter as she surveyed her handiwork, and followed it with further abuse in Greek.

Then suddenly she choked on her words and stared white-faced as Nick strode toward them. It was evident from his expression that he had witnessed the whole sordid little drama, and it would have been impossible for him not to have overheard Mariga's final spate of abuse.

Without speaking, he seized the strewn garments, stuffed them into the case and crammed the lid down. Then he dumped it inside the door, took Christine's hand and pulled her toward him.

"Now where do you think you're going?" he asked abruptly.

"I . . . I thought you were the taxi," she replied inanely. "I . . . I'm leaving."

"I gathered as much. I had a chat with Ruby and Clive on their way to the dig and I knew immediately from Ruby's manner that something was up. Well, you won't need that taxi. I'll drive you anywhere you want to go. But first I must talk to you."

Mariga had, by this time, recovered her aplomb. "Where are you going with her?" she shrilled.

"That," he remarked coolly, "is none of your business."

Mariga flung her head back, her eyes flashing with rage. "I've a right to know!" she yelled.

"From now on you've no rights whatsoever," he replied dispassionately. "I've no intention of spending the rest of my life with a virago. And now, Christine, are you coming?"

Before she could demur she found herself marched across the patio and up the hill leading to the temple of Aphrodite.

When they arrived at the ruins, Nick released her and breathlessly she sat down on one of the fallen marble pillars. Everything had happened so swiftly that she felt confused, but under her bewilderment there was a growing warm happiness.

"Why have we come up here?" she asked.

"What could be more suitable for a proposal than the temple of the goddess of love?" he answered softly.

"Oh, Nick!" She was on her feet and flew into his arms.

In silence they clung together for a long moment. Then, with arms entwined, they gazed across the azure blue sea to where Koula appeared like a pinpoint on the horizon. Strange to think that Nick's palace of marble would be her future home. Later on, high in her little kingdom, she would gaze across the water and remember this moment. She must often visit the temple, she told herself. It was here that she had finally found happiness.

"What are you thinking of?" she asked softly.

"That never again shall I have to come here to watch the light spring up in your window."

"Did you do that often?" she queried.

"Much more often than you realized," he replied.

She laid her cheek against his. "Oh, but I think I always sensed when you were here."

"That sounds ominous," he said, with mock alarm. "Does it mean that when we're married you'll be able to keep tabs on me every moment of the day?"

She shook her head and said seriously, "No. I'll always remember that you're Greek and that Greeks value their freedom more than anything else. I shouldn't want it any other way."

"It seems to me you'll make the perfect wife, Christine," he said softly. "And we must never forget our debt to Aphrodite. In the years to come we must return here each year in the spring and leave an offering for the goddess. I wonder what flowers she would prefer?"

"Orange blossom, of course," she whispered, as he took her in his arms again.